THE
HISTORICAL NIGHTS'
ENTERTAINMENT

BY

RAFAEL SABATINI

SECOND SERIES

BOSTON AND NEW YORK

HOUGHTON MIFFLIN COMPANY

The Riverside Press Cambridge

The Riverside Press

CAMBRIDGE · MASSACHUSETTS

PRINTED IN THE U.S.A.

TO

DAVID WHITELAW

MY DEAR DAVID,

Since the narratives collected here, as well as in the preceding volume under the title of "The Historical Nights' Entertainment"—narratives originally published in *The Premier Magazine*, which you so ably edit—owe their being to your suggestion, it is fitting that some acknowledgment of the fact should be made. To what is hardly less than a duty allow me to add the pleasure of dedicating to you, in earnest of my friendship and esteem, not merely this volume, but the work of which this volume is the second.

Sincerely yours

LONDON, *June*, 1919   RAFAEL SABATINI

NOTE

To this edition of the Second Series of *The Histori-cal Nights' Entertainment* are added three stories from the volume originally published under the title of *The Justice of the Duke*.

PREFACE

The kindly reception accorded to the first volume of "The Historical Nights' Entertainment," issued in December of 1917, has encouraged me to prepare the second series here assembled.

As in the case of the narratives that made up the first volume, I set out again with the same ambitious aim of adhering scrupulously in every instance to actual, recorded facts; and once again I find it desirable at the outset to reveal how far the achievement may have fallen short of the admitted aim.

On the whole, I have to confess to having allowed myself perhaps a wider latitude, and to having taken greater liberties than was the case with the essays constituting the previous collection. This, however, applies, where applicable, to the parts rather than to the whole.

The only entirely apocryphal narrative here included is the first — "The Absolution." This is one of those stories which, if resting upon no sufficient authority to compel its acceptance, will, nevertheless, resist all attempts at final refutation, having its roots at least in the soil of fact. It is given in the rather discredited Portuguese chronicles of Acenheiro, and finds place, more or less as related here, in Duarte Galvão's "Chronicle of Affonso Henriques," whence it was taken by the Portuguese historical writer, Alexandre Herculano, to be included in his "Lendas e Narrativas." If it is to be relegated to the limbo of

the ben trovato, at least I esteem it to afford us a
precious glimpse of the naïve spirit of the age in which
it is set, and find in that my justification for including
it.

The next to require apology is "His Insolence of
Buckingham," but only in so far as the incident of the
diamond studs is concerned. The remainder of the
narrative, the character of Buckingham, the details of
his embassy to Paris, and the particulars of his audacious courtship of Anne of Austria, rest upon unassail-
able evidence. I would have omitted the very apocryphal incident of the studs but that I considered it of
peculiar interest as revealing the source of the main
theme of one of the most famous historical romances
ever written — "The Three Musketeers." I give the
story as related by La Rochefoucauld in his "Mem-
oirs," whence Alexandre Dumas culled it that he
might turn it to such excellent romantic account. In
La Rochefoucauld's narrative it is the painter Gerbier
who, in a far less heroic manner, plays the part assigned by Dumas to d'Artagnan, and it is the Countess of Carlisle who carries out the political theft which
Dumas attributes to Milady. For the rest, I do not
invite you to attach undue credit to it, which is not,
however, to say that I account it wholly false.

In the case of "The Hermosa Fembra," I confess to
having blended together into one single narrative two
historical episodes closely connected in time and
place. Susan's daughter was, in fact, herself the betrayer of her father, and it was in penitence for that
unnatural act that she desired her skull to be exhib-
ited as I describe. Into the story of Susan's daughter
I have woven that of another New-Christian girl,

who, like the Hermosa Fembra, had taken a Castilian lover — in this case a youth of the house of Guzman. This youth was driven into concealment in circumstances more or less as I describe them. He overheard the Judaizing of several New-Christians there assembled, and bore word of it at once to Ojeda. The two episodes were separated in fact by an interval of three years, and the first afforded Ojeda a strong argument for the institution of the Holy Office in Seville. Between the two there are many points of contact, and each supplies what the other lacks to make an interesting narrative having for background the introduction of the Inquisition to Castile. The dénouement I supply is entirely fictitious and the introduction of Torquemada is quite arbitrary. Ojeda was the inquisitor who dealt with both cases. But if there I stray into fiction, at least I claim to have sketched a faithful portrait of the Grand Inquisitor as I know him from fairly exhaustive researches into his life and times.

The story of the False Demetrius is here related from the point of view of my adopted solution of what is generally regarded as an historical mystery. The mystery lies, of course, in the man's identity. He has been held by some to have been the unfrocked monk, Grishka Otropiev, by others to have been a son of Stephen Bathory, King of Poland. I am not aware that the theory that he was both at one and the same time has ever been put forward, and whilst admitting that it is speculative, yet I claim that no other would appear so aptly to fit all the known facts of his career or to shed light upon its mysteries.

Undoubtedly I have allowed myself a good deal of

licence and speculation in treating certain unwitnessed scenes in "The Barren Wooing." But the theory that I develop in it to account for the miscarriage of the matrimonial plans of Queen Elizabeth and Robert Dudley seems to me to be not only very fully warranted by de Quadra's correspondence, but the only theory that will convincingly explain the events. Elizabeth, as I show, was widely believed to be an accessory to the murder of Amy Robsart. But in carefully following her words and actions at that critical time, as reported by de Quadra, my reading of the transaction is as given here. The most damning fact against Elizabeth was held to be her own statement to de Quadra on the eve of Lady Robert Dudley's murder to the effect that Lady Robert was "already dead, or very nearly so." This foreknowledge of the fate of that unfortunate lady has been accepted as positive evidence that the Queen was a party to the crime at Cumnor, which was to set her lover free to marry again. Far from that, however, I account it positive proof of Elizabeth's innocence of any such part in the deed. Elizabeth was far too crafty and clear-sighted not to realize how her words must incriminate her afterwards if she knew that the murder of Lady Robert was projected. She must have been merely repeating what Dudley himself had told her; and what he must have told her — and she believed — was that his wife was at the point of a natural death. Similarly, Dudley would not have told her this, unless his aim had been to procure his wife's removal by means which would admit of a natural interpretation. Difficulties encountered, much as I relate them — and for which there is abundant evidence — drove his too-zealous agents to rather desperate lengths, and thus brought suspicion, not only upon the guilty Dudley, but also upon the innocent Queen. The manner of Amy's murder is pure conjecture; but it should not be far from what actually took place. The possibility of an accident — extraordinarily and suspiciously opportune for Dudley as it would have been — could not be altogether ruled out but for the further circumstance that Lady Robert had removed everybody from Cumnor on that day. To what can this point — unless we accept an altogether incredible chain of coincidence — but to some such plotting as I here suggest?

In the remaining six essays in this volume the liberties taken with the absolute facts are so slight as to require no apology or comment.

R. S.

LONDON, *June*, 1919

CONTENTS

xvi CONTENTS

THE HISTORICAL NIGHTS'
ENTERTAINMENT

SECOND SERIES

I

THE ABSOLUTION

AFFONSO HENRIQUES, FIRST KING OF PORTUGAL

IN 1093 the Moors of the Almoravide dynasty, under
the Caliph Yusuf, swept irresistibly upwards into
the Iberian Peninsula, recapturing Lisbon and San-
tarem in the west, and pushing their conquest as far
as the river Mondego.

To meet this revival of Mohammedan power,
Alfonso VI of Castile summoned the chivalry of
Christendom to his aid. Among the knights who
answered the call was Count Henry of Burgundy
(grandson of Robert, first Duke of Burgundy), to
whom Alfonso gave his natural daughter Theresa in
marriage, together with the Counties of Oporto and
Coimbra, with the title of Count of Portugal.

That is the first chapter of the history of Portugal.

Count Henry fought hard to defend his southern
frontiers from the incursion of the Moors until his
death in 1114. Thereafter his widow Theresa became
Regent of Portugal during the minority of their son,
Affonso Henriques. A woman of great energy, resource, and ambition, she successfully waged war

against the Moors, and in other ways laid the foundations upon which her son was to build the Kingdom of Portugal. But her passionate infatuation for one of her knights — Don Fernando Peres de Trava — and the excessive honours she bestowed upon him, made enemies for her in the new state, and estranged her from her son.

In 1127 Alfonso VII of Castile invaded Portugal, compelling Theresa to recognize him as her suzerain. But Affonso Henriques, now aged seventeen — and declared by the citizens of the capital to be of age and competent to reign — incontinently refused to recognize the submission made by his mother, and in the following year assembled an army for the purpose of expelling her and her lover from the country. The warlike Theresa resisted until defeated in the battle of San Mamede and taken prisoner.

He was little more than a boy, although four years were sped already since, as a mere lad of fourteen, he had kept vigil throughout the night over his arms in the Cathedral of Zamora, preparatory to receiving the honour of knighthood at the hands of his cousin, Alfonso VII of Castile. Yet already he was looked upon as the very pattern of what a Christian knight should be, worthy son of the father who had devoted his life to doing battle against the Infidel, wheresoever he might be found. He was well-grown and tall, and of a bodily strength that is almost a byword to this day in that Portugal of which he was the real founder and first king. He was skilled beyond the common wont in all knightly exercises of arms and horsemanship, and equipped with far more learning —

though much of it was ill-digested, as this story will serve to show — than the twelfth century considered useful or even proper in a knight. And he was at least true to his time in that he combined a fervid piety with a weakness of the flesh and an impetuous arrogance that was to bring him under the ban of greater excommunication at the very outset of his reign.

It happened that his imprisonment of his mother was not at all pleasing in the sight of Rome. Dona Theresa had powerful friends, who so used their influence at the Vatican on her behalf that the Holy Father — conveniently ignoring the provocation she had given and the scandalous, unmotherly conduct of which she had been guilty — came to consider the behaviour of the Infante of Portugal as reprehensibly unfilial, and commanded him to deliver Dona Theresa at once from duress.

This papal order, backed by a threat of excommunication in the event of disobedience, was brought to the young prince by the Bishop of Coimbra, whom he counted among his friends.

Affonso Henriques, ever impetuous and quick to anger, flushed scarlet when he heard that uncompromising message. His dark eyes smouldered as they considered the aged prelate.

"You come here to bid me let loose again upon this land of Portugal that author of strife, to deliver over the people once more to the oppression of the Lord of Trava?" he asked. "And you tell me that, unless by obeying this command I am false to the duty I owe this country, you will launch the curse of Rome against me? You tell me this?"

The Bishop, deeply stirred, torn between his duty to the Holy See and his affection for his Prince, bowed his head and wrung his hands. "What choice have I?" he asked, on a quavering note.

"I raised you from the dust." Thunder was rumbling in the Prince's voice. "Myself I placed the episcopal ring upon your finger."

"My lord, my lord! Could I forget? All that I have I owe to you — save only my soul, which I owe to God; my faith, which I owe to Christ; and my obedience, which I owe to our Holy Father the Pope."

The Prince considered him in silence, mastering his passionate, impetuous nature. "Go," he growled at last.

The prelate bowed his head, his eyes not daring to meet his Prince's.

"God keep you, lord," he almost sobbed, and so went out.

But though stirred by his affection for the Prince to whom he owed so much, though knowing in his inmost heart that Affonso Henriques was in the right, the Bishop of Coimbra did not swerve from his duty to Rome, which was as plain as it was unpalatable. Betimes next morning word was brought to Affonso Henriques in the Alcazar of Coimbra that a parchment was nailed to the door of the Cathedral, setting forth his excommunication, and that the Bishop — either out of fear or out of sorrow — had left the city, journeying northward towards Oporto.

Affonso Henriques passed swiftly from incredulity to anger; then almost as swiftly came to a resolve, which was as mad and harebrained as could have been expected from a lad in his eighteenth year who held the reins of power. Yet by its very directness and its superb ignoring of all obstacles, legal and canonical, it was invested with a certain wild sanity.

In full armour, a white cloak simply embroidered in gold at the edge and knotted at the shoulder, he rode to the Cathedral, attended by his half-brother, Pedro Affonso, and two of his knights, Emigio Moniz and Sancho Nunes. There on the great iron-studded doors he found, as he had been warned, the Roman parchment pronouncing him accursed, its sonorous Latin periods set forth in a fine round clerkly hand.

He swung down from his great horse and clanked up the Cathedral steps, his attendants following. He had for witnesses no more than a few loiterers, who had paused at sight of their Prince.

The interdict had so far attracted no attention, for in the twelfth century the art of letters was a mystery to which there were few initiates.

Affonso Henriques tore the sheepskin from its nails, and crumpled it in his hand; then he passed into the Cathedral, and thence came out presently into the cloisters. Overhead a bell was clanging by his orders, summoning the chapter.

To the Infante, waiting there in the sun-drenched close, came presently the canons, austere, aloof, majestic in their unhurried progress through the fretted cloisters, with flowing garments and hands tucked into their wide sleeves before them. In a semicircle they arrayed themselves before him, and waited impassively to learn his will. Overhead the bell had ceased.

Affonso Henriques wasted no words.

"I have summoned you," he announced, "to command that you proceed to the election of a bishop."

A rustle stirred through the priestly throng. The canons looked askance at the Prince and at one another. Then one of them spoke.

"Habemus episcopum," he said gravely, and several instantly made chorus: "We have a bishop."

The eyes of the young sovereign kindled. "You are wrong," he told them. "You had a bishop, but he is here no longer. He has deserted his see, after publishing this shameful thing." And he held aloft the crumpled interdict. "As I am a God-fearing, Christian knight, I will not live under this ban. Since the bishop who excommunicated me is gone, you will at once elect another in his place who shall absolve me."

They stood before him, silent and impassive, in their priestly dignity, and in their assurance that the law was on their side.

"Well?" the boy growled at them.

"Habemus episcopum," droned a voice again.

"Amen," boomed in chorus through the cloisters.

"I tell you that your bishop is gone," he insisted, his voice quivering now with anger, "and I tell you that he shall not return, that he shall never set foot again within my city of Coimbra. Proceed you, therefore, at once to the election of his successor."

"Lord," he was answered coldly by one of them, "no such election is possible or lawful."

"Do you dare stand before my face, and tell me this?" he roared, infuriated by their cold resistance. He flung out an arm in a gesture of terrible dismissal. "Out of my sight, you proud and evil men! Back to your cells, to await my pleasure. Since in your arrogant, stiff-necked pride you refuse to do my will, you shall receive the bishop I shall myself select."

He was so terrific in his rage that they dared not tell him that he had no power, Prince though he might be, to make such an election. They bowed to him, ever impassively, and with their hands still folded, unhurried as they had come, they now turned and filed past him in departure.

He watched them with scowling brows and tightened lips, Moniz and Nunes silent behind him. Suddenly those dark, watchful eyes of his were held by the last figure of all in that austere procession — a tall, gaunt young man, whose copper-coloured skin and hawk-featured face proclaimed his Moorish blood. Instantly, maliciously, it flashed through the Prince's boyish mind how he might make of this man an instrument to humble the pride of that insolent clergy. He raised his hand, and beckoned the cleric to him.

"What is your name?" he asked him.

"I am called Zuleyman, Lord," he was answered, and the name confirmed — where, indeed, no confirmation was necessary — the fellow's Moorish origin.

Affonso Henriques laughed. It would be an excellent jest to thrust upon these arrogant priests, who refused to appoint a bishop of their choice, a bishop who was little better than a blackamoor.

"Don Zuleyman," said the Prince, "I name you Bishop of Coimbra in the room of the rebel who has fled. You will prepare to celebrate High Mass this morning, and to pronounce my absolution."

The Christianized Moor fell back a step, his face

paling under its copper skin to a sickly grey. In the background, the hindmost members of the retreating clerical procession turned and stood at gaze, angered and scandalized by what they heard, which was indeed a thing beyond belief.

"Ah, no, my lord! Ah, no!" Don Zuleyman was faltering. "Not that!"

The prospect terrified him, and in his agitation he had recourse to Latin. "Domine, non sum dignus," he cried, and beat his breast.

But the uncompromising Affonso Henriques gave him back Latin for Latin.

"Dixi — I have spoken!" he answered sternly. "Do not fail me in obedience, on your life." And on that he clanked out again with his attendants, well-pleased with his morning's work.

As he had disposed with boyish, almost irresponsible rashness, and in flagrant contravention of all canon law, so it fell out. Don Zuleyman, wearing the bishop's robes and the bishop's mitre, intoned the "Kyrie Eleison" before noon that day in the Cathedral of Coimbra, and pronounced the absolution of the Infante of Portugal, who knelt so submissively and devoutly before him.

Affonso Henriques was very pleased with himself. He made a jest of the affair, and invited his intimates to laugh with him. But Emigio Moniz and the elder members of his Council refused to laugh. They looked with awe upon a deed that went perilously near to sacrilege, and implored him to take their own sober view of the thing he had done.

"By the bones of Saint James!" he cried. "A prince is not to be brow-beaten by a priest."

Such a view in the twelfth century was little short of revolutionary. The chapter of the Cathedral of Coimbra held the converse opinion that priests were not to be brow-beaten by a prince, and set themselves to make Affonso Henriques realize this to his bitter cost. They dispatched to Rome an account of his unconscionable, high-handed, incredible sacrilege, and invited Rome to administer condign spiritual flagellation upon this errant child of Mother Church. Rome made haste to vindicate her authority, and dispatched a legate to the recalcitrant, audacious boy who ruled in Portugal. But the distance being considerable, and means of travel inadequate and slow, it was not until Don Zuleyman had presided in the See of Coimbra for a full two months that the papal legate made his appearance in Affonso Henriques's capital.

A very splendid Prince of the Church was Cardinal Corrado, the envoy dispatched by Pope Honorius II, full armed with apostolic weapons to reduce the rebellious Infante of Portugal into proper subjection.

His approach was heralded by the voice of rumour. Affonso Henriques heard of it without perturbation. His conscience at ease in the absolution which he had wrung from Mother Church after his own fashion, he was entirely absorbed in preparations for a campaign against the Moors which was to widen his dominions. Therefore, when at length the thunderbolt descended, it fell — so far as he was concerned — from a sky entirely clear.

It was towards dusk of a summer evening when the legate, in a litter slung in line between two mules, entered Coimbra. He was attended by two nephews, Giannino and Pierluigi da Corrado, both patricians of

Rome, and a little knot of servants. Empanoplied in his sacred office, the Cardinal had no need of the protection of men-at-arms upon a journey through God-fearing lands.

He was borne straight to the old Moorish palace where the Infante resided, and came upon him there amid a numerous company in the great pillared hall. Against a background of battle trophies, livid weapons, implements of war, and suits of mail both Saracen and Christian, with which the bare walls were hung, moved a gaily clad, courtly gathering of nobles and their women-folk, when the great Cardinal, clad from head to foot in scarlet, entered unannounced.

Laughter rippled into silence. A hush descended upon the company, which stood now at gaze, considering the imposing and unbidden guest. Slowly the legate, followed by the two Roman youths, advanced down the hall, the soft pad of his slippered feet and the rustle of his silken robes being at first the only sound. On he came, until he stood before the shallow dais, where in a massively carved chair sat the Infante of Portugal, mistrustfully observing him. Affonso Henriques scented here an enemy, an ally of his mother's, the bearer of a fresh declaration of hostilities. Therefore, of deliberate purpose he kept his seat, as if to stress the fact that here he was the master.

"Lord Cardinal," he greeted the legate, "be welcome to my land of Portugal."

The Cardinal bowed stiffly, resentful of this reception. In his long journey across the Spains, princes and nobles had flocked to kiss his hand, and bend the knee before him, seeking his blessing. Yet this mere boy, beardless save for a silky down about his firm young cheeks, retained his seat and greeted him with no more submissiveness than if he had been the envoy of some temporal prince.

"I am the representative of our Holy Father," he announced, in a voice of stern reproof. "I am from Rome, with these my well-beloved nephews."

"From Rome?" quoth Affonso Henriques. For all his length of limb and massive thews he could be impish upon occasion. He was impish now. "Although no good has ever yet come to me from Rome, you make me hopeful. His Holiness will have heard of the preparations I am making for a war against the Infidel that shall carry the Cross where now stands the Crescent, and sends me, perhaps, a gift of gold to assist me in this holy work."

The mockery of it stung the legate sharply. His sallow, ascetic face empurpled.

"It is not gold I bring you," he answered, "but a lesson in the Faith which you would seem to have forgotten. I am come to teach you your Christian duty, and to require of you immediate reparation of the sacrilegious wrongs you have done. The Holy Father demands of you the instant reinstatement of the Bishop of Coimbra, whom you have driven out with threats of violence, and the degradation of the cleric you blasphemously appointed bishop in his stead."

"And is that all?" quoth the boy, in a voice dangerously quiet.

"No." Fearless in his sense of right, the legate towered before him. "It is demanded of you further that you instantly release the lady, your mother, from the unjust confinement in which you hold her."

"That confinement is not unjust, as all here can witness," the Infante answered. "Rome may believe it, because lies have been carried to Rome. Dona Theresa's life was a scandal, her regency an injustice to my people. She and the infamous Lord of Trava lighted the torch of civil war in these dominions. Learn here the truth, and carry it to Rome. Thus shall you do worthy service."

But the prelate was obstinate and proud.

"That is not the answer that our Holy Father awaits."

"It is the answer that I send."

"Rash, rebellious youth, beware!" The Cardinal's anger flamed up, and his voice swelled. "I come armed with spiritual weapons of destruction. Do not abuse the patience of Mother Church, or you shall feel the full weight of her wrath released against you."

Exasperated, Affonso Henriques bounded to his feet, his face livid now with passion, his eyes ablaze.

"Out! Away!" he cried. "Go, my lord, and go quickly, or as God watches us I will add here and now yet another sacrilege to those of which you accuse me."

The prelate gathered his ample robes about him. If pale, he was entirely calm once more. With stern dignity, he bowed to the angry youth, and so departed, but with such outward impassivity that it would have been difficult to say with whom lay the victory. If Affonso Henriques thought that night that he had conquered, morning was to shatter the illusion.

He was awakened early by a chamberlain at the urgent instances of Emigio Moniz, who was demanding immediate audience. Affonso Henriques sat up in bed, and bade him to be admitted.

The elderly knight and faithful counsellor came in, treading heavily. His swarthy face was overcast, his mouth set in stern lines under its grizzled beard.

"God keep you, lord," was his greeting, so lugubriously delivered as to sound like a pious, but rather hopeless, wish.

"And you, Emigio," answered him the Infante. "You are early astir. What is the cause?"

"Ill tidings, lord." He crossed the room, unlatched and flung wide a window. "Listen," he bade the Prince.

On the still morning air arose a sound like the drone of some gigantic hive, or of the sea when the tide is making. Affonso Henriques recognized it for the murmur of the multitude.

"What does it mean?" he asked, and thrust a sinewy leg from the bed.

"It means that the papal legate has done all that he threatened, and something more. He has placed your city of Coimbra under a ban of excommunication. The churches are closed, and until the ban is lifted no priest will be found to baptize, marry, shrive, or perform any other sacrament of Holy Church. The people are stricken with terror, knowing that they share the curse with you. They are massing below at the gates of the alcazar, demanding to see you that they may implore you to lift from them the horror of this excommunication."

Affonso Henriques had come to his feet by now, and he stood there staring at the old knight, his face blenched, his stout heart clutched by fear of these impalpable, blasting weapons that were being used against him.

"My God!" he groaned, and asked: "What must I do?"

Moniz was preternaturally grave. "It is of the first importance that the people should be pacified."

"But how?"

"There is one way only — by a promise that you will submit to the will of the Holy Father, and by penance seek absolution for yourself and your city."

A red flush swept into the young cheeks that had been so pale.

"What?" he cried, his voice a roar. "Release my mother, depose Zuleyman, recall that fugitive recreant who cursed me, and humble myself to seek pardon at the hands of this insolent Italian cleric? May my bones rot, may I roast forever in hell-fire if I show myself such a craven! And do you counsel it, Emigio — do you really counsel that?" He was in a towering rage.

"Listen to that voice," Emigio answered him, and waved a hand to the open window. "How else will you silence it?"

Affonso Henriques sat down on the edge of the bed, and took his head in his hands. He was checkmated — and yet . . .

He rose and beat his hands together, summoning chamberlain and pages to help him dress and arm.

"Where is the legate lodged?" he asked Moniz.

"He is gone," the knight answered him. "He left at cock-crow, taking the road to Spain along the Mondego — so I learnt from the watch at the River Gate."

"How came they to open for him?"

"His office, lord, is a key that opens all doors at any hour of day or night. They dared not detain or delay him."

"Ha!" grunted the Infante. "We will go after him, then." And he made haste to complete his dressing. Then he buckled on his great sword, and they departed.

In the courtyard of the alcazar, he summoned Sancho Nunes and a half-dozen men-at-arms to attend him, mounted a charger, and, with Emigio Moniz at his side and the others following, he rode out across the drawbridge into the open space that was thronged with the clamant inhabitants of the stricken city.

A great cry went up when he showed himself — a mighty appeal to him for mercy and the remission of the curse. Then silence fell, a silence that invited him to answer and give comfort.

He reined in his horse, and, standing in his stirrups very tall and virile, he addressed them.

"People of Coimbra," he announced, "I go to obtain this city's absolution from the ban that has been laid upon it. I shall return before sunset. Till then do you keep the peace."

The voice of the multitude was raised again, this time to hail him as the father and protector of the Portuguese, and to invoke the blessing of Heaven upon his handsome head.

Riding between Moniz and Nunes, and followed by his glittering men-at-arms, he crossed the city and took the road along the river by which it was known that the legate had departed. All that morning they rode briskly amain, the Infante fasting, as he had risen, yet unconscious of hunger and of all else but the purpose that was consuming him. He rode in utter silence, his face set, his brows stern; and Moniz watching him furtively the while, wondered what thoughts were stirring in that rash, impetuous young brain, and was afraid.

Towards noon at last they overtook the legate's party. They espied his mule-litter at the door of an inn in a little village some ten miles beyond the foot-hills of the Bussaco range. The Infante reined up sharply, a hoarse, fierce cry escaping him, akin to that of some creature of the wild when it espies its prey.

Moniz put forth a hand to seize his arm.

"My lord, my lord," he cried, fearfully, "what is your purpose?"

The Prince looked him between the eyes, and his lips curled in a smile that was not altogether sweet.

"I am going to beg Cardinal Corrado to have compassion on me," he answered, subtly mocking, and on that he swung down from his horse, and tossed the reins to a man-at-arms.

Into the inn he clanked, Moniz and Nunes following closely. He thrust aside the vintner who, not knowing him, would have hindered him, great lord though he seemed, from disturbing the holy guest who was honouring the house. He strode on, and into the room where the Cardinal with his noble nephews sat at dinner.

At sight of him, fearing violence, Giannino and Pierluigi came instantly to their feet, their hands upon their daggers. But Cardinal da Corrado sat unmoved. He looked up, a smile of ineffable gentleness upon his ascetic face.

"I had hoped that you would come after me, my son," he said. "If you come a penitent, then has my prayer been heard."

"A penitent!" cried Affonso Henriques. He laughed wickedly, and plucked his dagger from its sheath.

Sancho Nunes, in terror, set a detaining hand upon his Prince's arm.

"My lord," he cried in a voice that shook, "you will not strike the Lord's anointed — that were to destroy yourself forever."

"A curse," said Affonso Henriques, "perishes with him that uttered it." He could reason loosely, you see, this hot-blooded, impetuous young cutter of Gordian knots. "And it imports above all else that the curse should be lifted from my city of Coimbra."

"It shall be, my son, as soon as you show penitence and a Christian submission to the Holy Father's will," said the undaunted Cardinal.

"God give me patience with you," Affonso Henriques answered him. "Listen to me now, Lord Cardinal." And he leaned forward on his dagger, burying the point of it some inches into the deal table. "That you should punish me with the weapons of the Faith for the sins that you allege against me I can understand and suffer. There is reason in that, perhaps. But will you tell me what reasons there can be in punishing a whole city for an offence which, if it exists at all, is mine alone? — and in punishing it by a curse so terrible that all the consolations of religion are denied those true children of Mother Church, that no priestly office may be performed within the city, that men and women may not approach the altars of the Faith, that they must die unshriven with their sins upon them, and so be damned through all eternity? Where is the reason that urges this?"

The Cardinal's smile had changed from one of benignity to one of guile.

"Why, I will answer you. Out of their terror they will be moved to revolt against you, unless you relieve them of the ban. Thus, Lord Prince, I hold you in check. You make submission or else you are destroyed."

Affonso Henriques considered him a moment. "You answer me, indeed," said he, and then his voice swelled up in denunciation. "But this is statecraft, not religion. And when a prince has no statecraft to match that which is opposed to him, do you know what follows? He has recourse to force, Lord Cardinal. You compel me to it; upon your own head the consequences."

The legate almost sneered. "What is the force of your poor lethal weapons compared with the spiritual power I wield? Do you threaten me with death? Do you think I fear it?" He rose in a surge of sudden wrath, and tore open his scarlet robe. "Strike here with your poniard. I wear no mail. Strike if you dare, and by the sacrilegious blow destroy yourself in this world and the next."

The Infante considered him. Slowly he sheathed his dagger, smiling a little. Then he beat his hands together. His men-at-arms came in. ·

"Seize me those two Roman whelps," he commanded, and pointed to Giannino and Pierluigi. "Seize them, and make them fast. About it!"

"Lord Prince!" cried the legate in a voice of appeal, wherein fear and anger trembled.

It was the note of fear that heartened Affonso Henriques. "About it!" he cried again, though needlessly, for already his men-at-arms were at grips with the Cardinal's nephews. In a trice the kicking, biting, swearing pair were overpowered, deprived of arms, and pinioned. The men looked to their Prince for further orders. In the background Moniz and Nunes witnessed all with troubled countenances, whilst the Cardinal, beyond the table, white to the lips, demanded in a quavering voice to know what violence was intended, implored the Infante to consider, and in the same breath threatened him with dread consequences of this affront.

Affonso Henriques, unmoved, pointed through the window to a stalwart oak that stood before the inn.

"Take them out there, and hang them unshriven," he commanded.

The Cardinal swayed, and almost fell forward. He clutched the table, speechless with terror for those lads who were as the very apple of his eye, he who so fearlessly had bared his own breast to the steel.

The two comely Italian youths were dragged out writhing in their captors' hands.

At last the half-swooning legate found his voice. "Lord Prince," he gasped, "Lord Prince . . . you cannot do this infamy! You cannot! I warn you that . . . that . . ." The threat perished unuttered, slain by mounting terror. "Mercy! Have mercy, lord! as you hope for mercy!"

"What mercy do you practise, you who preach a

gospel of mercy in the world, and cry for mercy now?" the Infante asked him.

"But this is an infamy! What harm have those poor children done? What concern is it of theirs that I have offended you in performing my sacred duty?"

Swift into that opening flashed the home-thrust of the Infante's answer.

"What harm have my people of Coimbra done? What concern is it of theirs that I have offended you? Yet to master me you did not hesitate to strike at them with the spiritual weapons that are yours. To master you I do not hesitate to strike at your nephews with the lethal weapons that are mine. When you shall have seen them hang, you will understand the things that argument could not make clear to you. In the vileness of my act you will see a reflection of the vileness of your own, and perhaps your heart will be touched, your monstrous pride abated."

Outside, under the tree, the figures of the men-at-arms were moving. Expeditiously, and with indifference, they went about the preparations for the task entrusted to them.

The Cardinal writhed, and fought for breath. "Lord Prince, this must not be!" He stretched forth supplicating hands. "Lord Prince, you must release my nephews."

"Lord Cardinal, you must absolve my people."

"If ... if you will first make submission. My duty ... to the Holy See ... O God! Will nothing move you?"

"When they have been hanged you will understand, and out of your own affliction learn compassion." The Infante's voice was so cold, his mien so resolute, that the legate despaired of conquering his purpose. Abruptly he capitulated, even as the halters went about the necks of his two cherished lads.

"Stop!" he screamed. "Bid them stop! The curse shall be lifted."

Affonso Henriques opened the window with a lei-sureliness which to the legate seemed to belong to the realm of nightmare.

"Wait yet a moment," the Infante called to those outside, about whom by now a little knot of awe-stricken villagers had gathered. Then he turned again to Cardinal Corrado, who had sunk to his chair like a man exhausted, and sat now panting, his elbows on the table, his head in his hands. "Here," said the Prince, "are the terms upon which you may have their lives: Complete absolution, and Apostolic bene-diction for my people and myself this very night, I on my side making submission to the Holy Father's will to the extent of releasing my mother from duress, with the condition that she leaves Portugal at once and does not return. As for the banished bishop and his successor, matters must remain as they are; but you can satisfy your conscience on that score by your-self confirming the appointment of Don Zuleyman. Come, my lord, I am being generous, I think. In the enlargement of my mother I afford you the means of satisfying Rome. If you have learnt your lesson from what I here proposed, your conscience should satisfy you of the rest."

"Be it so," the Cardinal answered hoarsely. "I will return with you to Coimbra and do your will."

Thereupon, without any tinge of mockery, but in completest sincerity in token that the feud between them was now completely healed, Affonso Henriques went down upon his knees, like the true and humble son of Holy Church he accounted himself, to ask a blessing at the Cardinal's hands.

II

THE FALSE DEMETRIUS

BORIS GODUNOV AND THE PRETENDED SON OF IVAN THE TERRIBLE

THE news of it first reached him whilst he sat at supper in the great hall of his palace in the Kremlin. It came at a time when already there was enough to distract his mind; for although the table before him was spread and equipped as became an emperor's, the gaunt spectre of famine stalked outside in the streets of Moscow, and men and women were so reduced by it that cannibalism was alleged to be breaking out amongst them.

Alone, save for the ministering pages, sat Boris Godunov under the iron lamps that made of the table, with its white napery and vessels of gold and silver plate, an island of light in the gloom of that vast apartment. The air was fragrant with the scent of burning pine, for although the time of year was May, the nights were chill, and a great log-fire was blazing on the distant hearth. To him, as he sat there, came his trusted Basmanov with those tidings which startled him at first, seeming to herald that at last the sword of Nemesis was swung above his sinful head.

Basmanov, a flush tinting the prominent cheekbones of his sallow face, an excited glitter in his long eyes, began by ordering the pages out of earshot, then leaning forward quickly muttered forth his news.

At the first words of it, the Tsar's knife clashed into his golden platter, and his short, powerful hands clutched the carved arms of his great gilded chair. Quickly he controlled himself, and then as he continued to listen he was moved to scorn, and a faint smile began to stir under his grizzled beard.

A man had appeared in Poland — such was the burden of Basmanov's story — coming none knew exactly whence, who claimed to be Demetrius, the son of Ivan Vassielivitch, and lawful Tsar of Russia — Demetrius, who was believed to have died at Uglich ten years ago, and whose remains lay buried in Moscow, in the Church of Saint Michael. This man had found shelter in Lithuania, in the house of Prince Wisniowiecki, and thither the nobles of Poland were now flocking to do him homage, acknowledging him the son of Ivan the Terrible. He was said to be the living image of the dead Tsar, save that he was swarthy and black-haired, like the dowager Tsarina, and there were two warts on his face, such as it was remembered had disfigured the countenance of the boy Demetrius.

Thus Basmanov, adding that he had dispatched a messenger into Lithuania to obtain more precise confirmation of the story. That messenger — chosen in consequence of something else that Basmanov had been told — was Smirnoy Otrepiev.

The Tsar Boris sat back in his chair, his eyes on the gem-encrusted goblet, the stem of which his fingers were mechanically turning. There was now no vestige of the smile on his round white face. It had grown set and thoughtful.

"Find Prince Shuiski," he said presently, "and send him to me here."

Upon the tale the boyar had brought him he offered now no comment.

"We will talk of this again, Basmanov," was all he said in acknowledgment that he had heard, and in dismissal.

But when the boyar had gone, Boris Godunov heaved himself to his feet, and strode over to the fire, his great head sunk between his massive shoulders. He was a short, thick-set bow-legged man, inclining to corpulence. He set a foot, shod in red leather reversed with ermine, upon an andiron, and, leaning an elbow on the carved overmantel, rested his brow against his hand. His eyes stared into the very heart of the fire, as if they beheld there the pageant of the past, upon which his mind was bent.

Nineteen years were sped since Ivan the Terrible had passed away, leaving two sons, Feodor Ivanovitch, who had succeeded him, and the infant Demetrius. Feodor, a weakling who was almost imbecile, had married Irene, the daughter of Boris Godunov, whereby it had fallen out that Boris became the real ruler of Russia, the power behind the throne. But his insatiable ambition coveted still more. He must wear the crown as well as wield the sceptre; and this could not be until the Ruric dynasty which had ruled Russia for nearly seven centuries should be stamped out. Between himself and the throne stood his daughter's husband and their child, and the boy Demetrius, who had been dispatched with his mother, the dowager Tsarina, to Uglich. The three must be removed.

Boris began with the last, and sought at first to drive him out of the succession without bloodshed.

He attempted to have him pronounced illegitimate, on the ground that he was the son of Ivan's seventh wife (the Orthodox Church recognizing no wife as legitimate beyond the third). But in this he failed. The memory of the terrible Tsar, the fear of him, was still alive in superstitious Russia, and none dared to dishonour his son. So Boris had recourse to other and surer means. He dispatched his agents to Uglich, and presently there came thence a story that the boy, whilst playing with a knife, had been taken with a fit of epilepsy, and had fallen, running the blade into his throat. But it was not a story that could carry conviction to the Muscovites, since with it came the news that the town of Uglich had risen against the emissaries of Boris, charging them with the murder of the boy, and killing them out of hand.

Terrible had been the vengeance which Boris had exacted. Of the luckless inhabitants of the town two hundred were put to death by his orders, and the rest sent into banishment beyond the Ural Mountains, whilst the Tsarina Maria, Demetrius's mother, for having said that her boy was murdered at the instigation of Boris, was packed off to a convent, and had remained there ever since in close confinement.

That had been in 1591. The next to go was Feodor's infant son, and lastly — in 1598 — Feodor himself, succumbing to a mysterious illness, and leaving Boris a clear path to the throne. But he ascended it under the burden of his daughter's curse. Feodor's widow had boldly faced her father, boldly accused him of poisoning her husband to gratify his remorseless ambitions, and on a passionate appeal to God to let it be done by him as he had done by others she had

departed to a convent, swearing never to set eyes upon him again.

The thought of her was with him now, as he stood there looking into the heart of the fire; and perhaps it was the memory of her curse that turned his stout heart to water, and made him afraid where there could surely be no cause for fear. For five years now had he been Tsar of Russia, and in these five years he had taken such a grip of power as was not lightly to be loosened.

Long he stood there, and there he was found by the magnificent Prince Shuiski, whom he had bidden Basmanov to summon.

"You went to Uglich when the Tsarevitch Demetrius was slain," said Boris. His voice and mien were calm and normal. "Yourself you saw the body. There is no possibility that you could have been mistaken in it?"

"Mistaken?" The boyar was taken aback by the question. He was a tall man, considerably younger than Boris, who was in his fiftieth year. His face was lean and saturnine, and there was something sinister in the dark, close-set eyes under a single heavy line of eyebrow.

Boris explained his question, telling him what he had learnt from Basmanov. Basil Shuiski laughed. The story was an absurd one. Demetrius was dead. Himself he had held the body in his arms, and no mistake was possible.

Despite himself, a sigh of relief fluttered from the lips of Boris. Shuiski was right. It was an absurd story, this. There was nothing to fear. He had been a fool to have trembled for a moment.

Nevertheless, in the weeks that followed, he brooded more and more over all that Basmanov had said. It was in the thought that the nobility of Poland was flocking to the house of Wisniowiecki to do honour to this false son of Ivan the Terrible, that Boris found the chief cause of uneasiness. There was famine in Moscow, and empty bellies do not make for loyalty. Then, too, the Muscovite nobles did not love him. He had ruled too sternly, and had curbed their power. There were men like Basil Shuiski who knew too much — greedy, ambitious men, who might turn their knowledge to evil account. The moment might be propitious to the pretender, however false his claim. Therefore Boris dispatched a messenger to Wisniowiecki with the offer of a heavy bribe if he would yield up the person of this false Demetrius.

But that messenger returned empty-handed. He had reached Bragin too late. The pretender had already left the place, and was safely lodged in the castle of George Mniszek, the Palatine of Sandomir, to whose daughter Maryna he was betrothed. If these were ill tidings for Boris, there were worse to follow soon. Within a few months he learned from Sandomir that Demetrius had removed to Cracow, and that there he had been publicly acknowledged by Sigismund III of Poland as the son of Ivan Vassielivitch, the rightful heir to the crown of Russia. He heard, too, the story upon which this belief was founded. Demetrius had declared that one of the agents employed by Boris Godunov to procure his murder at Uglich had bribed his physician Simon to perform the deed. Simon had pretended to agree as the only means of saving him. He had dressed the son of a serf, who

slightly resembled Demetrius, in garments similar to those worn by the young Prince, and thereafter cut the lad's throat, leaving those who had found the body to presume it to be the Prince's. Meanwhile, Demetrius himself had been concealed by the physician, and very shortly thereafter carried away from Uglich, to be placed in safety in a monastery, where he had been educated.

Such, in brief, was the story with which Demetrius convinced the Court of Poland, and not a few who had known the boy at Uglich came forward now to identify with him the grown man, who carried in his face so strong a resemblance to Ivan the Terrible. That story which Boris now heard was soon heard by all Russia, and Boris realized that something must be done to refute it.

But something more than assurances — his own as- surances — were necessary if the Muscovites were to believe him. And so at last Boris bethought him of the Tsarina Maria, the mother of the murdered boy. He had her fetched to Moscow from her convent, and told her of this pretender who was setting up a claim to the throne of Russia, supported by the King of Poland.

She listened impassively, standing before him in the black robes and conventual coif which his tyranny had imposed upon her. When he had done, a faint smile swept over the face that had grown so hard in these last twelve years since that day when her boy had been slain almost under her very eyes.

"It is a circumstantial tale," she said. "It is per- haps true. It is probably true."

"True!" He bounded from his seat. "True?

What are you saying, woman? Yourself you saw the boy dead."

"I did, and I know who killed him."

"But you saw him. You recognized him for your own, since you set the people on to kill those whom you believed had slain him."

"Yes," she answered. And added the question: "What do you want of me now?"

"What do I want?" He was amazed that she should ask, exasperated. Had the conventual confinement turned her head? "I want your testimony. I want you to denounce this fellow for the impostor that he is. The people will believe you."

"You think they will?" Interest had kindled in her glance.

"What else? Are you not the mother of Demetrius, and shall not a mother know her own son?"

"You forget. He was ten years of age then — a child. Now he is a grown man of three-and-twenty. How can I be sure? How can I be sure of anything?"

He swore a full round oath at her. "Because you saw him dead."

"Yet I may have been mistaken. I thought I knew the agents of yours who killed him. Yet you made me swear — as the price of my brothers' lives — that I was mistaken. Perhaps I was more mistaken than we thought. Perhaps my little Demetrius was not slain at all. Perhaps this man's tale is true."

"Perhaps . . ." He broke off to stare at her, mistrustfully, searchingly. "What do you mean?" he asked her sharply.

Again that wan smile crossed the hard, sharp-featured face that once had been so lovely. "I mean

that if the devil came out of hell and called himse
my son, I should acknowledge him to your undoing.'

Thus the pent-up hate and bitterness of years of
brooding upon her wrongs broke forth. Taken aback,
he quailed before it. His jaw dropped foolishly, and
he stared at her with wide, unblinking eyes.

"The people will believe me, you say — they will
believe that a mother should know her own son.
Then are your hours of usurpation numbered."

If for a moment it appalled him, yet in the end,
forewarned, he was forearmed. It was foolish of her to
let him look upon the weapon with which she could
destroy him. The result of it was that she went back
to her convent under close guard, and was thereafter
confined with greater rigour than hitherto.

Desperately Boris heard how the belief in Demetrius was gaining ground in Russia with the people.
The nobles might still be sceptical, but Boris knew
that he could not trust them, since they had no cause
to love him. He began, perhaps, to realize that it is
not good to rule by fear.

And then at last came Smirnoy Otrepiev back from
Cracow, where he had been sent by Basmanov to obtain with his own eyes confirmation of the rumour
which had reached the boyar on the score of the pretender's real identity.

The rumour, he declared, was right. The false
Demetrius was none other than his own nephew,
Grishka Otrepiev, who had once been a monk, but,
unfrocked, had embraced the Roman heresy, and had
abandoned himself to licentious ways. You realize
now why Smirnoy had been chosen by Basmanov for
this particular mission.

The news heartened Boris. At last he could denounce the impostor in proper terms, and denounce him he did. He sent an envoy to Sigismund III to proclaim the fellow's true identity, and to demand his expulsion from the Kingdom of Poland; and his denunciation was supported by a solemn excommunication pronounced by the Patriarch of Moscow against the unfrocked monk, Grishka Otrepiev, who now falsely called himself Demetrius Ivanovitch.

But the denunciation did not carry the conviction that Boris expected. It was reported that the Tsarevitch was a courtly, accomplished man, speaking Polish and Latin, as well as Russian, skilled in horsemanship and in the use of arms, and it was asked how an unfrocked monk had come by these accomplishments. Moreover, although Boris, forewarned, had prevented the Tsarina Maria from supporting the pretender out of motives of revenge, he had forgotten her two brothers; he had not foreseen that, actuated by the same motives, they might do that which he had prevented her from doing. This was what occurred. The brothers Nagoy repaired to Cracow publicly to acknowledge Demetrius their nephew, and to enrol themselves under his banner.

Against this Boris realized that mere words were useless. The sword of Nemesis was drawn, indeed. His sins had found him out. Nothing remained him but to arm and go forth to meet the impostor, who was advancing upon Moscow with a great host of Poles and Cossacks.

He appraised the support of the Nagoys at its right value. They, too, had been at Uglich, and had seen the dead boy, almost seen him slain. Vengeance upon himself was their sole motive. But was it possible that Sigismund of Poland was really deceived, as well as the Palatine of Sandomir, whose daughter was betrothed to the adventurer, Prince Adam Wisnio-wiecki, in whose house the false Demetrius had first made his appearance, and all those Polish nobles who flocked to his banner? Or were they, too, moved by some ulterior motive which he could not fathom?

That was the riddle that plagued Boris Godunov what time — in the winter of 1604 — he sent his ar-mies to meet the invader. He sent them because, crippled now by gout, even the satisfaction of leading them was denied him. He was forced to stay at home in the gloomy apartments of the Kremlin, fretted by care, with the ghosts of his evil past to keep him com-pany, and assure him that the hour of judgment was at hand.

With deepening rage he heard how town after town capitulated to the adventurer, and mistrusting Bas-manov, who was in command, he sent Shuiski to re-place him. In January of 1605 the armies met at Dobrinichi, and Demetrius suffered a severe defeat, which compelled him to fall back on Putioli. He lost all his infantry, and every Russian taken in arms on the pretender's side was remorselessly hanged as Boris had directed.

Hope began to revive in the heart of Boris; but as months passed and no decision came, those hopes faded again, and the canker of the past gnawed at his vitals and sapped his strength. And then there was ever present to his mind the nightmare riddle of the pretender's identity. At last, one evening in April, he sent for Smirnoy Otrepiev to question him again concerning that nephew of his. Otrepiev came in fear this time. It is not good to be the uncle of a man who is giving so much trouble to a great prince.

Boris glared at him from blood-injected eyes. His round, white face was haggard, his cheeks sagged, and his fleshly body had lost all its erstwhile firm vigour.

"I have sent for you to question you again," he said, "touching this lewd nephew of yours, this Grishka Otrepiev, this unfrocked monk, who claims to be Tsar of Muscovy. Are you sure, man, that you have made no mistake — are you sure?"

Otrepiev was shaken by the Tsar's manner, by the ferocity of his mien. But he made answer: "Alas, Highness! I could not be mistaken. I am sure."

Boris grunted, and moved his body irritably in his chair. His terrible eyes watched Otrepiev mistrustfully. He had reached the mental stage in which he mistrusted everything and everybody.

"You lie, you dog," he snarled savagely.

"Highness, I swear . . ."

"Lies!" Boris roared him down. "And here's the proof. Would Sigismund of Poland have acknowledged him had he been what you say? When I denounced him the unfrocked monk Grishka Otrepiev, would not Sigismund have verified the statement had it been true?"

"The brothers Nagoy, the uncles of the dead Demetrius . . ." Otrepiev was beginning, when again Boris interrupted him.

"Their acknowledgment of him came after Sigismund's, after — long after — my denunciation." He broke into oaths. "I say you lie. Will you stand there and palter with me, man? Will you wait until the rack pulls you joint from joint before you speak the truth?"

"Highness!" cried Otrepiev, "I have served you faithfully these years."

"The truth, man; as you hope for life," thundered the Tsar, "the whole truth of this foul nephew of yours, if so be he is your nephew."

And Otrepiev spoke the whole truth at last in his great dread. "He is not my nephew."

"Not?" It was a roar of rage. "You dared lie to me?"

Otrepiev's knees were loosened by terror, and he went down upon them before the irate Tsar.

"I did not lie — not altogether. I told you a half-truth, Highness. His name is Grishka Otrepiev; it is the name by which he always has been known, and he is an unfrocked monk, all as I said, and the son of my brother's wife."

"Then . . . then . . ." Boris was bewildered. Suddenly he understood. "And his father?"

"Was Stephen Bathory, King of Poland. Grishka Otrepiev is King Stephen's natural son."

Boris seemed to fight for breath for a moment.

"This is true?" he asked, and himself answered the question. "Of course it is true. It is the light at last . . . at last. You may go."

Otrepiev stumbled out, thankful, surprised to escape so lightly. He could not know of how little account to Boris was the deception he had practised in comparison with the truth he had now revealed, a truth that shed a fearful, dazzling light upon the dark mystery of the false Demetrius. The problem that so long had plagued the Tsar was solved at last.

This pretended Demetrius, this unfrocked monk, was a natural son of Stephen Bathory, and a Roman Catholic. Such men as Sigismund of Poland and the Voyvode of Sandomir were not deceived on the score of his identity. They, and no doubt other of the leading nobles of Poland, knew the man for what he was, and because of it supported him, using the fiction of his being Demetrius Ivanovitch to impose upon the masses and facilitate the pretender's occupation of the throne of Russia. And the object of it was to set up in Muscovy a ruler who should be a Pole and a Roman Catholic. Boris knew the bigotry of Sigismund, who already had sacrificed a throne — that of Sweden — to his devout conscience, and he saw clearly to the heart of this intrigue. Had he not heard that a papal nuncio had been at Cracow, and that this nuncio had been a stout supporter of the pretender's claim? What could be the Pope's concern in the Muscovite succession? Why should a Roman priest support the claim of a prince to the throne of a country devoted to the Greek Faith?

At last all was clear indeed to Boris. Rome was at the bottom of this business, whose true aim was the Romanization of Russia; and Sigismund had fetched Rome into it, had set Rome on. Himself an elected King of Poland, Sigismund may have seen in the ambitious son of Stephen Bathory one who might perhaps supplant him on the Polish throne. To divert his ambition into another channel he had fathered — if he had not invented — this fiction that the pretender was the dead Demetrius.

Had that fool Smirnoy Otrepiev but dealt frankly with him from the first, what months of annoyance might he not have been spared; how easy it might have been to prick this bubble of imposture. But better late than never. To-morrow he would publish the true facts, and all the world should know the truth; and it was a truth that must give pause to those fools in this superstitious Russia, so devoted to the Orthodox Greek Church, who favoured the pretender. They should see the trap that was being baited for them.

There was a banquet in the Kremlin that night to certain foreign envoys, and Boris came to table in better spirits than he had been for many a day. He was heartened by the thought of what was now to do, by the conviction that he held the false Demetrius in the hollow of his hand. There to those envoys he would announce to-night what to-morrow he would announce to all Russia — tell them of the discovery he had made, and reveal to his subjects the peril in which they stood. Towards the close of the banquet he rose to address his guests, announcing that he had an important communication for them. In silence they waited for him to speak. And then, abruptly, with no word yet spoken, he sank back into his chair, fighting for breath, clawing the air, his face empurpling until suddenly the blood gushed copiously from his mouth and nostrils.

He was vouchsafed time in which to strip off his splendid apparel and wrap himself in a monk's robe, thus symbolizing the putting aside of earthly vanities, and then he expired.

It has been now and then suggested that he was poisoned. His death was certainly most opportune to Demetrius. But there is nothing in the manner of it to justify the opinion that it resulted from anything other than an apoplexy.

His death brought the sinister opportunist Shuiski back to Moscow to place Boris's son Feodor on the throne. But the reign of this lad of sixteen was very brief. Basmanov, who had gone back to the army, being now inspired by jealousy and fear of the ambitious Shuiski, went over at once to the pretender, and proclaimed him Tsar of Russia. Thereafter events moved swiftly. Basmanov marched on Moscow, entered it in triumph, and again proclaimed Demetrius, whereupon the people rose in revolt against the son of the usurper Boris, stormed the Kremlin, and strangled the boy and his mother.

Basil Shuiski would have shared their fate had he not bought his life at the price of betrayal. Publicly he declared to the Muscovites that the boy whose body he had seen at Uglich was not that of Demetrius, but of a peasant's son, who had been murdered in his stead.

That statement cleared the last obstacle from the pretender's path, and he advanced now to take possession of his throne. Yet before he occupied it, he showed the real principles that actuated him, proved how true had been Boris's conclusion. He ordered the arrest and degradation of the Patriarch who had denounced and excommunicated him, and in his place appointed Ignatius, Bishop of Riazan, a man suspected of belonging to the Roman communion.

On the 30th of June of that year 1605, Demetrius made his triumphal entry into Moscow. He went to prostrate himself before the tomb of Ivan the Terrible, and then to visit the Tsarina Maria, who, after a brief communion with him in private, came forth publicly to acknowledge him as her son.

Just as Shuiski had purchased his life by a falsehood, so did she purchase her enlargement from that convent where so long she had been a prisoner, and restoration to the rank that was her proper due. After all, she had cause for gratitude to Demetrius, who, in addition to restoring her these things, had avenged her upon the hated Boris Godunov.

His coronation followed in due season, and at last this amazing adventurer found himself firmly seated upon the throne of Russia, with Basmanov at his right hand to help and guide him. And at first all went well, and the young Tsar earned a certain measure of popularity. If his swarthy face was coarse-featured, yet his bearing was so courtly and gracious that he won his way quickly to the hearts of his people. For the rest he was of a tall, graceful figure, a fine horseman, and of a knightly address at arms.

But he soon found himself in the impossible position of having to serve two masters. On the one hand there was Russia, and the Orthodox Russians whose tsar he was, and on the other there were the Poles, who had made him so at a price, and who now demanded payment. Because he saw that this payment would be difficult and fraught with peril to himself, he would — after the common wont of princes who had attained their objects — have repudiated the debt. And so he was disposed to ignore, or at least to evade, the persistent reminders that reached him from the papal nuncio, to whom he had promised the introduction into Russia of the Roman faith.

But presently came a letter from Sigismund

couched in different terms. The King of Poland wrote to Demetrius that word had reached him that Boris Godunov was still alive, and that he had taken refuge in England, adding that he might be tempted to restore the fugitive to the throne of Muscovy.

The threat contained in that bitter piece of sarcasm aroused Demetrius to a sense of the responsibilities he had undertaken, which were precisely as Boris Godunov had surmised. As a beginning he granted the Jesuits permission to build a church within the sacred walls of the Kremlin, whereby he gave great scandal. Soon followed other signs that he was not a true son of the Orthodox Greek Church; he gave offence by his indifference to public worship, by his neglect of Russian customs, and by surrounding himself with Roman Catholic Poles, upon whom he conferred high offices and dignities.

And there were those at hand ready to stir up public feeling against him, resentful boyars quick to suspect that perhaps they had been swindled. Foremost among these was the sinister turncoat Shuiski, who had not derived from his perjury all the profit he expected, who resented, above all, to see Basmanov — who had ever been his rival — invested with a power second only to that of the Tsar himself. Shuiski, skilled in intrigue, went to work in his underground, burrowing fashion. He wrought upon the clergy, who in their turn wrought upon the populace, and presently all was seething disaffection under a surface apparently calm.

The eruption came in the following May, when Maryna, the daughter of the Palatine of Sandomir, made her splendid entry into Moscow, the bride-elect of the young Tsar. The dazzling procession and the feasting that followed found little favour in the eyes of the Muscovites, who now beheld their city aswarm with heretic Poles.

The marriage was magnificently solemnized on the 18th of May, 1606. And now Shuiski applied a match to the train he had so skilfully laid. Demetrius had caused a timber fort to be built before the walls of Moscow for a martial spectacle which he had planned for the entertainment of his bride. Shuiski put it abroad that the fort was intended to serve as an engine of destruction, and that the martial spectacle was a pretence, the real object being that from the fort the Poles were to cast firebrands into the city, and then proceed to the slaughter of the inhabitants.

No more was necessary to infuriate an already exasperated populace. They flew to arms, and on the night of the 29th of May they stormed the Kremlin, led on by the arch-traitor Shuiski himself, to the cry of "Death to the heretic! Death to the impostor!"

They broke into the palace, and swarmed up the stairs into the Tsar's bedchamber, slaying the faithful Basmanov, who stood sword in hand to bar the way and give his master time to escape. The Tsar leapt from a balcony thirty feet to the ground, broke his leg, and lay there helpless, to be dispatched by his enemies, who presently discovered him.

He died firmly and fearlessly protesting that he was Demetrius Ivanovitch. Nevertheless, he was Grishka Otrepiev, the unfrocked monk.

It has been said that he was no more than an instrument in the hands of priestcraft, and that because he played his part badly he met his doom. But something more he was. He was an instrument, indeed, not of priestcraft, but of Fate, to bring home to Boris Godunov the hideous sins that stained his soul, and to avenge his victims by personating one of them. In that personation he had haunted Boris as effectively as if he had been the very ghost of the boy murdered at Uglich, haunted and tortured, and finally broken him so that he died.

That was the part assigned him by Fate in the mysterious scheme of human things. And that part being played, the rest mattered little. In the nature of him and of his position it was impossible that his imposture should be other than ephemeral.

III

THE HERMOSA FEMBRA

APPREHENSION hung like a thundercloud over the city of Seville in those early days of the year 1481. It had been growing since the previous October, when the Cardinal of Spain and Frey Tomas de Torquemada, acting jointly on behalf of the sovereigns — Ferdinand and Isabella — had appointed the first inquisitors for Castile, ordering them to set up a Tribunal of the Faith in Seville, to deal with the apostatizing said to be rampant among the New-Christians, or baptized Jews, who made up so large a proportion of the population.

Among the many oppressive Spanish enactments against the children of Israel, it was prescribed that all should wear the distinguishing circlet of red cloth on the shoulder of their gabardines; that they should reside within the walled confines of their ghettos and never be found beyond them after nightfall, and that they should not practise as doctors, surgeons, apothecaries, or innkeepers. The desire to emancipate themselves from these and other restrictions upon their commerce with Christians, and from the generally intolerable conditions of bondage and ignominy imposed upon them, had driven many to accept baptism and embrace Christianity. But even such Christians as were sincere in their professions of failed to find in this baptism the peace they sought. Bitter racial hostility, though sometimes tempered, was never extinguished by their conversion.

Hence the alarm with which they viewed the gloomy, funereal, sinister pageant — the white-robed, black-mantled, and hooded inquisitors, with their attendant familiars and barefoot friars — headed by a Dominican bearing the white Cross, which invaded the city of Seville one day towards the end of December, and took its way to the Convent of Saint Paul, there to establish the Holy Office of the Inquisition. The fear of the New-Christians that they were to be the object of the attentions of this dread tribunal had sufficed to drive some thousands of them out of the city, to seek refuge in such feudal lordships as those of the Duke of Medina Sidonia, the Marquis of Cadiz, and the Count of Arcos.

This exodus had led to the publication by the newly appointed inquisitors of the edict of 2d January, in which they set forth that, inasmuch as it had come to their knowledge that many persons had departed out of Seville in fear of prosecution upon grounds of heretical pravity, they commanded the nobles of the Kingdom of Castile that within fifteen days they should make an exact return of the persons of both sexes who had sought refuge in their lordships or jurisdictions; that they arrest all these and lodge them in the prison of the Inquisition in Seville, confiscating their property, and holding it at the disposal of the inquisitors; that none should shelter any fugitive under ~~in~~ of greater excommunication and of other penal-~~ty~~ by law established against abettors of heretics.

~~The~~ harsh injustice that lay in this call to arrest

men and women, merely because they had departed from Seville before departure was in any way forbidden, revealed the severity with which the inquisitors intended to proceed. It completed the consternation of the New-Christians who had remained behind, and how numerous these were may be gathered from the fact that in the district of Seville alone they numbered a hundred thousand, many of them occupying, thanks to the industry and talent characteristic of their race, positions of great eminence. It even disquieted the well favoured young Don Rodrigo de Cardona, who in all his vain, empty, pampered, and rather vicious life had never yet known perturbation. Not that he was a New-Christian. He was of a lineage that went back to the Visigoths, of purest red Castilian blood, untainted by any strain of that dark-hued, unclean fluid alleged to flow in Hebrew veins. But it happened that he was in love with the daughter of the millionaire Diego de Susan, a girl whose beauty was so extraordinary that she was known throughout Seville and for many a mile around as "la Hermosa Fembra"; and he knew that such commerce — licit or illicitly conducted — was disapproved by the holy fathers. His relations with the girl had been perforce clandestine, because the disapproval of the holy fathers was matched in thoroughness by that of Diego de Susan. It had been vexatious enough on that account not to be able to boast himself the favoured of the beautiful and opulent Isabella de Susan; it was exasperating to discover now a new and more imperative reason for this odious secrecy.

Never sped a lover to his mistr

mind more aggrieved than tha

Rodrigo as, tight-wrapped in his black cloak, he gained the Calle de Ataud on that January night.

Anon, however, when by way of a garden gate and an easily escaladed balcony he found himself in the presence of Isabella, the delight of her effaced all other considerations. Her father was from home, as she had told him in the note that summoned him; he was away at Palacios on some merchant's errand, and would not return until the morrow. The servants were all abed, and so Don Rodrigo might put off his cloak and hat, and lounge at his ease upon the low Moorish divan, what time she waited upon him with a Saracen goblet filled with sweet wine of Malaga. The room in which she received him was one set apart for her own use, her bower, a long, low-ceilinged chamber, furnished with luxury and taste. The walls were hung with tapestries, the floor spread with costly Eastern rugs; on an inlaid Moorish table a tall, three-beaked lamp of beaten copper charged with aromatic oil shed light and perfume through the apartment.

Don Rodrigo sipped his wine, and his dark, hungry eyes followed her as she moved about him with vaguely voluptuous, almost feline grace. The wine, the heavy perfume of the lamp, and the beauty of her played havoc among them with his senses, so that he forgot for the moment his Castilian lineage and clean Christian blood, forgot that she derived from the accursed race of the Crucifiers. All that he remembered was that she was the loveliest woman in Seville, d...... .... the wealthiest man, and in that hour of ....led to convert into reality that which .... .ore than an infamous pretence.

He would loyally fulfil the false, disloyal promises he had made. He would take her to wife. It was a sacrifice which her beauty and her wealth should make worth while. Upon that impulse he spoke now, abruptly:

"Isabella, when will you marry me?"

She stood before him, looking down into his weak, handsome face, her fingers interlacing his own. She merely smiled. The question did not greatly move her. Not knowing him for the scoundrel that he was, guessing nothing of the present perturbation of his senses, she found it very natural that he should ask her to appoint the day.

"It is a question you must ask my father," she answered him.

"I will," said he, "to-morrow, on his return." And he drew her down beside him.

But that father was nearer than either of them dreamed. At that very moment the soft thud of the closing house-door sounded through the house. It brought her sharply to her feet, and loosed from his coiling arms, with quickened breath and blanching face. A moment she hung there, tense, then sped to the door of the room, set it ajar and listened.

Up the stairs came the sound of footsteps and of muttering voices. It was her father, and others with him.

With ever-mounting fear she turned drigo, and breathed the question: "If come here?"

The Castilian stood where he had divan, his face paler now than its pal wont, his eyes reflecting the fear that g

own. He had no delusion as to what action Diego de
Susan would take upon discovering him. These Jewish dogs were quickly stirred to passion, and as jealous
as their betters of the honour of their womenfolk. Already Don Rodrigo in imagination saw his clean red
Christian blood bespattering that Hebrew floor, for
he had no weapon save the heavy Toledo dagger at his
girdle, and Diego de Susan was not alone.

It was, he felt, a ridiculous position for a Hidalgo of
Spain. But his dignity was to suffer still greater damage. In another moment she had bundled him into an
alcove behind the arras at the chamber's end, a tiny
closet that was no better than a cupboard contrived
for the storing of household linen. She had moved
with a swift precision which at another time might
have provoked his admiration, snatching up his cloak
and hat, and other evidences of his presence, quenching the lamp, and dragging him to that place of
cramped concealment, which she remained to share
with him.

Came presently movements in the room beyond,
and the voice of her father:

"We shall be securest from intrusion here. It is my
daughter's room. If you will give me leave, I will go
down again to admit our other friends."

Those other friends, as Don Rodrigo gathered, continued to arrive for the next half-hour, until in the end
there must have been some twenty of them assembled
in that chamber. The mutter of voices had steadily
increased, but so confused that no more than odd
words, affording no clue to the reason of this gathering, had reached the hidden couple.

And then quite suddenly a silence fell, and on that

silence beat the sharp, clear voice of Diego de Susan addressing them.

"My friends," he said, "I have called you hither that we may concert measures for the protection of ourselves and all New-Christians in Seville from the fresh peril by which we are menaced. The edict of the inquisitors reveals how much we have to fear. You may gather from it that the court of the Holy Office is hardly likely to deal in justice, and that the most innocent may find himself at any moment exposed to its cruel mercies. Therefore it is for us now to consider how to protect ourselves and our property from the unscrupulous activities of this tribunal. You are the principal New-Christian citizens of Seville; you are wealthy, not only in property, but also in the good-will of the people, who trust and respect, and at need will follow, you. If nothing less will serve, we must have recourse to arms; and so that we are resolute and united, my friends, we shall prevail against the inquisitors."

Within the alcove, Don Rodrigo felt his skin roughening with horror at this speech, which breathed sedition not only against the sovereigns, but against the very Church. And with his horror was blent a certain increase of fear. If his situation had been perilous before, it was tenfold more dangerous now. Discovery, since he had overheard this treason, must mean his certain death. And Isabella, realizing the same to the exclusion of all else, clutched his arm and cowered against him in the dark.

There was worse to follow. Susan's address was received with a murmur of applause, and then others spoke, and several were named, and their presence thus disclosed. There was the influential Manuel Sauli, who next to Susan was the wealthiest man in Seville; there was Torralba, the Governor of Triana; Juan Abolafio, the farmer of the royal customs, and his brother Fernandez, the licentiate; and there were others — all of them men of substance, some even holding office under the Crown. Not one was there who dissented from anything that Susan had said; rather did each contribute some spur to the general resolve. In the end it was concerted that each of those present should engage himself to raise a proportion of the men, arms, and money that would be needed for their enterprise. And upon that the meeting was dissolved, and they departed. Susan himself went with them. He had work to do in the common cause, he announced, and he would do it that very night in which it was supposed that he was absent at Palacios.

At last, when all had gone, and the house was still again, Isabella and her lover crept forth from their concealment, and in the light of the lamp which Susan had left burning each looked into the other's white, startled face. So shaken was Don Rodrigo with horror of what he had overheard, and with the terror of discovery, that it was with difficulty he kept his teeth from chattering.

"Heaven protect us!" he gasped. "What Judaizing was this?"

"Judaizing!" she echoed. It was the term applied to apostasy, to the relapse of New-Christians to Judaism, an offence to be expiated at the stake. "Here was no Judaizing. Are you mad, Rodrigo? You heard no single word that sinned against the Faith."

"Did I not? I heard treason enough to . . ."

"No, nor treason either. You heard honourable, upright men considering measures of defence against oppression, injustice, and evil acquisitiveness masquerading in the holy garments of religion."

He stared askance at her for a moment, then his full lips curled into a sneer. "Of course you would seek to justify them," he said. "You are of that foul brood yourself. But you cannot think to cozen me, who am of clean Old-Christian blood and a true son of Mother Church. These men plot evil against the Holy Inquisition. Is that not Judaizing when it is done by Jews?"

She was white to the lips, and a new horror stared at him from her great dark eyes; her lovely bosom rose and fell in tumult. Yet still she sought to reason with him.

"They are not Jews — not one of them. Why, Perez is himself in holy orders. All of them are Christians, and . . ."

"Newly baptized!" he broke in, sneering viciously. "A defilement of that holy sacrament to gain them worldly advantages. That is revealed by what passed here just now. Jews they were born, the sons of Jews, and Jews they remain under their cloak of mock Christianity, to be damned as Jews in the end." He was panting now with fiery indignation; a holy zeal inflamed this profligate defiler. "God forgive me that ever I entered here. Yet I do believe that it was His will that I should come to overhear what is being plotted. Let me depart from hence."

With a passionate gesture of abhorrence he swung towards the door. Her clutch upon his arm arrested him.

"Whither do you go?" she asked him sharply. He looked now into her eyes, and of all that they contained he saw only fear; he saw nothing of the hatred into which her love had been transmuted in that moment by his unsparing insults to herself, her race, and her home, by the purpose which she clearly read in him.

"Whither?" he echoed, and sought to shake her off. "Whither my Christian duty bids me."

It was enough for her. Before he could prevent or suspect her purpose, she had snatched the heavy Toledo blade from his girdle, and armed with it stood between the door and him.

"A moment, Don Rodrigo. Do not attempt to advance, or, as Heaven watches us, I strike, and it may be that I shall kill you. We must talk awhile before you go."

Amazed, chapfallen, half-palsied, he stood before her, his fine religious zeal wiped out by fear of that knife in her weak woman's hand. Rapidly to-night was she coming into real knowledge of this Castilian gentleman, whom with pride she had taken for her lover. It was a knowledge that was to sear her presently with self-loathing and self-contempt. But for the moment her only consideration was that, as a direct result of her own wantonness, her father stood in mortal peril. If he should perish through the delation of this creature, she would account herself his slayer.

"You have not considered that the delation you intend will destroy my father," she said quietly.

"There is my Christian duty to consider," answered he, but without boldness now.

"Perhaps. But there is something you must set

against it. Have you no duty as a lover — no duty to me?"

"No earthly duty can weigh against a spiritual obligation . . ."

"Ah, wait! Have patience. You have not well considered, that is plain. In coming here in secret you wronged my father. You will not trouble to deny it. Jointly we wronged him, you and I. Will you then take advantage of something learnt whilst you were hiding there like a thief from the consequences of what you did, and so do him yet this further wrong?"

"Must I wrong my conscience?" he asked her sullenly.

"Indeed, I fear you must."

"Imperil my immortal soul?" He almost laughed. "You talk in vain."

"But I have something more than words for you." With her left hand she drew upon the fine gold chain about her neck, and brought forth a tiny jewelled cross. Passing the chain over her head, she held it out.

"Take this," she bade him. "Take it, I say. Now, with that sacred symbol in your hand, make solemn oath to divulge no word of what you have learnt here to-night, or else resign yourself to an unshriven death. For either you take that oath, or I rouse the servants and have you dealt with as one who has intruded here unbidden for an evil end." She backed away from him as she spoke, and threw wide the door. Then, confronting him from the threshold, she admonished him again, her voice no louder than a whisper. "Quick now! Resolve yourself. Will you die here with all your sins upon you, and so destroy for all eternity the immortal soul that urges you to this betrayal, or will you take the oath that I require?"

He began an argument that was like a sermon of the Faith. But she cut him short. "For the last time!" she bade him. "Will you decide?"

He chose the coward's part, of course, and did violence to his fine conscience. With the cross in his hand he repeated after her the words of the formidable oath that she administered, an oath which it must damn his immortal soul to break. Because of that, because she imagined that she had taken the measure of his faith, she returned him his dagger, and let him go at last. She imagined that she had bound him fast in irrefragable spiritual bonds.

And even on the morrow, when her father and all those who had been present at that meeting at Susan's house were arrested by order of the Holy Office of the Inquisition, she still clung to that belief. Yet presently a doubt crept in, a doubt that she must at all costs resolve. And so presently she called for her litter, and had herself carried to the Convent of Saint Paul, where she asked to see Frey Alfonso de Ojeda, the Prior of the Dominicans of Seville.

She was left to wait in a square, cheerless, dimly lighted room pervaded by a musty smell, that had for only furniture a couple of chairs and a praying-stool, and for only ornament a great, gaunt crucifix hanging upon one of its whitewashed walls.

Thither came presently two Dominican friars. One of these was a harsh-featured man of middle height and square build, the uncompromising zealot Ojeda. The other was tall and lean, stooping slightly at the shoulders, haggard and pale of countenance, with deep-set, luminous dark eyes, and a tender, wistful mouth. This was the Queen's confessor, Frey Tomas de Torquemada, Grand Inquisitor of Castile. He approached her, leaving Ojeda in the background, and stood a moment regarding her with eyes of infinite kindliness and compassion.

"You are the daughter of that misguided man, Diego de Susan," he said, in a gentle voice. "God help and strengthen you, my child, against the trials that may be in store for you. What do you seek at our poor hands? Speak, child, without fear."

"Father," she faltered, "I come to implore your pity."

"No need to implore it, child. Should I withhold pity who stand myself in need of pity, being a sinner — as are we all."

"It is for my father that I come to beg your mercy."

"So I supposed." A shade crossed the gentle, wistful face; the tender melancholy deepened in the eyes that regarded her. "If your father is innocent of what has been alleged against him, the benign tribunal of the Holy Office will bring his innocence to light, and rejoice therein; if he is guilty, if he has strayed — as we may all stray unless fortified by heavenly grace — he shall be given the means of expiation, that his salvation may be assured him."

She shivered at the words. She knew the mercy in which the inquisitors dealt, a mercy so spiritual that it took no account of the temporal agonies inflicted to ensure it.

"My father is innocent of any sin against the Faith," said she.

"Are you so sure?" croaked the harsh voice of

Ojeda, breaking in. "Consider well. Remember that your duty as a Christian is above your duty as a daughter."

Almost had she bluntly demanded the name of her father's accuser, that thus she might reach the object of her visit. Betimes she checked the rash impulse, perceiving that subtlety was here required; that a direct question would close the door to all information. Skilfully, then, she chose her line of attack.

"I am sure," she exclaimed, "that he is a more fervent and pious Christian — New-Christian though he be — than his accuser."

The wistfulness faded from Torquemada's eyes. They grew keen, as became the eyes of an inquisitor, the eyes of a sleuth, quick to fasten on a spoor. But he shook his head.

Ojeda advanced. "That I cannot believe," said he. "The delation was made from a sense of duty so pure that the delator did not hesitate to confess the sin of his own commission through which he had discovered the treachery of Don Diego and his associates."

She could have cried out in anguish at this answer to her unspoken question. Yet she controlled herself, and that no single doubt should linger, she thrust boldly home.

"He confessed it?" she cried, seemingly aghast. The friar slowly nodded. "Don Rodrigo confessed?" she insisted, as will the incredulous.

Abruptly the friar nodded again; and as abruptly checked, recollecting himself.

"Don Rodrigo?" he echoed, and asked: "Who mentioned Don Rodrigo?"

But it was too late. His assenting nod had betrayed

the truth, had confirmed her worst fear. She swayed a little; the room swam round her, she felt as she would swoon. Then blind indignation against that forsworn betrayer surged to revive her. If it was through her weakness and undutifulness that her father had been destroyed, through her strength should he be avenged, though in doing so she pulled down and destroyed herself.

"And he confessed to his own sin?" she was repeating slowly, ever on that musing, incredulous note. "He dared confess himself a Judaizer?"

"A Judaizer!" Sheer horror now overspread the friar's grim countenance. "A Judaizer! Don Rodrigo? Oh, impossible!"

"But I thought you said he had confessed."

"Why, yes, but . . . but not to that."

Her pale lips smiled, sadly contemptuous. "I see. He set limits of prudence upon his confession. He left out his Judaizing practices. He did not tell you, for instance, that this delation was an act of revenge against me who refused to marry him, having discovered his unfaith, and fearing its consequences in this world and the next."

Ojeda stared at her in sheer, incredulous amazement.

And then Torquemada spoke: "Do you say that Don Rodrigo de Cardona is a Judaizer? Oh, it is unbelievable."

"Yet I could give you evidence that should convince you."

"Then so you shall. It is your sacred duty, lest you become an abettor of heresy, and yourself liable to the extreme penalty."

It would be a half-hour later, perhaps, when she quitted the Convent of Saint Paul to return home, with hell in her heart, knowing in life no purpose but that of avenging the parent her folly had destroyed. As she was being carried past the Alcazar, she espied across the open space a tall, slim figure in black, in whom she recognized her lover, and straightway she sent the page who paced beside her litter to call him to her side. The summons surprised him after what had passed between them; moreover, considering her father's present condition, he was reluctant to be seen in attendance upon the beautiful, wealthy Isabella de Susan. Nevertheless, urged on by curiosity, he went.

Her greeting increased his surprise.

"I am in deep distress, Rodrigo, as you may judge," she told him sadly. "You will have heard what has befallen my father?"

He looked at her sharply, yet saw nothing but loveliness rendered more appealing by sorrow. Clearly she did not suspect him of betrayal; did not realize that an oath extorted by violence — and an oath, moreover, to be false to a sacred duty — could not be accounted binding.

"I . . . I heard of it an hour ago," he lied a thought unsteadily. "I . . . I commiserate you deeply."

"I deserve commiseration," answered she, "and so does my poor father, and those others. It is plain that amongst those he trusted there was a traitor, a spy, who went straight from that meeting to inform against them. If I but had a list it were easy to discover the betrayer. One need but ascertain who is the one of all who were present whose arrest has been omitted." Her lovely, sorrowful eyes turned full upon him. "What is to become of me now, alone in the world?" she asked him. "My father was my only friend."

The subtle appeal of her did its work swiftly. Besides, he saw here a noble opportunity worth surely some little risk.

"Your only friend?" he asked her thickly. "Was there no one else? Is there no one else, Isabella?"

"There was," she said, and sighed heavily. "But after what befell last night, when . . . You know what is in my mind. I was distraught then, mad with fear for this poor father of mine, so that I could not even consider his sin in its full heinousness, nor see how righteous was your intent to inform against him. Yet I am thankful that it was not by your delation that he was taken. The thought of that is to-day my only consolation."

They had reached her house by now. Don Rodrigo put forth his arm to assist her to alight from her litter, and begged leave to accompany her within. But she denied him.

"Not now — though I am grateful to you, Rodrigo. Soon, if you will come and comfort me, you may. I will send you word when I am more able to receive you — that is, if I am forgiven for . . ."

"Not another word," he begged her. "I honour you for what you did. It is I who should sue to you for forgiveness."

"You are very noble and generous, Don Rodrigo. God keep you!" And so she left him.

She had found him — had she but known it — a dejected, miserable man in the act of reckoning up all that he had lost. In betraying Susan he had acted upon an impulse that sprang partly from rage, and partly from a sense of religious duty. In counting later the cost to himself, he cursed the folly of his rage, and began to wonder if such strict observance of religious duty was really worth while to a man who had his way to make in the world. In short, he was in the throes of reaction. But now, in her unsuspicion, he found his hopes revive. She need never know. The Holy Office preserved inviolate secrecy on the score of delations — since to do otherwise might be to discourage delators — and there were no confrontations of accuser and accused, such as took place in temporal courts. Don Rodrigo left the Calle de Ataud better pleased with the world than he had been since morning.

On the morrow he went openly to visit her; but he was denied, a servant announcing her indisposed. This fretted him, damped his hopes, and thereby increased his longing. But on the next day he received from her a letter which made him the most ample amends:

RODRIGO, — There is a matter on which we must come early to an understanding. Should my poor father be convicted of heresy and sentenced, it follows that his property will be confiscated, since as the daughter of a convicted heretic I may not inherit. For myself I care little; but I am concerned for you, Rodrigo, since if in spite of what has happened you would still wish to make me your wife, as you declared on Monday, it would be my wish to come to you well dowered. Now the inheritance which would be confiscated by the Holy Office from the daughter of a heretic might not be so confiscated from the wife of a gentleman of Castile. I say no more. Consider this well, and decide as your heart dictates. I shall receive you to-morrow if you come to me.

ISABELLA

She bade him consider well. But the matter really needed little consideration. Diego de Susan was sure to go to the fire. His fortune was estimated at ten million maravedis. That fortune, it seemed, Rodrigo was given the chance to make his own by marrying the beautiful Isabella at once, before sentence came to be passed upon her father. The Holy Office might impose a fine, but would not go further where the inheritance of a Castilian nobleman of clean lineage was concerned. He was swayed between admiration of her shrewdness and amazement at his own good fortune. Also vanity was immensely flattered.

He sent her three lines to protest his undying love, and his resolve to marry her upon the morrow, and went next day in person, as she had bidden him, to carry out the resolve.

She received him in the mansion's best room, a noble chamber furnished with a richness such as no other house in Seville could have boasted. She had arrayed herself for the interview with an almost wanton cunning that should enhance her natural endowments. Her high-waisted gown, low-cut and close-fitting in the bodice, was of cloth of gold, edged with miniver at skirt and cuffs and neck. On her white bosom hung a priceless carcanet of limpid diamonds, and through the heavy tresses of her bronze-coloured hair was coiled a string of lustrous pearls.

Never had Don Rodrigo found her more desirable; never had he felt so secure and glad in his possession of her. The quickening blood flushing now his olive face, he gathered her slim shapeliness into his arms, kissing her cheek, her lips, her neck.

"My pearl, my beautiful, my wife!" he murmured, rapturously. Then added the impatient question: "The priest? Where is the priest that shall make us one?"

Deep, unfathomable eyes looked up to meet his burning glance. Languorously she lay against his breast, and her red lips parted in a smile that maddened him.

"You love me, Rodrigo — in spite of all?"

"Love you!" It was a throbbing, strangled cry, an almost inarticulate ejaculation. "Better than life — better than salvation."

She fetched a sign, as of deep content, and nestled closer. "Oh, I am glad — so glad — that your love for me is truly strong. I am about to put it to the test, perhaps."

He held her very close. "What is this test, beloved?"

"It is that I want this marriage knot so tied that it shall be indissoluble save by death."

"Why, so do I," quoth he, who had so much to gain.

"And, therefore, because after all, though I profess Christianity, there is Jewish blood in my veins, I would have a marriage that must satisfy even my father when he regains his freedom, as I believe he will — for, after all, he is not charged with any sin against the Faith."

She paused, and he was conscious of a premonitory chill upon his ardour.

"What do you mean?" he asked her, and his voice was strained.

"I mean — you'll not be angry with me? — I mean that I would have us married not only by a Christian priest, and in the Christian manner, but also and first of all by a rabbi, and in accordance with the Jewish rites."

Upon the words, she felt his encircling arms turn limp, and relax their grip upon her, whereupon she clung to him the more tightly.

"Rodrigo! Rodrigo! If you truly love me, if you truly want me, you'll not deny me this condition, for I swear to you that once I am your wife you shall never hear anything again to remind you that I am of Jewish blood."

His face turned ghastly pale, his lips writhed and twitched, and beads of sweat stood out upon his brow.

"My God!" he groaned. "What do you ask? I . . . I can't. It were a desecration, a defilement."

She thrust him from her in a passion. "You regard it so? You protest love, and in the very hour when I propose to sacrifice all to you, you will not make this little sacrifice for my sake, you even insult the faith that was my forbears', if it is not wholly mine. I misjudged you, else I had not bidden you here to-day. I think you had better leave me."

Trembling, appalled, a prey to an ineffable tangle of emotion, he sought to plead, to extenuate his attitude, to move her from her own. He ranted torrentially, but in vain. She stood as cold and aloof as earlier she had been warm and clinging. He had proved the measure of his love. He could go his ways.

The thing she proposed was to him, as he had truly said, a desecration, a defilement. Yet to have dreamed yourself master of ten million maravedis, and a matchless woman, is a dream not easily relinquished. There was enough cupidity in his nature, enough neediness in his condition, to make the realization of that dream worth the defilement of the abominable marriage rites upon which she insisted. But fear remained where Christian scruples were already half-effaced.

"You do not realize," he cried. "If it were known that I so much as contemplated this, the Holy Office would account it clear proof of apostasy, and send me to the fire."

"If that were your only objection, it were easily overcome," she informed him coldly. "For who should ever inform against you? The rabbi who is waiting above-stairs dare not for his own life's sake betray us, and who else will ever know?"

"You can be sure of that?"

He was conquered. But she played him yet awhile, compelling him in his turn to conquer the reluctance which his earlier hesitation had begotten in her, until it was he who pleaded insistently for this Jewish marriage that filled him with such repugnance.

And so at last she yielded, and led him up to that bower of hers in which the conspirators had met.

"Where is the rabbi?" he asked impatiently, looking round that empty room.

"I will summon him if you are quite sure that you desire him."

"Sure? Have I not protested enough? Can you still doubt me?"

"No," she said. She stood apart, conning him steadily. "Yet I would not have it supposed that you were in any way coerced to this." They were odd words; but he heeded not their oddness. He was hardly master of the wits which in themselves were never of the brightest. "I require you to declare that it is your own desire that our marriage should be solemnized in accordance with the Jewish rites and the law of Moses."

And he, fretted now by impatience, anxious to have this thing done and ended, made answer hastily:

"Why to be sure I do declare it to be my wish that we should be so married — in the Jewish manner, and in accordance with the law of Moses. And now, where is the rabbi?" He caught a sound and saw a quiver in the tapestries that masked the door of the alcove. "Ah! He is here, I suppose . . ."

He checked abruptly, and recoiled as from a blow, throwing up his hands in a convulsive gesture. The tapestry had been swept aside, and forth stepped not the rabbi he expected, but a tall, gaunt man, stooping slightly at the shoulders, dressed in the white habit and black cloak of the order of Saint Dominic, his face lost in the shadows of a black cowl. Behind him stood two lay brothers of the order, two armed familiars of the Holy Office, displaying the white cross on their sable doublets.

Terrified by that apparition, evoked, as it seemed, by those terribly damning words he had pronounced, Don Rodrigo stood blankly at gaze a moment, not even seeking to understand how this dread thing had come to pass.

The friar pushed back his cowl, as he advanced,

and displayed the tender, compassionate, infinitely wistful countenance of Frey Tomas de Torquemada. And infinitely compassionate and wistful came the voice of that deeply sincere and saintly man.

"My son, I was told this of you — that you were a Judaizer — yet before I could bring myself to believe so incredible a thing in one of your lineage, I required the evidence of my own senses. Oh, my poor child, by what wicked counsels have you been led so far astray?" The sweet, tender eyes of the inquisitor were luminous with unshed tears. Sorrowing pity shook his gentle voice.

And then Don Rodrigo's terror changed to wrath, and this exploded. He flung out an arm towards Isabella in passionate denunciation.

"It was that woman who bewitched and fooled and seduced me into this. It was a trap she baited for my undoing."

"It was, indeed. She had my consent to do so, to test the faith which I was told you lacked. Had your heart been free of heretical pravity the trap had never caught you; had your faith been strong, my son, you could not been have seduced from loyalty to your Redeemer."

"Father! Hear me, I implore you!" He flung down upon his knees, and held out shaking, supplicating hands.

"You shall be heard, my son. The Holy Office does not condemn any man unheard. But what hope can you put in protestations? I had been told that your life was disorderly and vain, and I grieved that it should be so, trembled for you when I heard how wide you opened the gates of your soul to evil. But remembering that age and reason will often make good and penitent amends for the follies of early life, I hoped and prayed for you. Yet that you should Judaize — that you should be bound in wedlock by the unclean ties of Judaism — Oh!" The melancholy voice broke off upon a sob, and Torquemada covered his pale face with his hands — long, white, emaciated, almost transparent hands. "Pray now, my child, for grace and strength," he exhorted. "Offer up the little temporal suffering that may yet be yours in atonement for your error, and so that your heart be truly contrite and penitent, you shall deserve salvation from that Divine Mercy which is boundless. You shall have my prayers, my son. I can do no more. Take him hence."

On the 6th of February of that year 1481, Seville witnessed the first auto-de-fé, the sufferers being Diego de Susan, his fellow-conspirators, and Don Rodrigo de Cardona. The function presented but little of the ghastly pomp that was soon to distinguish these proceedings. But the essentials were already present.

In a procession headed by a Dominican bearing aloft the green Cross of the Inquisition, swathed in a veil of crêpe, behind whom walked two by two the members of the Confraternity of Saint Peter the Martyr, the familiars of the Holy Office, came the condemned, candle in hand, barefoot, in the ignominious yellow penitential sack. Hemmed about by halberdiers, they were paraded through the streets to the Cathedral, where Mass was said and a sermon of the Faith preached to them by the stern Ojeda. Thereafter they were conveyed beyond the city to the meadows of Tablada, where the stake and faggots awaited them.

Thus the perjured accuser perished in the same holocaust with the accused. Thus was Isabella de Susan, known as "la Hermosa Fembra," avenged by falseness upon the worthless lover who made her by falseness the instrument of her father's ruin.

For herself, when all was over, she sought the refuge of a convent. But she quitted it without professing. The past gave her no peace, and she returned to the world to seek in excesses an oblivion which the cloister denied her and only death could give. In her will she disposed that her skull should be placed over the doorway of the house in the Calle de Ataud, as a measure of posthumous atonement for her sins. And there the fleshless, grinning skull of that once lovely head abode for close upon four hundred years. It was still to be seen there when Bonaparte's legions demolished the Holy Office of the Inquisition.

IV

THE PASTRY-COOK OF MADRIGAL

THE STORY OF THE FALSE SEBASTIAN OF PORTUGAL

THERE is not in all that bitter tragi-comic record of human frailty which we call History a sadder story than this of the Princess Anne, the natural daughter of the splendid Don John of Austria, natural son of the Emperor Charles V, and, so, half-brother to the bowelless King Philip II of Spain. Never was woman born to royal or semi-royal state who was more utterly the victim of the circumstances of her birth.

Of the natural sons of princes something could be made, as witness the dazzling career of Anne's own father; but for natural daughters — and especially for one who, like herself, bore a double load of cadency — there was little use or hope. Their royal blood set them in a class apart; their bastardy denied them the worldly advantages of that spurious eminence. Their royal blood prescribed that they must mate with princes; their bastardy raised obstacles to their doing so. Therefore, since the world would seem to hold no worthy place for them, it was expedien' to withdraw them from the world before its vanities beglamoured them, and to immure them in convents, where they might aspire with confidence to the sterile dignity of abbesshood.

Thus it befell with Anne. At the early age of six she had been sent to the Benedictine convent at Burgos, and in adolescence removed thence to the Monastery of Santa Maria la Real at Madrigal, where it was foreordained that she should take the veil. She went unwillingly. She had youth, and youth's hunger of life, and not even the repressive conditions in which she had been reared had succeeded in extinguishing her high spirit or in concealing from her the fact that she was beautiful. On the threshold of that convent which by her dread uncle's will was to be her living tomb, above whose gates her spirit may have beheld the inscription, "Lasciate ogni speranza, voi ch' entrate!" she made her protest, called upon the bishop who accompanied her to bear witness that she did not go of her own free will.

But what she willed was a matter of no account. King Philip's was, under God's, the only will in Spain. Still, less, perhaps, to soften the sacrifice imposed upon her than because of what he accounted due to one of his own blood, His Catholic Majesty accorded her certain privileges unusual to members of religious communities: he granted her a little civil list — two ladies-in-waiting and two grooms — and conferred upon her the title of Excellency, which she still retained even when after her hurried novitiate of a single year she had taken the veil. She submitted where to have striven would have been to have spent herself in vain; but her resignation was only of the body, and this dejected body moved mechanically through the tasks and recreations that go to make up the grey monotone of conventual existence; in which one day is as another day, one hour as another hour; in which the seasons of the year lose their significance; in which time has no purpose save for its subdivision into periods devoted to sleeping and waking, to eating and fasting, to praying and contemplating, until life loses all purpose and object, and sterilizes itself into preparation for death.

Though they might command and compel her body, her spirit remained unfettered in rebellion. Anon the claustral apathy might encompass her; in time and by slow degrees she might become absorbed into the grey spirit of the place. But that time was not yet. For the present she must nourish her caged and starving soul with memories of glimpses caught in passing of the bright, active, stirring world without; and where memory stopped she had now beside her a companion to regale her with tales of high adventure and romantic deeds and knightly feats, which served but to feed and swell her yearnings.

This companion, Frey Miguel de Souza, was a Portuguese friar of the order of Saint Augustine, a learned, courtly man who had moved in the great world and spoke with the authority of an eye-witness. And above all he loved to talk of that last romantic King of Portugal, with whom he had been intimate, that high-spirited, headstrong, gallant, fair-haired lad Sebastian, who at the age of four-and-twenty had led the disastrous overseas expedition against the Infidel which had been shattered on the field of Alcacer-el-Kebir some fifteen years ago.

He loved to paint for her in words the dazzling knightly pageants he had seen along the quays at Lisbon, when that expedition was embarking with crusader ardour, the files of Portuguese knights and

men-at-arms, the array of German and Italian mercenaries, the young king in his bright armour, bare of
head — an incarnation of Saint Michael — moving
forward exultantly amid flowers and acclamations to
take ship for Africa. And she would listen with
parted lips and glistening eyes, her slim body bending
forward in her eagerness to miss no word of this great
epic. Anon, when he came to tell of that disastrous
day of Alcacer-el-Kebir, her dark, eager eyes would
fill with tears. His tale of it was hardly truthful. He
did not say that military incompetence and a presumptuous vanity which would listen to no counsels
had been the cause of a ruin that had engulfed the
chivalry of Portugal, and finally the very kingdom
itself. He represented the defeat as due to the overwhelming numbers of the Infidel, and dwelt at length
upon the closing scene, told her in fullest detail how
Sebastian had scornfully rejected the counsels of
those who urged him to fly when all was lost, how
the young king, who had fought with a lion-hearted
courage, unwilling to survive the day's defeat, had
turned and ridden back alone into the Saracen host
to fight his last fight and find a knightly death.
Thereafter he was seen no more.

It was a tale she never tired of hearing, and it
moved her more and more deeply each time she
listened to it. She would ply him with questions
touching this Sebastian, who had been her cousin,
concerning his ways of life, his boyhood, and his
enactments when he came to the crown of Portugal.
And all that Frey Miguel de Souza told her served
but to engrave more deeply upon her virgin mind the
adorable image of the knightly king. Ever present

in the daily thoughts of this ardent girl, his empanoplied figure haunted now her sleep, so real and
vivid that her waking senses would dwell fondly upon
the dream-figure as upon the memory of some one
seen in actual life; likewise she treasured up the memory of the dream-words he had uttered, words it
would seem begotten of the longings of her starved
and empty heart, words of a kind not calculated to
bring peace to the soul of a nun professed. She was
enamoured, deeply, fervently, and passionately
enamoured of a myth, a mental image of a man who
had been dust these fifteen years. She mourned him
with a fond widow's mourning; prayed daily and
nightly for the repose of his soul, and in her exaltation waited now almost impatiently for death that
should unite her with him. Taking joy in the thought
that she should go to him a maid, she ceased at last to
resent the maidenhood that had been imposed upon
her.

One day a sudden, wild thought filled her with a
strange excitement.

"Is it so certain that he is dead?" she asked.
"When all is said, none actually saw him die, and
you tell me that the body surrendered by Mulai-
Ahmed-ben-Mahomet was disfigured beyond recogni-
tion. Is it not possible that he may have survived?"

The lean, swarthy face of Frey Miguel grew
pensive. He did not impatiently scorn the suggestion
as she had half-feared he would.

"In Portugal," he answered slowly, "it is firmly
believed that he lives, and that one day he will come,
like another Redeemer, to deliver his country from
the thrall of Spain."

"Then . . . then . . ."

Wistfully, he smiled. "A people will always believe what it wishes to believe."

"But you, yourself?" she pressed him.

He did not answer her at once. The cloud of
thought deepened on his ascetic face. He half-turned
from her — they were standing in the shadow of the
fretted cloisters — and his pensive eyes roamed over
the wide quadrangle that was at once the convent
garden and burial ground. Out there in the sunshine
amid the hum of invisible but ubiquitously pulsat-
ing life, three nuns, young and vigorous, their arms
bared to the elbows, the skirts of their black habits
shortened by a cincture of rope, revealing feet roughly
shod in wood, were at work with spade and mattock,
digging their own graves in memento mori. Amid
the shadows of the cloisters, within sight but beyond
earshot, hovered Dona Maria de Grado and Dona
Luiza Nieto, the two nobly born nuns appointed by
King Philip to an office as nearly akin to that of
ladies-in-waiting as claustral conditions would permit.

At length Frey Miguel seemed to resolve himself.

"Since you ask me, why should I not tell you?
When I was on my way to preach the funeral oration
in the Cathedral at Lisbon, as befitted one who had
been Don Sebastian's preacher, I was warned by a
person of eminence to have a care of what I said of
Don Sebastian, for not only was he alive, but he
would be secretly present at the Requiem."

He met her dilating glance, noted the quivering of
her parted lips.

"But that," he added, "was fifteen years ago, and

since then I have had no sign. At first I thought it possible ... there was a story afloat that might have been true ... But fifteen years!" He sighed, and shook his head.

"What ... what was the story?" She was trembling from head to foot.

"On the night after the battle three horsemen rode up to the gates of the fortified coast-town of Arzilla. When the timid guard refused to open to them, they announced that one of them was King Sebastian, and so won admittance. One of the three was wrapped in a cloak, his face concealed, and his two companions were observed to show him the deference due to royalty."

"Why, then ..." she was beginning.

"Ah, but afterwards," he interrupted her — "afterwards, when all Portugal was thrown into commotion by that tale, it was denied that King Sebastian had been among these horsemen. It was affirmed to have been no more than a ruse of those men's to gain the shelter of the city."

She questioned and cross-questioned him upon that, seeking to draw from him the admission that it was possible denial and explanation obeyed the wishes of the hidden prince.

"Yes, it is possible," he admitted at length, "and it is believed by many to be the fact. Don Sebastian was as sensitive as high-spirited. The shame of his defeat may have hung so heavily upon him that he preferred to remain in hiding, and to sacrifice a throne of which he now felt himself unworthy. Half Portugal believes it so, and waits and hopes."

When Frey Miguel parted from her that day, he

took with him the clear conviction that not in all Portugal was there a soul who hoped more fervently than she that Don Sebastian lived, or yearned more passionately to acclaim him should he show himself. And that was much to think, for the yearning of Portugal was as the yearning of the slave for freedom.

Sebastian's mother was King Philip's sister, whereby King Philip had claimed the succession, and taken possession of the throne of Portugal. Portugal writhed under the oppressive heel of that foreign rule, and Frey Miguel de Souza himself, a deeply, passionately patriotic man, had been foremost among those who had sought to liberate her. When Don Antonio, the sometime Prior of Crato, Sebastian's natural cousin, and a bold, ambitious, enterprising man, had raised the standard of revolt, the friar had been the most active of all his coadjutors. In those days Frey Miguel, who was the Provincial of his order, a man widely renowned for his learning and experience of affairs, who had been preacher to Don Sebastian and confessor to Don Antonio, had wielded a vast influence in Portugal. That influence he had unstintingly exerted on behalf of the pretender, to whom he was profoundly devoted. After Don Antonio's army had been defeated on land by the Duke of Alba, and his fleet shattered in the Azores in 1582 by the Marquis of Santa Cruz, Frey Miguel found himself deeply compromised by his active share in the rebellion. He was arrested and suffered a long imprisonment in Spain. In the end, because he expressed repentance, and because Philip II, aware of the man's gifts and worth, desired to attach him to himself by gratitude, he was enlarged, and appointed Vicar of Santa Maria la Real, where he was now become confessor, counsellor, and confidant of the Princess Anne of Austria.

But his gratitude to King Philip was not of a kind to change his nature, to extinguish his devotion to the pretender, Don Antonio — who, restlessly ambitious, continued ceaselessly to plot abroad — or yet to abate the fervour of his patriotism. The dream of his life was ever the independence of Portugal, with a native prince upon the throne. And because of Anne's fervent hope, a hope that grew almost daily into conviction, that Sebastian had survived and would return one day to claim his kingdom, those two at Madrigal, in that quiet eddy of the great stream of life, were drawn more closely to each other.

But as the years passed, and Anne's prayers remained unanswered and the deliverer did not come, her hopes began to fade again. Gradually she reverted to her earlier frame of mind in which all hopes were set upon a reunion with the unknown beloved in the world to come.

One evening in the spring of 1594 — four years after the name of Sebastian had first passed between the priest and the Princess — Frey Miguel was walking down the main street of Madrigal, a village whose every inhabitant was known to him, when he came suddenly face to face with a stranger. A stranger would in any case have drawn his attention, but there was about this man something familiar to the friar, something that stirred in him vague memories of things long forgotten. His garb of shabby black was that of a common townsman, but there was something in his air and glance, his soldierly carriage, and the tilt of his bearded chin, that belied his garb. He bore upon his person the stamp of intrepidity and assurance.

Both halted, each staring at the other, a faint smile on the lips of the stranger — who, in the fading light, might have been of any age from thirty to fifty — a puzzled frown upon the brow of the friar. Then the man swept off his broad-brimmed hat.

"God save your paternity," was his greeting.

"God save you, my son," replied Frey Miguel, still pondering him. "I seem to know you. Do I?"

The stranger laughed. "Though all the world forget, your paternity should remember me."

And then Frey Miguel sucked in his breath sharply. "My God!" he cried, and set a hand upon the fellow's shoulder, looking deeply into those bold, grey eyes. "What make you here?"

"I am a pastry-cook."

"A pastry-cook? You?"

"One must live, and it is a more honest trade than most. I was in Valladolid, when I heard that your paternity was the Vicar of the convent here, and so for the sake of old times — of happier times — I bethought me that I might claim your paternity's support." He spoke with a careless arrogance, half-tinged with mockery.

"Assuredly . . ." began the priest, and then he checked. "Where is your shop?"

"Just down the street. Will your paternity honour me?"

Frey Miguel bowed, and together they departed.

For three days thereafter the convent saw the friar only in the celebration of the Mass. But on the morning of the fourth, he went straight from the sacristy to the parlour, and, despite the early hour, desired to see her excellency.

"Lady," he told her, "I have great news; news that will rejoice your heart." She looked at him, and saw the feverish glitter in his sunken eyes, the hectic flush on his prominent cheek-bones. "Don Sebastian lives. I have seen him."

A moment she stared at him as if she did not understand. Then she paled until her face became as white as the nun's coif upon her brow; her breath came in a faint moan, she stiffened, and swayed upon her feet, and caught at the back of a prie-dieu to steady and save herself from falling. He saw that he had blundered by his abruptness, that he had failed to gauge the full depth of her feelings for the Hidden Prince, and for a moment feared that she would swoon under the shock of the news he had so recklessly delivered.

"What do you say? Oh, what do you say?" she moaned, her eyes half-closed.

He repeated the news in more measured, careful terms, exerting all the magnetism of his will to sustain her reeling senses. Gradually she quelled the storm of her emotions.

"And you say that you have seen him? Oh!" Once more the colour suffused her cheeks, and her eyes glowed, her expression became radiant. "Where is he?"

"Here. Here in Madrigal."

"In Madrigal?" She was all amazement. "But why in Madrigal?"

"He was in Valladolid, and there heard that I —

his sometime preacher and counsellor — was Vicar here at Santa Maria la Real. He came to seek me. He comes disguised, under the false name of Gabriel de Espinosa, and setting up as a pastry-cook until his term of penance shall be completed, and he shall be free to disclose himself once more to his impatiently awaiting people."

It was bewildering, intoxicating news to her. It set her mind in turmoil, made of her soul a battle-ground for mad hope and dreadful fear. This dream-prince, who for four years had been the constant companion of her thoughts, whom her exalted, ardent, imaginative, starved soul had come to love with a con-suming passion, was a living reality near at hand, to be seen in the flesh by the eyes of her body. It was a thought that set her in an ecstasy of terror, so that she dared not ask Frey Miguel to bring Don Sebas-tian to her. But she plied him with questions, and so elicited from him a very circumstantial story.

Sebastian, after his defeat and escape, had made a vow upon the Holy Sepulchre to lay aside the royal dignity of which he deemed that he had proved him-self unworthy, and to do penance for the pride that had brought him down, by roaming the world in humble guise, earning his bread by the labour of his hands and the sweat of his brow like any common hind, until he should have purged his offence and rendered himself worthy once more to resume the estate to which he had been born.

It was a tale that moved her pity to the point of tears. It exalted her hero even beyond the eminence he had already held in her fond dreams, particularly when to that general outline were added in the days that followed details of the wanderings and sufferings of the Hidden Prince. At last, some few weeks after that first startling announcement of his presence, in the early days of August of that year 1594, Frey Miguel proposed to her the thing she most desired, yet dared not beg.

"I have told His Majesty of your attachment to his memory in all these years in which we thought him dead, and he is deeply touched. He desires your leave to come and prostrate himself at your feet."

She crimsoned from brow to chin, then paled again; her bosom heaved in tumult. Between dread and yearning she spoke a faint consent.

Next day he came, brought by Frey Miguel to the convent parlour, where her excellency waited, her two attendant nuns discreetly in the background. Her eager, frightened eyes beheld a man of middle height, dignified of mien and carriage, dressed with extreme simplicity, yet without the shabbiness in which Frey Miguel had first discovered him.

His hair was of a light brown — the colour to which the golden locks of the boy who had sailed for Africa some fifteen years ago might well have faded — his beard of an auburn tint, and his eyes were grey. His face was handsome, and save for the colour of his eyes and the high arch of his nose presented none of the distinguishing and marring features peculiar to the House of Austria, from which Don Sebastian derived through his mother.

Hat in hand, he came forward, and went down on one knee before her.

"I am here to receive your excellency's commands," he said.

She steadied her shuddering knees and trembling lips.

"Are you Gabriel de Espinosa, who has come to Madrigal to set up as a pastry-cook?" she asked him.

"To serve your excellency."

"Then be welcome, though I am sure that the trade you least understand is that of a pastry-cook."

The kneeling man bowed his handsome head, and fetched a deep sigh.

"If in the past I had better understood another trade, I should not now be reduced to following this one."

She urged him now to rise, whereafter the entertainment between them was very brief on that first occasion. He departed upon a promise to come soon again, and the undertaking on her side to procure for his shop the patronage of the convent.

Thereafter it became his custom to attend the morning Mass celebrated by Frey Miguel in the convent chapel — which was open to the public — and afterwards to seek the friar in the sacristy and accompany him thence to the convent parlour, where the Princess waited, usually with one or another of her attendant nuns. These daily interviews were brief at first, but gradually they lengthened until they came to consume the hours to dinner-time, and presently even that did not suffice, and Sebastian must come again later in the day.

And as the interviews increased and lengthened, so they grew also in intimacy between the royal pair, and plans for Sebastian's future came to be discussed. She urged him to proclaim himself. His penance had been overlong already for what was really no fault at all, since it is the heart rather than the deed that Heaven judges, and his heart had been pure, his intention in making war upon the Infidel loftily pious. Diffidently he admitted that it might be so, but both he and Frey Miguel were of opinion that it would be wiser now to await the death of Philip II, which, considering his years and infirmities, could not be long delayed. Out of jealousy for his possessions, King Philip might oppose Sebastian's claims.

Meanwhile these daily visits of Espinosa's, and the long hours he spent in Anne's company gave, as was inevitable, rise to scandal, within and without the convent. She was a nun professed, interdicted from seeing any man but her confessor other than through the parlour grating, and even then not at such length or with such constancy as this. The intimacy between them — fostered and furthered by Frey Miguel — had so ripened in a few weeks that Anne was justified in looking upon him as her saviour from the living tomb to which she had been condemned, in hoping that he would restore her to the life and liberty for which she had ever yearned by taking her to Queen when his time came to claim his own. What if she was a nun professed? Her profession had been against her will, preceded by only one year of noviatiate, and she was still within the five probationary years prescribed. Therefore, in her view, her vows were revocable.

But this was a matter beyond the general consideration or knowledge, and so the scandal grew. Within the convent there was none bold enough, considering Anne's royal rank, to offer remonstrance or advice, particularly, too, considering that her behaviour had the sanction of Frey Miguel, the convent's spiritual adviser. But from without, from the Provincial of the Order of Saint Augustine, came at last a letter to Anne, respectfully stern in tone, to inform her that the numerous visits she received from a pastry-cook were giving rise to talk, for which it would be wise to cease to give occasion. That recommendation scorched her proud, sensitive soul with shame. She sent her servant Roderos at once to fetch Frey Miguel, and placed the letter in his hands.

The friar's dark eyes scanned it, and grew troubled.

"It was to have been feared," he said, and sighed. "There is but one remedy, lest worse follow and all be ruined. Don Sebastian must go."

"Go?" Fear robbed her of breath. "Go where?"

"Away from Madrigal — anywhere — and at once; to-morrow at latest." And then, seeing the look of horror in her face, "What else, what else?" he added, impatiently. "This meddlesome Provincial may be stirring up trouble already."

She fought down her emotion. "I . . . I shall see him before he goes?" she begged.

"I don't know. It may not be wise. I must consider." He flung away in deepest perturbation, leaving her with a sense that life was slipping from her.

That late September evening, as she sat stricken in her room, hoping against hope for at least another glimpse of him, Dona Maria de Grado brought word that Espinosa was even then in the convent in Frey Miguel's cell. Fearful lest he should be smuggled thence without her seeing him, and careless of the impropriety of the hour — it was already eight o'clock

and dusk was falling—she at once dispatched Roderos to the friar, bidding him bring Espinosa to her in
the parlour.

The friar obeyed, and the lovers — they were no
less by now — came face to face in anguish.

"My lord, my lord," she cried, casting all prudence
to the winds, "what is decided?"

"That I leave in the morning," he answered.

"To go where?" She was distraught.

"Where?" He shrugged. "To Valladolid at first,
and then . . . where God pleases."

"And when shall I see you again?"

"When . . . when God pleases."

"Oh, I am terrified . . . if I should lose you . . . if I
should never see you more!" She was panting, distraught.

"Nay, lady, nay," he answered. "I shall come for
you when the time is ripe. I shall return by All
Saints', or by Christmas at the latest, and I shall
bring with me one who will avouch me."

"What need any to avouch you to me?" she protested, on a note of fierceness. "We belong to each
other, you and I. But you are free to roam the
world, and I am caged here and helpless . . ."

"Ah, but I shall free you soon, and we'll go hence
together. See." He stepped to the table. There was
an ink-horn, a box of pounce, some quills, and a
sheaf of paper there. He took up a quill, and wrote —
with labour, for princes are notoriously poor scholars:

I, Don Sebastian, by the Grace of God King of Portugal,
take to wife the most serene Dona Ana of Austria, daughter
of the most serene Prince, Don John of Austria, by virtue
of the dispensation which I hold from two pontiffs.

And he signed it — after the manner of the Kings of Portugal in all ages — "El Rey" — the King.

"Will that content you, lady?" he pleaded, handing it to her.

"How shall this scrawl content me?"

"It is a bond I shall redeem as soon as Heaven will permit."

Thereafter she fell to weeping, and he to protesting, until Frey Miguel urged him to depart, as it grew late. And then she forgot her own grief, and became all solicitude for him, until naught would content her but she must empty into his hands her little store of treasure — a hundred ducats and such jewels as she possessed, including a gold watch set with diamonds and a ring bearing a cameo portrait of King Philip, and last of all a portrait of herself, of the size of a playing-card.

At last, as ten was striking, he was hurried away. Frey Miguel had gone on his knees to him, and kissed his hand, what time he had passionately urged him not to linger; and then Sebastian had done the same by the Princess, both weeping now. At last he was gone, and on the arm of Dona Maria de Grado the forlorn Anne staggered back to her cell to weep and pray.

In the days that followed she moved, pale and listless, oppressed by her sense of loss and desolation, a desolation which at last she sought to mitigate by writing to him to Valladolid, whither he had repaired. Of all those letters only two survive.

My king and lord [she wrote in one of these], alas! How we suffer by absence! I am so filled with the pain of it that if I did not seek the relief of writing to Your Majesty and thus spend some moments in communion with you, there would be an end to me. What I feel to-day is what I feel every day when I recall the happy moments so deliciously spent, which are no more. This privation is for me so severe a punishment of Heaven that I should call it unjust, for without cause I find myself deprived of the happiness missed by me for so many years and purchased at the price of suffering and tears. Ah, my lord, how willingly, nevertheless, would I not suffer all over again the misfortunes that have crushed me if thus I might spare Your Majesty the least of them. May He who rules the world grant my prayers and set a term to so great an unhappiness, and to the intolerable torment I suffer through being deprived of the presence of Your Majesty. It were impossible for long to suffer so much pain and live.

I belong to you, my lord; you know it already. The troth I plighted to you I shall keep in life and in death, for death itself could not tear it from my soul, and this immortal soul will harbour it through eternity. . . .

Thus and much more in the same manner wrote the niece of King Philip of Spain to Gabriel Espinosa, the pastry-cook, in his Valladolid retreat. How he filled his days we do not know, beyond the fact that he moved freely abroad. For it was in the streets of that town that meddlesome Fate brought him face to face one day with Gregorio Gonzales, under whom Espinosa had been a scullion once in the service of the Count of Nyeba.

Gregorio hailed him, staring round-eyed; for although Espinosa's garments were not in their first freshness they were far from being those of a plebeian.

"In whose service may you be now?" quoth the intrigued Gregorio, so soon as greetings had passed between them.

Espinosa shook off his momentary embarrassment, and took the hand of his sometime comrade. "Times are changed, friend Gregorio. I am not in anybody's service, rather do I require servants myself."

"Why, what is your present situation?"

Loftily Espinosa put him off. "No matter for that," he answered, with a dignity that forbade further questions. He gathered his cloak about him to proceed upon his way. "If there is anything you wish for, I shall be happy, for old times' sake, to oblige you."

But Gregorio was by no means disposed to part from him. We do not readily part from an old friend whom we rediscover in an unsuspected state of affluence. Espinosa must home with Gregorio. Gregorio's wife would be charmed to renew his acquaintance, and to hear from his own lips of his improved and prosperous state. Gregorio would take no refusal, and in the end Espinosa, yielding to his insistence, went with him to the sordid quarter where Gregorio had his dwelling.

About an unclean table of pine, in a squalid room, sat the three — Espinosa, Gregorio, and Gregorio's wife; but the latter displayed none of the signs of satisfaction at Espinosa's prosperity which Gregorio had promised. Perhaps Espinosa observed her evil envy, and it may have been to nourish it — which is the surest way to punish envy — that he made Gregorio a magnificent offer of employment.

"Enter my service," said he, "and I will pay you fifty ducats down and four ducats a month."

Obviously they were incredulous of his affluence. To convince them he displayed a gold watch — most rare possession — set with diamonds, a ring of price, and other costly jewels. The couple stared now with dazzled eyes.

"But didn't you tell me when we were in Madrid together that you had been a pastry-cook at Ocaña?" burst from Gregorio.

Espinosa smiled. "How many kings and princes have been compelled to conceal themselves under disguises?" he asked oracularly. And seeing them stricken, he must play upon them further. Nothing, it seems, was sacred to him — not even the portrait of that lovely, desolate royal lady in her convent at Madrigal. Forth he plucked it. and thrust it to them across the stains of wine and oil that befouled their table.

"Look at this beautiful lady, the most beautiful in Spain," he bade them. "A prince could not have a lovelier bride."

"But she is dressed as a nun," the woman protested. "How, then, can she marry?"

"For kings there are no laws," he told her with finality.

At last he departed, but bidding Gregorio to think of the offer he had made him. He would come again for the cook's reply, leaving word meanwhile of where he was lodged.

They deemed him mad, and were disposed to be derisive. Yet the woman's disbelief was quickened into malevolence by the jealous fear that what he had told them of himself might, after all, be true. Upon that malevolence she acted forthwith, lodging an information with Don Rodrigo de Santillan, the Alcalde of Valladolid.

Very late that night Espinosa was roused from his sleep to find his room invaded by alguaziles — the police of the Alcalde. He was arrested and dragged before Don Rodrigo to give an account of himself and of certain objects of value found in his possession — more particularly of a ring, on the cameo of which was carved a portrait of King Philip.

"I am Gabriel de Espinosa," he answered firmly, "a pastry-cook of Madrigal."

"Then how come you by these jewels?"

"They were given me by Dona Ana of Austria to sell for her account. That is the business that has brought me to Valladolid."

"Is this Dona Ana's portrait?"

"It is."

"And this lock of hair? Is that also Dona Ana's? And do you, then, pretend that these were also given you to sell?"

"Why else should they be given me?"

Don Rodrigo wondered. They were useless things to steal, and as for the lock of hair, where should the fellow find a buyer for that? The Alcalde conned his man more closely, and noted that dignity of bearing, that calm assurance which usually is found upon birth and worth. He sent him to wait in prison, what time he went to ransack the fellow's house in Madrigal.

Don Rodrigo was prompt in acting; yet even so his prisoner mysteriously found means to send a warning that enabled Frey Miguel to forestall the Alcalde. Before Don Rodrigo's arrival, the friar had abstracted from Espinosa's house a box of papers which he reduced to ashes. Unfortunately Espinosa had been careless. Four letters not confided to the box were discovered by the alguaziles. Two of them were from Anne — one of which supplies the extract I have given; the other two from Frey Miguel himself.

Those letters startled Don Rodrigo de Santillan. He was a shrewd reasoner and well-informed. He knew how the justice of Castile was kept on the alert by the persistent plottings of the Portuguese pretender, Don Antonio, sometime Prior of Crato. He was intimate with the past life of Frey Miguel, knew his self-sacrificing patriotism and passionate devotion to the cause of Don Antonio, remembered the firm dignity of his prisoner, and leapt at a justifiable conclusion. The man in his hands — the man whom the Princess Anne addressed in such passionate terms by the title of Majesty — was the Prior of Crato. He conceived that he had stumbled here upon something grave and dangerous. He ordered the arrest of Frey Miguel, and then proceeded to visit Dona Ana at the convent. His methods were crafty, and depended upon the effect of surprise. He opened the interview by holding up before her one of the letters he had found, asking her if she acknowledged it for her own.

She stared a moment panic-stricken; then snatched it from his hands, tore it across, and would have torn again, but that he caught her wrists in a grip of iron to prevent her, with little regard in that moment for the blood royal in her veins. King Philip was a stern master, pitiless to blunderers, and Don Rodrigo knew he never would be forgiven did he suffer that precious letter to be destroyed.

Overpowered in body and in spirit, she surrendered the fragments and confessed the letter her own.

"What is the real name of this man, who calls himself a pastry-cook, and to whom you write in such terms as these?" quoth the magistrate.

"He is Don Sebastian, King of Portugal." And to that declaration she added briefly the story of his escape from Alcacer-el-Kebir and subsequent penitential wanderings.

Don Rodrigo departed, not knowing what to think or believe, but convinced that it was time he laid the whole matter before King Philip. His Catholic Majesty was deeply perturbed. He at once dispatched Don Juan de Llano, the Apostolic Commissary of the Holy Office, to Madrigal to sift the matter, and ordered that Anne should be solitarily confined in her cell, and her nuns-in-waiting and servants placed under arrest.

Espinosa, for greater security, was sent from Valladolid to the prison of Medina del Campo. He was taken thither in a coach with an escort of arquebusiers.

"Why convey a poor pastry-cook with so much honour?" he asked his guards, half-mockingly.

Within the coach he was accompanied by a soldier named Cervatos, a travelled man, who fell into talk with him, and discovered that he spoke both French and German fluently. But when Cervatos addressed him in Portuguese the prisoner seemed confused, and replied that, although he had been in Portugal, he could not speak the language.

Thereafter, throughout that winter, examinations of the three chief prisoners — Espinosa, Frey Miguel, and the Princess Anne — succeeded one another with a wearisome monotony of results. The Apostolic

Commissary interrogated the Princess and Frey Miguel; Don Rodrigo conducted the examinations of Espinosa. But nothing was elicited that took the matter forward or tended to dispel its mystery.

The Princess replied with a candour that became more and more tinged with indignation under the persistent and at times insulting interrogatories. She insisted that the prisoner was Don Sebastian, and wrote passionate letters to Espinosa, begging him for her honour's sake to proclaim himself what he really was, declaring to him that the time had come to cast off all disguise.

Yet the prisoner, unmoved by these appeals, persisted that he was Gabriel de Espinosa, a pastry-cook. But the man's bearing, and the air of mystery cloaking him, seemed in themselves to belie that asseveration. That he could not be the Prior of Crato, Don Rodrigo had now assured himself. He fenced skilfully under examination, ever evading the magistrate's practised point when it sought to pin him, and he was no less careful to say nothing that should incriminate either of the other two prisoners. He denied that he had ever given himself out to be Don Sebastian, though he admitted that Frey Miguel and the Princess had persuaded themselves that he was that lost prince.

He pleaded ignorance when asked who were his parents, stating that he had never known either of them — an answer this which would have fitted the case of Don Sebastian, who was born after his father's death, and quitted in early infancy by his mother.

As for Frey Miguel, he stated boldly under examination the conviction that Don Sebastian had survived the African expedition, and the belief that Espinosa might well be the missing monarch. He protested that he had acted in good faith throughout, and without any thought of disloyalty to the King of Spain.

Late one night, after he had been some three months in prison, Espinosa was roused from sleep by an unexpected visit from the Alcalde. At once he would have risen and dressed.

"Nay," said Don Rodrigo, restraining him, "that is not necessary for what is intended."

It was a dark phrase which the prisoner, sitting up in bed with tousled hair, and blinking in the light of the torches, instantly interpreted into a threat of torture. His face grew white.

"It is impossible," he protested. "The King cannot have ordered what you suggest. His Majesty will take into account that I am a man of honour. He may require my death, but in an honourable manner, and not upon the rack. And as for its being used to make me speak, I have nothing to add to what I have said already."

The stern, dark face of the Alcalde was overspread by a grim smile.

"I would have you remark that you fall into contradictions. Sometimes you pretend to be of humble and lowly origin, and sometimes a person of honourable degree. To hear you at this moment one might suppose that to submit you to torture would be to outrage your dignity. What then ..."

Don Rodrigo broke off suddenly to stare, then snatched a torch from the hand of his alguaziles and held it close to the face of the prisoner, who cowered now, knowing full well what it was the Alcalde had detected. In that strong light Don Rodrigo saw that the prisoner's hair and beard had turned grey at the roots, and so received the last proof that he had to do with the basest of impostures. The fellow had been using dyes, the supply of which had been cut short by his imprisonment. Don Rodrigo departed well satisfied with the results of that surprise visit.

Thereafter Espinosa immediately shaved himself. But it was too late, and even so, before many weeks were past his hair had faded to its natural grey, and he presented the appearance of what in fact he was — a man of sixty, or thereabouts.

Yet the torture to which he was presently submitted drew nothing from him that could explain all that yet remained obscure. It was from Frey Miguel, after a thousand prevarications and tergiversations, that the full truth — known to himself alone — was extracted by the rack.

He confessed that, inspired by the love of country and the ardent desire to liberate Portugal from the Spanish yoke, he had never abandoned the hope of achieving this, and of placing Don Antonio, the Prior of Crato, on the throne of his ancestors. He had devised a plan, primarily inspired by the ardent nature of the Princess Anne and her impatience of the conventual life. It was while casting about for the chief instrument that he fortuitously met Espinosa in the streets of Madrigal. Espinosa had been a soldier, and had seen the world. During the war between Spain and Portugal he had served in the armies of King Philip, had befriended Frey Miguel when the friar's convent was on the point of being invaded by soldiery, and had rescued him from the peril of it. Thus they had become acquainted, and Frey Miguel had had an instance of the man's resource and courage. Further, he was of the height of Don Sebastian and of the build to which the King might have grown in the years that were sped, and he presented other superficial resemblances to the late king. The colour of his hair and beard could be corrected; and he might be made to play the part of the Hidden Prince for whose return Portugal was waiting so passionately and confidently. There had been other impostors aforetime, but they had lacked the endowments of Espinosa, and their origins could be traced without difficulty. In addition to these natural endowments, Espinosa should be avouched by Frey Miguel — than whom nobody in the world was better qualified in such a matter — and by the niece of King Philip, to whom he would be married when he raised his standard. It was arranged that the three should go to Paris so soon as the arrangements were complete, where the pretender would be accredited by the exiled friends of Don Antonio residing there — the Prior of Crato being a party to the plot. From France Frey Miguel would have worked in Portugal through his agents, and presently would have gone there himself to stir up a national movement in favour of a pretender so fully accredited. Thus he had every hope of restoring Portugal to her independence. Once this should have been accomplished, Don Antonio would appear in Lisbon, unmask the impostor, and himself assume the crown of the kingdom which had been forcibly and definitely wrenched from Spain.

That was the crafty plan which the priest had laid

with a singleness of aim and a detachment from minor considerations that never hesitated to sacrifice the Princess, together with the chief instrument of the intrigue. Was the liberation of a kingdom, the deliverance of a nation from servitude, the happiness of a whole people, to weigh in the balance against the fates of a natural daughter of Don John of Austria and a soldier of fortune turned pastry-cook? Frey Miguel thought not, and his plot might well have succeeded but for the base strain in Espinosa and the man's overweening vanity, which had urged him to dazzle the Gonzales at Valladolid. That vanity sustained him to the end, which he suffered in October of 1595, a full year after his arrest. To the last he avoided admissions that should throw light upon his obscure identity and origin.

"If it were known who I am . . ." he would say, and there break off.

He was hanged, drawn, and quartered, and he endured his fate with calm fortitude. Frey Miguel suffered in the same way with the like dignity, after having undergone degradation from his priestly dignity.

As for the unfortunate Princess Anne, crushed under a load of shame and humiliation, she had gone to her punishment in the previous July. The Apostolic Commissary notified her of the sentence which King Philip had confirmed. She was to be transferred to another convent, there to undergo a term of four years' solitary confinement in her cell, and to fast on bread and water every Friday. She was pronounced incapable of ever holding any office, and was to be treated on the expiry of her term as an ordinary nun, her civil list abolished, her title of Excellency to be extinguished, together with all other honours and privileges conferred upon her by King Philip.

The piteous letters of supplication that she addressed to the King, her uncle, still exist. But they left the cold, implacable Philip of Spain unmoved. Her only sin was that, yielding to the hunger of her starved heart, and chafing under the ascetic life imposed upon her, she had allowed herself to be fascinated by the prospect of becoming the protectress of one whom she believed to be an unfortunate and romantic prince, and of exchanging her convent for a throne.

Her punishment — poor soul — endured for close upon forty years, but the most terrible part of it was not that which lay within the prescription of King Philip, but that which arose from her own broken and humiliated spirit. She had been uplifted a moment by a glorious hope, to be cast down again in the blackest despair, to which a shame unspeakable and a tortured pride were added.

Than hers, as I have said, there is in history no sadder story.

V

THE END OF THE "VERT GALANT"

THE ASSASSINATION OF HENRY IV

IN the year 1609 died the last Duke of Cleves, and King Henry IV of France and Navarre fell in love with Charlotte de Montmorency.

In their conjunction these two events were to influence the destinies of Europe. In themselves they were trivial enough, since it was as much a commonplace that an old gentleman should die as that Henry of Béarn should fall in love. Love had been the main relaxation of his otherwise strenuous life, and neither the advancing years — he was fifty-six at this date — nor the recriminations of Maria de' Medici, his longsuffering Florentine wife, sufficed to curb his zest.

Possibly there may have been a husband more unfaithful than King Henry; probably there was not. His gallantries were outrageous, his taste in women catholic, and his illegitimate progeny outnumbered that of his grandson, the English sultan Charles II. He differs, however, from the latter in that he was not quite as Oriental in the manner of his self-indulgence. Charles, by comparison, was a mere dullard who turned Whitehall into a seraglio. Henry preferred the romantic manner, the high adventure, and knew how to be gallant in two senses.

This gallantry of his is not, perhaps, seen to best advantage in the affair of Charlotte de Montmorency.

To begin with, he was, as I have said, in his fifty-sixth year, an age at which it is difficult, without being ridiculous, to unbridle a passion for a girl of twenty. Unfortunately for him, Charlotte does not appear to have found him so. On the contrary, her lovely, empty head was so turned by the flattery of his addresses that she came to reciprocate the passion she inspired.

Her family had proposed to marry her to the gay and witty Marshal de Bassompierre; and although his heart was not at all engaged, the marshal found the match extremely suitable, and was willing enough, until the King declared himself. Henry used the most impudent frankness.

"Bassompierre, I will speak to you as a friend," said he. "I am in love, and desperately in love, with Mademoiselle de Montmorency. If you should marry her, I should hate you. If she should love me, you would hate me. A breach of our friendship would desolate me, for I love you with sincere affection."

That was enough for Bassompierre. He had no mind to go further with a marriage of convenience which in the sequel would most probably give him to choose between assuming the ridiculous rôle of a complacent husband and being involved in a feud with his Prince. He said as much, and thanked the King for his frankness, whereupon Henry, liking him more than ever for his good sense, further opened his mind to him.

"I am thinking of marrying her to my nephew, Condé. Thus I shall have her in my family to be the comfort of my old age, which is coming on. Condé, who thinks of nothing but hunting, shall have a hundred thousand livres a year with which to amuse himself."

Bassompierre understood perfectly the kind of bargain that was in Henry's mind. As for the Prince de Condé, he appears to have been less acute, no doubt because his vision was dazzled by the prospect of a hundred thousand livres a year. So desperately poor was he that for half that sum he would have taken Lucifer's own daughter to wife, without stopping to consider the disadvantages it might entail.

The marriage was quietly celebrated at Chantilly in February of 1609. Trouble followed fast. Not only did Condé perceive at last precisely what was expected of him, and indignantly rebel against it, but the Queen, too, was carefully instructed in the matter by Concino Concini and his wife Leonora Galigai, the ambitious adventurers who had come from Florence in her train, and who saw in the King's weakness their own opportunity.

The scandal that ensued was appalling. Never before had the relations between Henry and his Queen been strained so nearly to breaking-point. And then, whilst the trouble of Henry's own making was growing about him until it threatened to overwhelm him, he received a letter from Vaucelas, his ambassador at Madrid, containing revelations that changed his annoyance into stark apprehension.

When the last Duke of Cleves died a few months before, "leaving all the world his heirs" — to use Henry's own phrase — the Emperor had stepped in, and overriding the rights of certain German princes had bestowed the fief upon his own nephew, the Archduke Leopold. Now this was an arrangement that did not suit Henry's policy at all, and being then — as the result of a wise husbanding of resources — the most powerful prince in Europe, Henry was not likely to submit tamely to arrangements that did not suit him. His instructions to Vaucelas were to keep open the difference between France and the House of Austria arising out of this matter of Cleves. All Europe knew that Henry desired to marry the Dauphin to the heiress of Lorraine, so that this State might one day be united with France; and it was partly to support this claim that he was now disposed to attach the German princes to his interests.

Yet what Vaucelas told him in that letter was that certain agents at the Court of Spain, chief among whom was the Florentine ambassador, acting upon instructions from certain members of the household of the Queen of France, and from others whom Vaucelas said he dared not mention, were intriguing to blast Henry's designs against the House of Austria, and to bring him willy-nilly into a union with Spain. These agents had gone so far in their utter disregard of Henry's own intentions as to propose to the Council of Madrid that the alliance should be cemented by a marriage between the Dauphin and the Infanta.

That letter sent Henry early one morning hot-foot to the Arsenal, where Sully, his Minister of State, had his residence. Maximilien de Béthune, Duke of Sully, was not merely the King's servant, he was his closest friend, the very keeper of his soul; and the King leaned upon him and sought his guidance not only in State affairs, but in the most intimate and domestic matters. Often already had it fallen to Sully to patch up the differences created between husband and wife by Henry's persistent infidelities.

The King, arriving like the whirlwind, turned everybody out of the closet in which the Duke — but newly risen — received him in bed-gown and night-cap. Alone with his minister, Henry came abruptly to the matter.

"You have heard what is being said of me?" he burst out. He stood with his back to the window, a sturdy, erect, soldierly figure, a little above the middle height, dressed like a captain of fortune in jerkin and long boots of grey leather, and a grey hat with a wine-coloured ostrich plume. His countenance matched his raiment. Keen-eyed, broad of brow, with a high-bridged, pendulous nose, red lips, a tuft of beard and a pair of grizzled, bristling mostachos, he looked half-hero, half-satyr; half-captain, half-Polichinelle.

Sully, tall and broad, the incarnation of respectability and dignity, despite bed-gown and slippers and the nightcap covering his high, bald crown, made no pretence of misunderstanding him.

"Of you and the Princesse de Condé, you mean, Sire?" quoth he, and gravely he shook his head. "It is a matter that has filled me with apprehension, for I foresee from it far greater trouble than from any former attachment of yours."

"So they have convinced you, too, Grand Master!" Henry's tone was almost sorrowful. "Yet I swear that all is greatly exaggerated. It is the work of that dog Concini. Ventre Saint Gris! If he has no respect for me, at least he might consider how he slanders a child of such grace and wit and beauty, a lady of her high birth and noble lineage."

There was a dangerous quiver of emotion in his

voice that was not missed by the keen ears of Sully.
Henry moved from the window, and flung into a chair.

"Concini works to enrage the Queen against me,
and to drive her to take violent resolutions which
might give colour to their pernicious designs."

"Sire!" It was a cry of protest from Sully.

Henry laughed grimly at his minister's incredulity,
and plucked forth the letter from Vaucelas.

"Read that."

Sully read, and, aghast at what the letter told him,
ejaculated: "They must be mad!"

"Oh, no," said the King. "They are not mad.
They are most wickedly sane, which is why their designs fill me with apprehension. What do you infer,
Grand Master, from such deliberate plots against
resolutions from which they know that nothing can
turn me while I have life?"

"What can I infer?" quoth Sully, aghast.

"In acting thus — in daring to act thus," the King
expounded, "they proceed as if they knew that I can
have but a short time to live."

"Sire!"

"What else? They plan events which cannot take
place until I am dead."

Sully stared at his master for a long moment, in
stupefied silence, his loyal Huguenot soul refusing to
discount by flattery the truth that he perceived.

"Sire," he said at last, bowing his fine head, "you
must take your measures."

"Aye, but against whom? Who are these that
Vaucelas says he dare not name? Can you suggest another than . . ." He paused, shrinking in horror from
completing the utterance of his thought. Then, with

an abrupt gesture, he went on, ". . . than the Queen herself?"

Sully quietly placed the letter on the table, and sat down. He took his chin in his hand, and looked squarely across at Henry.

"Sire, you have brought this upon yourself. You have exasperated Her Majesty; you have driven her in despair to seek and act upon the councils of this scoundrel Concini. There never was an attachment of yours that did not beget trouble with the Queen, but never such trouble as I have been foreseeing from your attachment to the Princess of Condé. Sire, will you not consider where you stand?"

"They are lies, I tell you," Henry stormed. But Sully the uncompromising gravely shook his head. "At least," Henry amended, "they are gross exaggerations. Oh, I confess to you, my friend, that I am sick with love of her. Day and night I see nothing but her gracious image. I sigh and fret and fume like any callow lad of twenty. I suffer the tortures of the damned. And yet . . . and yet, I swear to you, Sully, that I will curb this passion, though it kill me. I will stifle these fires, though they consume my soul to ashes. No harm shall come to her from me. No harm has come yet. I swear it. These stories that are put about are the inventions of Concini to set my wife against me. Do you know how far he and his wife have dared to go? They have persuaded the Queen to eat nothing that is not prepared in the kitchen they have set up for her in their own apartments. What can you conclude from that but that they suggest that I desire to poison her?"

"Why suffer it, Sire?" quoth Sully gravely. "Send

the pair packing back to Florence, and so be rid of them."

Henry rose in agitation. "I have a mind to. Ventre Saint Gris! I have a mind to. Yes, it is the only thing. You can manage it, Sully. Disabuse her mind of her suspicions regarding the Princess of Condé; make my peace with her; convince her of my sincerity, of my firm intention to have done with gallantry, so that she on her side will make me the sacrifice of banishing the Concinis. You will do this, my friend?"

It was no less than Sully had been expecting from past experience, and the task was one in which he was by now well practised; but the situation had never before been quite so difficult. He rose.

"Why, surely, Sire," said he. "But Her Majesty on her side may require something more to reconcile her to the sacrifice. She may reopen the question of her coronation so long and — in her view — so unreasonably postponed."

Henry's face grew overcast, his brows knit. "I have always had an instinct against it, as you know, Grand Master," said he, "and this instinct is strengthened by what that letter has taught me. If she will dare so much, having so little real power, what might she not do if . . ." He broke off, and fell to musing. "If she demands it, we must yield, I suppose," he said at length. "But give her to understand that if I discover any more of her designs with Spain I shall be provoked to the last degree against her. And as an antidote to these machinations at Madrid you may publish my intention to uphold the claims of the German princes in the matter of Cleves, and let all the world know that we are arming to that end."

He may have thought — as was long afterwards alleged — that the threat itself should be sufficient, for there was at that time no power in Europe that could have stood against his armies in the field.

On that they parted, with a final injunction from Sully that Henry should see the Princesse de Condé no more.

"I swear to you, Grand Master, that I will use restraint and respect the sacred tie I formed between my nephew and Charlotte solely so that I might impose silence upon my own passion."

And the good Sully writes in comment upon this: "I should have relied absolutely upon these assurances had I not known how easy it is for a heart tender and passionate as was his to deceive itself" — which is the most amiable conceivable way of saying that he attached not the slightest faith to the King's promise.

Nevertheless, he went about the task of making the peace between the royal couple with all the skill and tact that experience had taught him; and he might have driven a good bargain on his master's behalf but for his master's own weakness in supporting him. Maria de' Medici would not hear of the banishment of the Concinis, to whom she was so deeply attached. She insisted with perfect justice that she was a bitterly injured woman, and refused to entertain any idea of reconciliation save with the condition that arrangements for her coronation as Queen of France — which was no more than her due — should be made at once, and that the King should give an undertaking not to make himself ridiculous any longer by his pursuit of the Princess of Condé. Of the matters contained in the letter of Vaucelas she denied all knowledge, nor would suffer any further inquisition.

From Henry's point of view this was anything but satisfactory. But he yielded. Conscience made a coward of him. He had wronged her so much in one way that he must make some compensating concessions to her in another. This weakness was part of his mental attitude towards her, which swung constantly between confidence and diffidence, esteem and indifference, affection and coldness; at times he inclined to put her from him entirely; at others he opined that no one on his Council was more capable of the administration of affairs. Even in the indignation aroused by the proof he held of her disloyalty, he was too just not to admit the provocation he had given her. So he submitted to a reconciliation on her own terms, and pledged himself to renounce Charlotte. We have no right to assume from the sequel that he was not sincere in the intention.

By the following May events proved the accuracy of Sully's judgment. The Court was at Fontainebleau when the last bulwark of Henry's prudence was battered down by the vanity of that lovely fool, Charlotte, who must be encouraging her royal lover to resume his flattering homage. But both appear to have reckoned without the lady's husband.

Henry presented Charlotte with jewels to the value of eighteen thousand livres, purchased from Messier, the jeweller of the Pont au Change; and you conceive what the charitable ladies of the Court had to say about it. At the first hint of scandal, Monsieur de Condé put himself into a fine heat, and said things which pained and annoyed the King exceedingly.

Henry had amassed a considerable and varied experience of jealous husbands in his time; but he had never met one quite so intolerable as this nephew of his. He complained of it in a letter to Sully:

MY FRIEND, — Monsieur the Prince is here, but he acts like a man possessed. You will be angry and ashamed at the things he says of me. I shall end by losing all patience with him. In the mean while I am obliged to talk to him with severity.

More severe than any talk was Henry's instruction to Sully to withhold payment of the last quarter of the Prince's allowance, and to give refusals to his creditors and purveyors. Thus he intended also, no doubt, to make it clear to Condé that he did not receive a pension of a hundred thousand livres a year for nothing.

"If this does not keep him in bounds," Henry concluded, "we must think of some other method, for he says the most injurious things of me."

So little did it keep the Prince in bounds — as Henry understood the phrase — that he immediately packed his belongings, and carried his wife off to his country house. It was quite in vain that Henry wrote to him representing that this conduct was dishonouring to them both, and that the only place for a prince of the blood was the Court of his sovereign.

The end of it all was that the reckless and romantic Henry took to night-prowling about the grounds of Condé's château. In the disguise of a peasant you see His Majesty of France and Navarre, whose will was law in Europe, shivering behind damp hedges, ankle-deep in wet grass, spending long hours in love-lorn,

ecstatic contemplation of her lighted window, and all
— so far as we can gather — for no other result than
the aggravation of certain rheumatic troubles which
should have reminded him that he was no longer of an
age to pursue these amorous pernoctations.

But where his stiffening joints failed, the Queen succeeded. Henry had been spied upon, of course, as he
always was when he strayed from the path of matrimonial rectitude. The Concinis saw to that. And
when they judged the season ripe, they put Her Majesty in possession of the facts. So inflamed was she
by this fresh breach of trust that war was declared
anew between the royal couple, and the best that
Sully's wit and labours could now accomplish was a
sort of armed truce.

And then at last in the following November the
Prince de Condé took the desperate resolve of quitting
France with his wife, without troubling — as was his
duty — to obtain the King's consent. On the last
night of that month, as Henry was at cards in the
Louvre, the Chevalier du Guet brought him the news
of the Prince's flight.

"I never in my life," says Bassompierre, who was
present, "saw a man so distracted or in so violent a
passion."

He flung down his cards, and rose, sending his chair
crashing over behind him. "I am undone!" was his
cry. "Undone! This madman has carried off his wife
— perhaps to kill her." White and shaking, he turned
to Bassompierre. "Take care of my money," he bade
him, "and go on with the game."

He lurched out of the room, and dispatched a messenger to the Arsenal to fetch Monsieur de Sully.

Sully obeyed the summons and came at once, but in an extremely bad temper, for it was late at night, and he was overburdened with work.

He found the King in the Queen's chamber, walking backward and forward, his head sunk upon his breast, his hands clenched behind him. The Queen, a squarely built, square-faced woman, sat apart, attended by a few of her ladies and one or two gentlemen of her train. Her countenance was set and inscrutable, and her brooding eyes were fixed upon the King.

"Ha, Grand Master!" was Henry's greeting, his voice harsh and strained. "What do you say to this? What is to be done now?"

"Nothing at all, Sire," says Sully, as calm as his master was excited.

"Nothing! What sort of advice is that?"

"The best advice that you can follow, Sire. This affair should be talked of as little as possible, nor should it appear to be of any consequence to you, or capable of giving you the least uneasiness."

The Queen cleared her throat huskily. "Good advice, Monsieur le Duc," she approved him. "He will be wise to follow it" — her voice strained, almost threatening. "But in this matter I doubt wisdom and he have long since become strangers."

That put him in a passion, and in a passion he left her to do the maddest thing he had ever done. In the garb of a courier, and with a patch over one eye to complete his disguise, he set out in pursuit of the fugitives. He had learnt that they had taken the road to Landrecy, which was enough for him. Stage by stage he followed them in that flight to Flanders, picking up the trail as he went, and never pausing until he had reached the frontier without overtaking them.

It was all most romantic, and the lady, when she learnt of it, shed tears of mingled joy and rage, and wrote him impassioned letters in which she addressed him as her knight, and implored him, as he loved her, to come and deliver her from the detestable tyrant who held her in thrall. Those perfervid appeals completed his undoing, drove him mad, and blinded him to everything — even to the fact that his wife, too, was shedding tears, and that these were of rage undiluted by any more tender emotion.

He began by sending Praslin to require the Archduke to order the Prince of Condé to leave his dominions. And when the Archduke declined with dignity to be guilty of any such breach of the law of nations, Henry dispatched Cœuvres secretly to Brussels to carry off thence the Princess. But Maria de' Medici was on the alert, and frustrated the design by sending a warning of what was intended to the Marquis Spinola, as a result of which the Prince de Condé and his wife were housed for greater security in the Archduke's own palace.

Checkmated at all points, yet goaded further by the letters which he continued to receive from that most foolish of princesses, Henry took the wild decision that to obtain her he would invade the Low Countries as the first step in the execution of that design of a war with Spain which hitherto had been little more than a pretence. The matter of the Duchy of Cleves was a pretext ready to his hand. To obtain the woman he desired he would set Europe in a blaze.

He took that monstrous resolve at the very beginning of the new year, and in the months that followed France rang with preparations. It rang, too, with other things which should have given him pause. It rang with the voice of preachers giving expression to the popular view that Cleves was not worth fighting for, that the war was unrighteous — a war undertaken by Catholic France to defend Protestant interests against the very champions of Catholicism in Europe. And soon it began to ring, too, with prophecies of the King's approaching end.

These prognostics rained upon him from every quarter. Thomassin, and the astrologer La Brosse, warned him of a message from the stars that May would be fraught with danger for him. From Rome — from the very Pope himself — came notice of a conspiracy against him in which he was told that the very highest in the land were engaged. From Embrun, Bayonne, and Douai came messages of like purport, and early in May a note was found one morning on the altar of the church of Montargis announcing the King's approaching death.

But that is to anticipate. Meanwhile, Henry had pursued his preparations undeterred by either warnings or prognostications. There had been so many conspiracies against his life already that he was become careless and indifferent in such matters. Yet surely there never had been one that was so abundantly heralded from every quarter, or ever one that was hatched under conditions so propitious as those which he had himself created now. In his soul he was not at ease, and the source of his uneasiness was the coronation of the Queen, for which the preparations were now going forward.

He must have known that if danger of assassination threatened him from any quarter, it was most to be feared from those whose influence with the Queen was almost such as to give them a control over her — the Concinis and their unavowed but obvious ally the Duke of Epernon. If he were dead, and the Queen so left that she could be made absolute regent during the Dauphin's minority, it was those adventurers who would become through her the true rulers of France, and so enrich themselves and gratify to the full their covetous ambitions. He saw clearly that his safety lay in opposing this coronation — already fixed for the 13th May — which Maria de' Medici was so insistent should take place before his departure for the wars. The matter so preyed upon his mind that at last he unburdened himself to Sully one day at the Arsenal.

"Oh, my friend," he cried, "this coronation does not please me. My heart tells me that some fatality will follow."

He sat down, grasping the case of his reading-glass, whilst Sully could only stare at him amazed by this outburst. Thus he remained awhile in deep thought. Then he started up again.

"Pardieu!" he cried. "I shall be murdered in this city. It is their only resource. I see it plainly. This cursed coronation will be the cause of my death."

"What a thought, Sire!"

"You think that I have been reading the almanach or paying heed to the prophets, eh? But listen to me now, Grand Master." And wrinkles deepened about the bold, piercing eyes. "It is four months and more since we announced our intention of going to war, and France has resounded with our preparations. We have made no secret of it. Yet in Spain not a finger has been lifted in preparation to resist us, not a sword has been sharpened. Upon what does Spain build? Whence her confidence that in despite of my firm resolve and my abundant preparations, despite the fact announced that I am to march on the 17th of this month, despite the fact that my troops are already in Champagne with a train of artillery so complete and well-furnished that France has never seen the like of it, and perhaps never will again — whence the confidence that despite all this there is no need to prepare defences? Upon what do they build, I say, when they assume, as assume they must, that there will be no war? Resolve me that, Grand Master."

But Sully, overwhelmed, could only gasp and ejaculate.

"You had not thought of it, eh? Yet it is clear enough. Spain builds on my death. And who are the friends of Spain here in France? Who was it intrigued with Spain in such a way and to such ends as in my lifetime could never have been carried to an issue? Ha! You see."

"I cannot, Sire. It is too horrible. It is impossible!" cried that loyal, honest gentleman. "And yet if you are convinced of it, you should break off this coronation, your journey, and your war. If you wish it so, it is not difficult to satisy you."

"Aye, that is it." He came to his feet, and gripped the Duke's shoulder in his strong, nervous hand. "Break off this coronation, and never let me hear of it again. That will suffice. Thus I can rid my mind of apprehensions, and leave Paris with nothing to fear."

"Very well. I will send at once to Notre Dame and to Saint Denis, to stop the preparations and dismiss the workmen."

"Ah, wait." The eyes, that for a moment had sparkled with new hope, grew dull again; the lines of care descended between the brows. "Oh, what to decide! What to decide! It is what I wish, my friend. But how will my wife take it?"

"Let her take it as she will. I cannot believe that she will continue obstinate when she knows what apprehensions you have of disaster."

"Perhaps not, perhaps not," he answered. But his tone was not sanguine. "Try to persuade her, Sully. Without her consent I cannot do this thing. But you will know how to persuade her. Go to her."

Sully suspended the preparations for the coronation, and sought the Queen. For three days, he tells us, he used prayers, entreaties, and arguments with which to endeavour to move her. But all was labour lost. Maria de' Medici was not to be moved. To all Sully's argument she opposed an argument that was unanswerable.

Unless she were crowned Queen of France, as was her absolute right, she would be a person of no account and subject to the Council of Regency during the King's absence, a position unworthy and intolerable to her, the mother of the Dauphin.

And so it was Henry's part to yield. His hands were tied by the wrongs that he had done, and the culminating wrong that he was doing her by this very war, as he had himself openly acknowledged. He had chanced one day to ask the papal nuncio what Rome thought of this war.

"Those who have the best information," the nuncio answered boldly, "are of opinion that the principal object of the war is the Princess of Condé whom Your Majesty wishes to bring back to France."

Angered by this priestly insolence, Henry's answer had been an impudently defiant acknowledgment of the truth of that allegation.

"Yes, by God!" he cried. "Yes — most certainly I want to have her back, and I will have her back; no one shall hinder me, not even God's vicegerent on earth."

Having uttered those words, which he knew to have been carried to the Queen, and to have wounded her perhaps more deeply than anything that had yet happened in this affair, his conscience left him, despite his fears, powerless now to thwart her even to the extent of removing those pernicious familiars of hers of whose plottings he had all but positive evidence.

And so the coronation was at last performed with proper pomp and magnificence at Saint Denis on Thursday, the 13th May. It had been concerted that the festivities should last four days and conclude on the Sunday with the Queen's public entry into Paris. On the Monday the King was to set out to take command of his armies, which were already marching upon the frontiers.

Thus Henry proposed, but the Queen — convinced by his own admission of the real aim and object of the war, and driven by outraged pride to hate the man who offered her this crowning insult, and determined that at all costs it must be thwarted — had lent an ear to Concini's purpose to avenge her, and was ready to repay infidelity with infidelity. Concini and his fellow-conspirators had gone to work so confidently that a week before the coronation a courier had appeared in Liège, announcing that he was going with news of Henry's assassination to the Princes of Germany, whilst at the same time accounts of the King's death were being published in France and Italy.

Meanwhile, whatever inward misgivings Henry may have entertained, outwardly at least he appeared serene and good-humoured at his wife's coronation, gaily greeting her at the end of the ceremony by the title of "Madam Regent."

The little incident may have touched her, arousing her conscience. For that night she disturbed his slumbers by sudden screams, and when he sprang up in solicitous alarm she falteringly told him of a dream in which she had seen him slain, and fell to imploring him with a tenderness such as had been utterly foreign to her of late to take great care of himself in the days to come. In the morning she renewed those entreaties, beseeching him not to leave the Louvre that day, urging that she had a premonition it would be fatal to him.

He laughed for answer. "You have heard of the predictions of La Brosse," said he. "Bah! You should not attach credit to such nonsense."

Anon came the Duke of Vendôme, his natural son by the Marquise de Verneuil, with a like warning and a like entreaty, only to receive a like answer.

Being dull and indisposed as a consequence of last night's broken rest, Henry lay down after dinner. But finding sleep denied him, he rose, pensive and gloomy, and wandered aimlessly down, and out into the courtyard. There an exempt of the guard, of whom he casually asked the time, observing the King's pallor and listlessness, took the liberty of suggesting that His Majesty might benefit if he took the air.

That chance remark decided Henry's fate. His eyes quickened responsively. "You advise well," said he. "Order my coach. I will go to the Arsenal to see the Duc de Sully, who is indisposed."

On the stones beyond the gates, where lackeys were wont to await their masters, sat a lean fellow of some thirty years of age, in a dingy, clerkly attire, so repulsively evil of countenance that he had once been arrested on no better grounds than because it was deemed impossible that a man with such a face could be other than a villain.

Whilst the coach was being got ready, Henry reëntered the Louvre, and startled the Queen by announcing his intention. With fearful insistence she besought him to countermand the order, and not to leave the palace.

"I will but go there and back," he said, laughing at her fears. "I shall have returned before you realize that I have gone." And so he went, never to return alive.

He sat at the back of the coach, and the weather being fine all the curtains were drawn up so that he might view the decorations of the city against the Queen's public entry on Sunday. The Duc d'Epernon was on his right, the Duc de Montbazon and the Marquis de la Force on his left. Lavordin and Roquelaure were in the right boot, whilst near the left boot, opposite to Henry, sat Mirebeau and du Plessis Liancourt. He was attended only by a small number of gentlemen on horseback, and some footmen.

The coach turned from the Rue Saint Honoré into the narrow Rue de la Ferronerie, and there was brought to a halt by a block occasioned by the meeting of two carts, one laden with hay, the other with wine. The footmen went ahead with the exception of two. Of these, one advanced to clear a way for the royal vehicle, whilst the other took the opportunity to fasten his garter.

At that moment, gliding like a shadow between the coach and the shops, came that shabby, hideous fellow who had been sitting on the stones outside the Louvre an hour ago. Raising himself by deliberately standing upon one of the spokes of the stationary wheel, he leaned over the Duc d'Epernon, and, whipping a long, stout knife from his sleeve, stabbed Henry in the breast. The King, who was in the act of reading a letter, cried out, and threw up his arms in an instinctive warding movement, thereby exposing his heart. The assassin stabbed again, and this time the blade went deep.

With a little gasping cough, Henry sank together, and blood gushed from his mouth.

The predictions were fulfilled; the tale borne by the courier riding through Liège a week ago was made true, as were the stories of his death already at that very hour circulating in Antwerp, Malines, Brussels, and elsewhere.

The murderer aimed yet a third blow, but this at last was parried by Epernon, whereupon the fellow stepped back from the coach, and stood there, making no attempt to escape, or even to rid himself of the incriminating knife. Saint Michel, one of the King's gentlemen-in-waiting, who had followed the coach, whipped out his sword and would have slain him on the spot had he not been restrained by Epernon. The footmen seized the fellow, and delivered him over to the captain of the guard. He proved to be a school-master of Angoulême — which was Epernon's coun-try. His name was Ravaillac.

The curtains of the coach were drawn, the vehicle was put about, and driven back to the Louvre, whilst to avoid all disturbance it was announced to the peo-ple that the King was merely wounded.

But Saint Michel went on to the Arsenal, taking with him the knife that had stabbed his master, to bear the sinister tidings to Henry's loyal and devoted friend. Sully knew enough to gauge exactly whence the blow had proceeded. With anger and grief in his heart he got to horse, ill as he was, and, calling to-gether his people, set out presently for the Louvre, with a train one hundred strong, which was presently increased to twice that number by many of the King's faithful servants who joined his company as he ad-vanced. In the Rue de la Pourpointière a man in passing slipped a note into his hand. It was a brief scrawl:

Monsieur, where are you going? It is done. I have seen him dead. If you enter the Louvre, you will not escape any more than he did.

Nearing Saint Innocent, the warning was repeated, this time by a gentleman named du Jon, who stopped to mutter:

"Monsieur le Duc, our evil is without remedy.

Look to yourself, for this strange blow will have fearful consequences."

Again in the Rue Saint Honoré another note was thrown him, whose contents were akin to those of the first. Yet with misgivings mounting swiftly to certainty, Sully rode amain towards the Louvre, his train by now amounting to some three hundred horse. But at the end of the street he was stopped by Monsieur de Vitry, who drew rein as they met.

"Ah, monsieur," Vitry greeted him, "where are you going with such a following? They will never suffer you to enter the Louvre with more than two or three attendants, which I would not advise you to do. For this plot does not end here. I have seen some persons so little sensible of the loss they have sustained that they cannot even simulate the grief they should feel. Go back, monsieur. There is enough for you to do without going to the Louvre."

Persuaded by Vitry's solemnity, and by what he knew in his heart, Sully faced about and set out to retrace his steps. But presently he was overtaken by a messenger from the Queen, begging him to come at once to her at the Louvre, and to bring as few persons as possible with him. "This proposal," he writes, "to go alone and deliver myself into the hands of my enemies, who filled the Louvre, was not calculated to allay my suspicions."

Moreover, he received word at that moment that an exempt of the guards and a force of soldiers were already at the gates of the Arsenal, that others had been sent to the Temple where the powder was stored, and others again to the treasurer of the Exchequer to stop all the money there.

"Convey to the Queen my duty and service," he bade the messenger, "and assure her that until she acquaints me with her orders I shall continue assiduously to attend the affairs of my office." And with that he went to shut himself up in the Bastille, whither he was presently followed by a stream of Her Majesty's envoys, all bidding him to the Louvre. But Sully, ill as he was, and now utterly prostrated by all that he had endured, put himself to bed and made of his indisposition a sufficient excuse.

Yet on the morrow he allowed himself to be persuaded to obey her summons, receiving certain assurances that he had no ground for any apprehensions. Moreover, he may by now have felt a certain security in the esteem in which the Parisians held him. An attempt against him in the Louvre itself would prove that the blow that had killed his master was not the independent act of a fanatic, as it was being represented; and vengeance would follow swiftly upon the heads of those who would thus betray themselves of having made of that poor wretch's fanaticism an instrument to their evils ends.

In that assurance he went, and he has left on record the burning indignation aroused in him at the signs of satisfaction, complacency, and even mirth that he discovered in that house of death. The Queen herself, however, overwrought by the events, and perhaps conscience-stricken by the tragedy which in the eleventh hour she had sought to avert, burst into tears at sight of Sully, and brought in the Dauphin, who flung himself upon the Duke's neck.

"My son," the Queen addressed him, "this is Monsieur de Sully. You must love him well, for he was one of the best and most faithful servants of the King your father, and I entreat him to continue to serve you in the same manner."

Words so fair might have convinced a man less astute that all his suspicions were unworthy. But, even then, the sequel would very quickly have undeceived him. For very soon thereafter his fall was brought about by the Concinis and their creatures, so that no obstacle should remain between themselves and the full gratification of their fell ambitions.

At once he saw the whole policy of the dead King subversed; he saw the renouncing of all ancient alliances, and the union of the crowns of France and Spain; the repealing of all acts of pacification; the destruction of the Protestants; the dissipation of the treasures amassed by Henry; the disgrace of those who would not receive the yoke of the new favourites. All this Sully witnessed in his declining years, and he witnessed, too, the rapid rise to the greatest power and dignity in the State of that Florentine adventurer, Concino Concini — now bearing the title of Marshal d'Ancre — who had so cunningly known how to profit by a Queen's jealousy and a King's indiscretions.

As for the miserable Ravaillac, it is pretended that he maintained under torture and to the very hour of his death that he had no accomplices; that what he had done he had done to prevent an unrighteous war against Catholicism and the Pope — which was, no doubt, the falsehood with which those who used him played upon his fanaticism and whetted him to their service. I say "pretended" because, after all, complete records of his examinations are not discoverable, and there is a story that when at the point of death, seeing himself abandoned by those in whom perhaps he had trusted, he signified a desire to confess, and did so confess; but the notary Voisin, who took his depositions in articulo mortis, set them down in a hand so slovenly as to be afterwards undecipherable.

That may or may not be true. But the statement, that when the President du Harlay sought to pursue inquiries into certain allegations by a woman named d'Escaman, which incriminated the Duc d'Epernon, he received a royal order to desist, rests upon sound authority.

That is the story of the assassination of Henry IV retold in the light of certain records which appear to me to have been insufficiently studied. They should suggest a train of speculation leading to inferences which, whilst obvious, I hesitate to define absolutely.

"If it be asked," says Perefixe, "who were the friends that suggested to Ravaillac so damnable a design, history replies that it is ignorant and that upon an action of such consequences it is not permissible to give suspicions and conjectures for certain truths. The judges themselves who interrogated him dared not open their mouths, and never mentioned the matter but with gestures of horror and amazement."

VI

THE BARREN WOOING

THE MURDER OF AMY ROBSART

THERE had been a banquet, followed by a masque, and this again by a dance in which the young Queen had paired off with Lord Robert Dudley, who in repute was the handsomest man in Europe, just as in fact he was the vainest, shallowest, and most unscrupulous. There had been homage and flattery lavishly expressed, and there was a hint of masked hostility from certain quarters to spice the adventure, and to thrill her bold young spirit. Never yet in all the months of her reign since her coronation in January of last year had she felt so much a queen, and so conscious of the power of her high estate; never so much a woman, and so conscious of the weakness of her sex. The interaction of those conflicting senses wrought upon her like a heady wine. She leaned more heavily upon the silken arm of her handsome Master of the Horse, and careless in her intoxication of what might be thought or said, she — who by the intimate favour shown him had already loosed the tongue of Scandal and set it chattering in every court in Europe — drew him forth from that thronged and glittering chamber of the Palace of Whitehall into the outer solitude and friendly gloom.

And he, nothing loath to obey the suasion of that white hand upon his arm, exultant, indeed, to parade before them all the power he had with her, went willingly enough. Let Norfolk and Sussex scowl, let Arundel bite his lip until it bled, and sober Cecil stare cold disapproval. They should mend their countenances soon, and weigh their words or be forever silenced, when he was master in England. And that he would soon be master he was assured to-night by every glance of her blue eyes, by the pressure of that fair hand upon his arm, by the languishing abandonment with which that warm young body swayed towards him, as they passed out from the blaze of lights and the strains of music into the gloom and silence of the gallery leading to the terrace.

"Out — let us go out, Robin. Let me have air," she almost panted, as she drew him on.

Assuredly he would be master soon. Indeed, he might have been master already but for that wife of his, that stumbling-block to his ambition, who practised the housewifely virtues at Cumnor Place, and clung so tenaciously and so inconsiderately to life in spite of all his plans to relieve her of the burden of it.

For a year and more his name had been coupled with the Queen's in a tale that hurt her honour as a woman and imperilled her dignity as a sovereign. Already, in October of 1559, Alvarez de Quadra, the Spanish ambassador, had written home: "I have learnt certain things as to the terms on which the Queen and Lord Robert stand towards each other which I could not have believed."

That was at a time when de Quadra was one of a dozen ambassadors who were competing for her hand, and Lord Robert had, himself, appeared to be an ally of de Quadra and an advocate of the Spanish marriage with the Archduke Charles. But it was a pretence which nowise deceived the astute Spaniard, who employed a legion of spies to keep him well informed.

"All the dallying with us," he wrote, "all the dallying with the Swede, all the dallying there will be with the rest, one after another, is merely to keep Lord Robert's enemies in play until his villainy about his wife can be executed."

What that particular villainy was, the ambassador had already stated earlier in his letter. "I have learnt from a person who usually gives me true information that Lord Robert has sent to have his wife poisoned."

What had actually happened was that Sir Richard Verney — a trusted retainer of Lord Robert's — had reported to Dr. Bayley, of New College, Oxford, that Lady Robert Dudley was "sad and ailing," and had asked him for a potion. But the doctor was learned in more matters than physic. He had caught an echo of the tale of Lord Robert's ambition, he had heard a whisper that whatever suitors might come from overseas for Elizabeth, she would marry none but "my lord" — as Lord Robert was now commonly styled. More, he had aforetime heard rumours of the indispositions of Lady Robert, yet had never found those rumours verified by the fact. Some months ago, it had been reported that her ladyship was suffering from cancer of the breast and likely soon to die of it. Yet Dr. Bayley had reason to know that a healthier woman did not live in Berkshire.

The good doctor was a capable deductive reasoner, and the conclusion to which he came was that if they poisoned her under cover of his potion — she standing in no need of physic — he might afterwards be hanged as a cover for their crime. So he refused to prescribe as he was invited, nor troubled to make a secret of invitation and refusal.

For a while, then, Lord Robert had prudently held his hand; moreover, the urgency there had been a year ago, when that host of foreign suitors laid siege to Elizabeth of England, had passed, and his lordship could afford to wait. But now of a sudden the urgency was returned. Under the pressure brought to bear upon her to choose a husband, Elizabeth had half-committed herself to marry the Archduke Charles, promising the Spanish ambassador a definite answer within a few days.

Lord Robert had felt the earth to be quaking under him; he had seen the ruin of his high ambitions; he had watched with rage the expanding mockery upon the countenances of Norfolk, Sussex, and those others who hated and despised him; and he had cursed that wife of his who knew not when to die. But for that obstinacy with which she clung to life he had been the Queen's husband these many months, so making an end to suspense and to the danger that lies in delay.

To-night the wantonness with which the Queen flaunted before the eyes of all her Court the predilection in which she held him, came not merely to lull his recent doubts and fears, to feed his egregious vanity, and to assure him that in her heart he need fear no rival; it came also to set his soul aquiver with impotent rage. He had but to put forth his hands to possess himself of this splendid prize. Yet those hands of his were bound while that woman lived at Cumnor. Conceive his feelings as they stole away together like any pair of lovers.

Arm in arm they came by a stone gallery, where a stalwart scarlet sentinel, a yeoman of the guard, with a Tudor rose embroidered in gold upon his back, stood under a lamp set in the wall, with grounded pike and body stiffly erect.

The tall young Queen was in crimson satin with cunningly wrought silver embroideries, trimmed with tufted silver fringe, her stomacher stiff with silver bullion studded with gold rosettes and Roman pearls, her bodice cut low to display her splendid neck, decked by a carcanet of pearls and rubies, and surmounted by a fan-like ruff of guipure, high behind and sloping towards the bust. Thus she appeared to the sentinel as the rays of the single lamp behind him struck fire from her red-gold hair. As if by her very gait to express the wantonness of her mood, she pointed her toes and walked with head thrown back, smiling up into the gipsy face of her companion, who was arrayed from head to foot in shimmering ivory satin, with an elegance no man in England could have matched.

They came by that stone gallery to a little terrace above the Privy Steps. A crescent moon hung low over the Lambeth marshes across the river. From a barge that floated gay with lights in mid-stream came a tinkle of lutes, and the sweet voice of a singing boy. A moment the lovers stood at gaze, entranced by the beauty of the soft, tepid September night, so subtly adapted to their mood. Then she fetched a sigh, and hung more heavily upon his arm, leaned nearer to his tall, vigorous, graceful figure.

"Robin, Robin!" was all she said, but in her voice throbbed a world of passionate longing, an exquisite blend of delight and pain.

Judging the season ripe, his arm flashed round her, and drew her fiercely close. For a moment she was content to yield, her head against his stalwart shoulder, a very woman nestling to the mate of her choice, surrendering to her master. Then the queen in her awoke and strangled nature. Roughly she disengaged herself from his arm, and stood away, her breathing quickened.

"God's death, Robin!" There was a harsh note in the voice that lately had cooed so softly. "You are strangely free, I think."

But he, impudence incarnate, nothing abashed, accustomed to her gusty moods, to her alternations between the two natures she had inherited — from overbearing father and wanton mother — was determined at all costs to take the fullest advantage of the hour, to make an end of suspense.

"I am not free, but enslaved — by love and worship of you. Would you deny me? Would you?"

"Not I, but Fate," she answered heavily, and he knew that the woman at Cumnor was in her mind.

"Fate will soon mend the wrong that Fate has done — very soon now." He took her hand, and, melted again from her dignity, she let it lie in his. "When that is done, sweet, than will I claim you for my own."

"When that is done, Robin?" she questioned almost fearfully, as if a sudden dread suspicion broke upon her mind. "When what is done?"

He paused a moment to choose his words, what time she stared intently into the face that gleamed white in the surrounding gloom.

"When that poor ailing spirit is at rest." And he added: "It will be soon."

"Thou hast said the same aforetime, Robin. Yet it has not so fallen out."

"She has clung to life beyond what could have been believed of her condition," he explained, unconscious of any sinister ambiguity. "But the end, I know, is very near — a matter but of days."

"Of days!" she shivered, and moved forward to the edge of the terrace, he keeping step beside her. Then she stood awhile in silence, looking down at the dark oily surge of water. "You loved her once, Robin?" she asked, in a queer, unnatural voice.

"I never loved but once," answered that perfect courtier.

"Yet you married her — men say it was a love marriage. It was a marriage, anyway, and you can speak so calmly of her death?" Her tone was brooding. She sought understanding that should silence her own lingering doubt of him.

"Where lies the blame? Who made me what I am?" Again his bold arm encompassed her. Side by side they peered down through the gloom at the rushing waters, and he seized an image from them. "Our love is like that seething tide," he said. "To resist it is to labour in agony awhile, and then to perish."

"And to yield is to be swept away."

"To happiness," he cried, and reverted to his earlier prayer. "Say that when ... that afterwards, I may claim you for my own. Be true to yourself, obey the voice of instinct, and so win to happiness."

She looked up at him, seeking to scan the handsome face in that dim light that baffled her, and he observed the tumultuous heave of her white breast.

"Can I trust thee, Robin? Can I trust thee? Answer me true!" she implored him, adorably weak, entirely woman now.

"What does your own heart answer you?" quoth he, leaning close above her.

"I think I can, Robin. And, anyway, I must. I cannot help myself. I am but a woman, after all," she murmured, and sighed. "Be it as thou wilt. Come to me again when thou art free."

He bent lower, murmuring incoherently, and she put up a hand to pat his swarthy bearded cheek.

"I shall make thee greater than any man in England, so thou make me happier than any woman."

He caught the hand in his and kissed it passionately, his soul singing a triumph song within him. Norfolk and Sussex and those other scowling ones should soon be whistled to the master's heel.

As they turned arm in arm into the gallery to retrace their steps, they came suddenly face to face with a slim, sleek gentleman, who bowed profoundly, a smile upon his crafty, shaven, priestly face. In a smooth voice and an accent markedly foreign, he explained that he, too, sought the cool of the terrace, not thinking to intrude; and upon that, bowing again, he passed on and effaced himself. It was Alvarez de Quadra, Bishop of Aquila, the Argus-eyed ambassador of Spain.

The young face of the Queen hardened.

"I would I were as well served abroad as the King of Spain is here," she said aloud, that the retreating ambassador might hear the dubious compliment; and for my lord's ear alone she added under her breath: "The spy! Philip of Spain will hear of this."

"So that he hears something more, what shall it signify?" quoth my lord, and laughed.

They paced the length of the gallery in silence, past the yeoman of the guard, who kept his watch, and into the first ante-chamber. Perhaps it was that meeting with de Quadra and my lord's answer to her comment that prompted what now she asked: "What is it ails her, Robin?"

"A wasting sickness," he answered, never doubting to whom the question alluded.

"You said, I think, that . . . that the end is very near."

He caught her meaning instantly. "Indeed, if she is not dead already, she is very nearly so."

He lied, for never had Amy Dudley been in better health. And yet he spoke the truth, for in so much as her life depended upon his will, it was as good as spent. This was, he knew, a decisive moment of his career. The hour was big with fate. If now he were weak or hesitant, the chance might slip away and be forever lost to him. Elizabeth's moods were as uncertain as were certain the hostile activities of my lord's enemies. He must strike quickly whilst she was in her present frame of mind, and bring her to wedlock, be it in public or in private. But first he must shake off the paralyzing encumbrance of that housewife down at Cumnor.

I believe — from evidence that I account abundant — that he considered it with the cold remorselessness of the monstrous egotist he was. An upstart, great-grandson to a carpenter, noble only in two descents, and in both of them stained by the block, he found a queen — the victim of a physical passion that took no account of the worthlessness underlying his splendid exterior — reaching out a hand to raise

him to a throne. Being what he was, he weighed his
young wife's life at naught in the evil scales of his ambition. And yet he had loved her once, more truly
perhaps than he could now pretend to love the Queen.

It was some ten years since, as a lad of eighteen,
he had taken Sir John Robsart's nineteen-year-old
daughter to wife. She had brought him considerable
wealth and still more devotion. Because of this devotion she was content to spend her days at Cumnor,
whilst he ruffled it at Court; content to take such
crumbs of attention as he could spare her upon occasion. And during the past year, whilst he had been
plotting her death, she had been diligently caring for
his interests and fostering the prosperity of the Berkshire estate. If he thought of this at all, he allowed
no weakly sentiment to turn him from his purpose.
There was too much at stake for that — a throne, no
less.

And so, on the morning after that half-surrender of
Elizabeth's, we find my lord closeted with his hench-
man, Sir Richard Verney. Sir Richard — like his
master — was a greedy, unscrupulous, ambitious
scoundrel, prepared to go to any lengths for the sake
of such worldly advancement as it lay in my lord's
power to give him. My lord perforce used perfect
frankness with this perfect servant.

"Thou'lt rise or fall with me, Dick," quoth he.
"Help me up, then, and so mount with me. When I
am King, as soon now I shall be, look to me. Now to
the thing that is to do. Thou'lt have guessed it."

To Sir Richard it was an easy guess, considering
how much already he had been about this business.
He signified as much.

My lord shifted in his elbow-chair, and drew his embroidered bedgown of yellow satin closer about his shapely limbs.

"Hast failed me twice before, Richard," said he. "God's death, man, fail me not again, or the last chance may go the way of the others. There's a magic in the number three. See that I profit by it, or I am undone, and thou with me."

"I'd not have failed before but for that suspicious dotard Bayley," grumbled Verney. "Your lordship bade me see that all was covered."

"Aye, aye. And I bid thee so again. On thy life, leave no footprints by which we may be tracked. Bayley is not the only physician in Oxford. About it, then, and swiftly. Time is the very soul of fortune in this business, with the Spaniard straining at the leash, and Cecil and the rest pleading his case with her. Succeed, and thy fortune's made; fail, and trouble not to seek me again."

Sir Richard bowed, and took his leave. As he reached the door, his lordship stayed him. "If thou bungle, do not look to me. The Court goes to Windsor to-morrow. Bring me word there within the week." He rose, magnificently tall and stately, in his bedgown of embroidered yellow satin, his handsome head thrown back, and went after his retainer. "Thou'lt not fail me, Dick," said he, a hand upon the lesser scoundrel's shoulder. "There is much at issue for me, and for thee with me."

"I will not fail you, my lord," Sir Richard rashly promised, and on that they parted.

Sir Richard did not mean to fail. He knew the importance of succeeding, and he appreciated the urgency of the business as much as did my lord himself. But between his cold, remorseless will to succeed and success itself there lay a gulf which it needed all his resource to bridge. He paid a short visit to Lady Robert at Cumnor, and professed deepest concern to find in her a pallor and an ailing air which no one else had yet observed. He expressed himself on the subject to Mrs. Buttelar and the other members of her ladyship's household, reproaching them with their lack of care of their mistress. Mrs. Buttelar became indignant under his reproaches.

"Nay, now, Sir Richard, do you wonder that my lady is sad and downcast with such tales as are going of my lord's doings at Court, and of what there is 'twixt the Queen and him? Her ladyship may be too proud to complain, but she suffers the more for that, poor lamb. There was talk of a divorce awhile ago that got to her ears."

"Old wives' tales," snorted Sir Richard.

"Likely," agreed Mrs. Buttelar. "Yet when my lord neither comes to Cumnor, nor requires her ladyship to go to him, what is she to think, poor soul?"

Sir Richard made light of all, and went off to Oxford to find a physician more accommodating than Dr. Bayley. But Dr. Bayley had talked too much, and it was in vain that Sir Richard pleaded with each of the two physicians he sought that her ladyship was ailing — "sad and heavy" — and that he must have a potion for her.

Each in turn shook his head. They had no medicine for sorrow was their discreet answer. From his description of her condition, said each, it was plain that her ladyship's sickness was of the mind, and, con-

sidering the tales that were afloat, neither was surprised.

Sir Richard went back to his Oxford lodging with
the feeling of a man checkmated. For two whole days
of that precious time he lay there considering what to
do. He thought of going to seek a physician in Abingdon. But fearing no better success in that quarter,
fearing, indeed, that in view of the rumours abroad he
would merely be multiplying what my lord called
"footprints," he decided to take some other way to
his master's ends. He was a resourceful, inventive
scoundrel, and soon he had devised a plan.

On Friday he wrote from Oxford to Lady Robert,
stating that he had a communication for her on the
subject of his lordship as secret as it was urgent.
That he desired to come to her at Cumnor again, but
dared not do so openly. He would come if she would
contrive that her servants should be absent, and he
exhorted her to let no one of them know that he was
coming, else he might be ruined, out of his desire to
serve her.

That letter he dispatched by the hand of his servant Nunweek, desiring him to bring an answer. It
was a communication that had upon her ladyship's
troubled mind precisely the effect that the rascal conceived. There was about Sir Richard's personality
nothing that could suggest the villain. He was a
smiling, blue-eyed, florid gentleman, of a kindly manner that led folk to trust him. And on the occasion of
his late visit to Cumnor he had displayed such tender
solicitude that her ladyship — starved of affection as
she was — had been deeply touched.

His letter so cunningly couched filled her with

vague alarm and with anxiety. She had heard so many and such afflicting rumours, and had received in my lord's cruel neglect of her such circumstantial confirmation of them, that she fastened avidly upon what she deemed the chance of learning at last the truth. Sir Richard Verney had my lord's confidence, and was much about the Court in his attendance upon my lord. He would know the truth, and what could this letter mean but that he was disposed to tell it.

So she sent him back a line in answer, bidding him come on Sunday afternoon. She would contrive to be alone in the house, so that he need not fear being seen by any.

As she promised, so she performed, and on the Sunday packed off her household to the fair that was being held at Abingdon that day, using insistence with the reluctant, and particularly with one of her women, a Mrs. Oddingsell, who expressed herself strongly against leaving her ladyship alone in that lonely house. At length, however, the last of them was got off, and my lady was left impatiently to await her secret visitor. It was late afternoon when he arrived, accompanied by Nunweek, whom he left to hold the horses under the chestnuts in the avenue. Himself he reached the house across the garden, where the blighting hand of autumn was already at work.

Within the porch he found her waiting, fretted by her impatience.

"It is very good in you to have come, Sir Richard," was her gracious greeting.

"I am your ladyship's devoted servant," was his sufficient answer, and he doffed his plumed bonnet, and bowed low before her. "We shall be private in your bower above stairs," he added.

"Why, we are private anywhere. I am all alone, as you desired."

"That is very wise — most wise," said he. "Will your ladyship lead the way?"

So they went up that steep, spiral staircase, which had loomed so prominently in the plans the ingenious scoundrel had evolved. Across the gallery on the first floor they entered a little room whose windows overlooked the garden. This was her bower — an intimate cosy room, reflecting on every hand the gentle, industrious personality of the owner. On an oak table near the window were spread some papers and account-books concerned with the estate — with which she had sought to beguile the time of waiting. She led the way towards this, and, sinking into the high-backed chair that stood before it, she looked up at him expectantly. She was pale, there were dark stains under her eyes, and wistful lines had crept into the sweet face of that neglected wife.

Contemplating his poor victim now, Sir Richard may have compared her with the woman by whom my lord desired so impatiently to supplant her. She was tall and beautifully shaped, despite an almost maidenly slenderness. Her countenance was gentle and adorable, with its soft grey eyes and light brown hair, and tender, wistful mouth.

It was not difficult to believe that Lord Robert had as ardently desired her to wife five years ago as he now desired to be rid of her. Then he obeyed the insistent spur of passion; now he obeyed the remorseless spur of ambition. In reality, then as now, his beacon-light was love of self.

Seeing her so frail and trusting, trembling in her anxious impatience to hear the news of her lord which he had promised her, Sir Richard may have felt some pang of pity. But, like my lord, he was of those whose love of self suffers the rivalry of no weak emotion.

"Your news, Sir Richard," she besought him, her dove-like glance upon his florid face — less florid now than was its wont.

He leaned against the table, his back to the window. "Why, it is briefly this," said he. "My lord . . ."

And then he checked, and fell into a listening attitude. "What was that? Did you hear anything, my lady?"

"No. What is it?" Her face betrayed alarm, her anxiety mounting under so much mystery.

"Sh! Stay you here," he enjoined. "If we are spied upon . . ." He left the sentence there. Already he was moving quickly, stealthily, towards the door. He paused before opening it. "Stay where you are, my lady," he enjoined again, so gravely that she could have no thought of disobeying him. "I will return at once."

He stepped out, closed the door, and crossed to the stairs. There he stooped. From his pouch he had drawn a fine length of whipcord, attached at one end to a tiny bodkin of needle sharpness. That bodkin he drove into the edge of one of the panels of the wainscot, in line with the topmost step; drawing the cord taut at a height of a foot or so above this step, he made fast its other end to the newel-post at the stairhead. He had so rehearsed the thing in his mind that the performance of it occupied but a few seconds. Such dim light of that autumn afternoon as reached the spot would leave that fine cord invisible.

Sir Richard went back to her ladyship. She had not moved in his absence, so brief as scarcely to have left her time in which to resolve upon disobeying his injunction.

"We move in secret like conspirators," said he, "and so we are easily affrighted. I should have known it could be none but my lord himself . . ."

"My lord!" she interrupted, coming excitedly to her feet. "Lord Robert?"

"To be sure, my lady. It was he had need to visit you in secret — for did the Queen have knowledge of his coming here, it would mean the Tower for him. You cannot think what, out of love for you, his lordship suffers. The Queen . . ."

"But do you say that he is here, man . . . here?" her voice shrilled up in excitement.

"He is below, my lady. Such is his peril that he dared not set foot in Cumnor until he was certain beyond doubt that you are here alone."

"He is below!" she cried, and a flush dyed her pale cheeks, a light of gladness quickened her sad eyes. Already she had gathered from his cunning words a new and comforting explanation of the things reported to her. "He is below!" she repeated. "Oh!" She turned from him, and in an instant was speeding towards the door.

He stood rooted there, his nether lip between his teeth, his face a ghastly white, whilst she ran on.

"My lord! Robin! Robin!" he heard her calling, as she crossed the corridor. Then came a piercing scream that echoed through the silent house; a pause; a crashing thud below; and — silence.

Sir Richard remained by the table, immovable.

Blood was trickling down his chin. He had sunk his teeth through his lip when that scream rang out. A long moment thus, as if entranced, awe-stricken. Then he braced himself, and went forward, reeling at first like a drunken man. But by the time he had reached the stairs he was master of himself again. Swiftly, for all his trembling fingers, he unfastened the cord's end from the newel-post. The wrench upon it had already pulled the bodkin from the wainscot. He went down that abrupt spiral staircase at a moderate pace, mechanically coiling the length of whipcord, and bestowing it with the bodkin in his pouch again, and all the while his eyes were fixed upon the grey bundle that lay so still at the stairs' foot.

He came to it at last, and, pausing, looked more closely. He was thankful that there was not the need to touch it. The position of the brown-haired head was such as to leave no doubt of the complete success of his design. Her neck was broken. Lord Robert Dudley was free to marry the Queen.

Deliberately Sir Richard stepped over the huddled body of that poor victim of a knave's ambition, crossed the hall, and passed out, closing the door. An excellent day's work, thought he, most excellently accomplished. The servants, returning from Abingdon Fair on that Sunday evening, would find her there. They would publish the fact that in their absence her ladyship had fallen downstairs and broken her neck, and that was the end of the matter.

But that was not the end at all. Fate, the ironic interloper, had taken a hand in this evil game.

The Court had moved a few days earlier to Windsor, and thither on the Friday — the 6th of September — came Alvarez de Quadra to seek the definite answer which the Queen had promised him on the subject of the Spanish marriage. What he had seen that night at Whitehall, coupled with his mistrust of her promises and experience of her fickleness, had rendered him uneasy. Either she was trifling with him, or else she was behaving in a manner utterly unbecoming the future wife of the Archduke. In either case some explanation was necessary. De Quadra must know where he stood. Having failed to obtain an audience before the Court left London, he had followed it to Windsor, cursing all women and contemplating the advantages of the Salic law.

He found at Windsor an atmosphere of constraint, and it was not until the morrow that he obtained an audience with the Queen. Even then this was due to chance rather than to design on the part of Elizabeth. For they met on the terrace as she was returning from hunting. She dismissed those about her, including the stalwart Robert Dudley, and, alone with de Quadra, invited him to speak.

"Madame," he said, "I am writing to my master, and I desire to know whether Your Majesty would wish me to add anything to what you have announced already as your intention regarding the Archduke."

She knit her brows. The wily Spaniard fenced so closely that there was no alternative but to come to grips.

"Why, sir," she answered dryly, "you may tell His Majesty that I have come to an absolute decision — which is that I will not marry the Archduke."

The colour mounted to the Spaniard's sallow

cheeks. Iron self-control alone saved him from utter-ing unpardonable words. Even so he spoke sternly:

"This, Madame, is not what you have led me to be-lieve when last we talked upon the subject."

At another time Elizabeth might have turned upon him and rent him for that speech. But it happened that she was in high good-humour that afternoon, and disposed to indulgence. She laughed, surveying her-self in the small steel mirror that dangled from her waist.

"You are ungallant to remind me, my lord," said she. "My sex, you may have heard, is privileged to change of mind."

"Then, Madame, I pray that you may change it yet again." His tone was bitter.

"Your prayer will not be heard. This time I am re-solved."

De Quadra bowed. "The King, my master, will not be pleased, I fear."

She looked him straightly in the face, her dark eyes kindling.

"God's death!" said she, "I marry to please my-self, and not the King your master."

"You are resolved on marriage, then?" flashed he.

"An it please you," she mocked him archly, her mood of joyousness already conquering her momen-tary indignation.

"What pleases you must please me also, Madame," he answered, in a tone so cold that it belied his words. "That it please you is reason enough why you should marry . . . Whom did Your Majesty say?"

"Nay. I named no names. Yet one so astute

might hazard a shrewd guess." Half-challenging, half-coy, she eyed him over her fan.

"A guess? Nay, Madame. I might affront Your Majesty."

"How so?"

"If I were deluded by appearances. If I named a subject who signally enjoys your royal favour."

"You mean Lord Robert Dudley." She paled a little, and her bosom's heave was quickened. "Why should the guess affront me?"

"Because a queen — a wise queen, Madame — does not mate with a subject — particularly with one who has a wife already."

He had stung her. He had wounded at once the pride of the woman and the dignity of the queen, yet in a way that made it difficult for her to take direct offence. She bit her lip and mastered her surge of anger. Then she laughed, a thought sneeringly.

"Why, as to my Lord Robert's wife, it seems you are less well-informed than usual, sir. Lady Robert Dudley is dead, or very nearly so."

And as blank amazement overspread his face, she passed upon her way and left him.

But anon, considering, she grew vaguely uneasy, and that very night expressed her afflicting doubt to my lord, reporting to him de Quadra's words. His lordship, who was mentally near-sighted, laughed.

"He'll change his tone before long," said he.

She set her hands upon his shoulders, and looked up adoringly into his handsome gipsy face. Never had he known her so fond as in these last days since her surrender to him that night upon the terrace at Whitehall, never had she been more the woman and less the queen in her bearing towards him.

"You are sure, Robin? You are quite sure?" she pleaded.

He drew her close, she yielding herself to his embrace. "With so much at stake could I be less than sure, sweet?" said he, and so convinced her — the more easily since he afforded her the conviction she desired.

That was on the night of Saturday, and early on Monday came the news which justified him of his assurances. It was brought him to Windsor by one of Amy's Cumnor servants, a fellow named Bowes, who, with the others, had been away at Abingdon Fair yesterday afternoon, and had returned to find his mistress dead at the stairs' foot — the result of an accident, as all believed.

It was not quite the news that my lord had been expecting. It staggered him a little that an accident so very opportune should have come to resolve his difficulties, obviating the need for recourse to those more dangerous measures with which he had charged Sir Richard Verney. He perceived how suspicion might now fall upon himself, how his enemies would direct it, and on the instant made provision. There and then he seized a pen, and wrote to his kinsman, Sir Thomas Blount, who even then was on his way to Cumnor. He stated in the letter what he had learnt from Bowes, bade Blount engage the coroner to make the strictest investigation, and send for Amy's natural brother, Appleyard. "Have no respect to any living person," was the final injunction of that letter which he sent Blount by the hand of Bowes.

And, then, before he could carry to the Queen the news of this accident which had broken his matrimonial shackles, Sir Richard Verney arrived with the true account. He had expected praise and thanks from his master. Instead, he met first dismay, and then anger and fierce reproaches.

"My lord, this is unjust," the faithful retainer protested. "Knowing the urgency, I took the only way — contrived the accident."

"Pray God," said Dudley, "that the jury find it to have been an accident; for if the truth should come to be discovered, I leave you to the consequences. I warned you of that before you engaged in this. Look for no help from me."

"I look for none," said Sir Richard, stung to hot contempt by the meanness and cowardice so characteristic of the miserable egotist he served. "Nor will there be the need, for I have left no footprints."

"I hope that may be so, for I tell you, man, that I have ordered a strict inquiry, bidding them have no respect to any living person, and to that I shall adhere."

"And if, in spite of that, I am not hanged?" quoth Sir Richard, a sneer upon his white face.

"Come to me again when the affair is closed, and we will talk of it."

Sir Richard went out, rage and disgust in his heart, leaving my lord with rage and fear in his.

Grown calmer now, my lord dressed himself with care and sought the Queen to tell her of the accident that had removed the obstacle to their marriage. And that same night Her Majesty coldly informed de Quadra that Lady Robert Dudley had fallen down a flight of stairs and broken her neck.

The Spaniard received the information with a countenance that was inscrutable.

"Your Majesty's gift of prophecy is not so widely known as it deserves to be," was his cryptic comment.

She stared at him blankly a moment. Then a sudden uneasy memory awakened by his words, she drew him forward to a window embrasure apart from those who had stood about her, and for the greater security addressed him, as he tells us, in Italian.

"I do not think I understand you, sir. Will you be plain with me?" She stood erect and stiff, and frowned upon him after the manner of her bullying father. But de Quadra held the trumps, and was not easily intimidated.

"About the prophecy?" said he. "Why, did not Your Majesty foretell the poor lady's death a full day before it came to pass? Did you not say that she was already dead, or nearly so?"

He saw her blench; saw fear stare from those dark eyes that could be so very bold. Then her ever-ready anger followed swiftly.

"'Sblood, man! What do you imply?" she cried, and went on without waiting for his answer. "The poor woman was sick and ill, and must soon have succumbed; it will no doubt be found that the accident which anticipated nature was due to her condition."

Gently he shook his head, relishing her discomfiture, taking satisfaction in torturing her who had flouted him and his master, in punishing her whom he had every reason to believe guilty.

"Your Majesty, I fear, has been ill-informed on that score. The poor lady was in excellent health — and like to have lived for many years — at least, so I gather from Sir William Cecil, whose information is usually exact."

She clutched his arm. "You told him what I had said?"

"It was indiscreet, perhaps. Yet, how was I to know . . .?" He left his sentence there. "I but expressed my chagrin at your decision on the score of the Archduke — hardly a wise decision, if I may be so bold," he added slyly.

She caught the suggestion of a bargain, and became instantly suspicious.

"You transcend the duties of your office, my lord," she rebuked him, and turned away.

But soon that night she was closeted with Dudley, and closely questioning him about the affair. My lord was mightily vehement.

"I take Heaven to be my witness," quoth he, when she all but taxed him with having procured his lady's death, "that I am innocent of any part in it. My injunctions to Blount, who has gone to Cumnor, are that the matter be sifted without respect to any person, and if it can be shown that this is other than the accident I deem it, the murderer shall hang."

She flung her arms about his neck, and laid her head on his shoulder. "Oh, Robin, Robin, I am full of fears," she wailed, and was nearer to tears than he had ever seen her.

But, anon, as the days passed their fears diminished, and finally the jury at Cumnor — delayed in their finding, and spurred by my lord to exhaustive inquiries — returned a verdict of "found dead," which in all the circumstances left his lordship — who was known, moreover, to have been at Windsor when his lady died — fully acquitted. Both he and the Queen took courage from that finding, and made no secret of it now that they would very soon be wed.

But there were many whom that finding did not convince, who read my lord too well, and would never suffer him to reap the fruits of his evil deed. Prominent among these were Arundel — who himself had aimed at the Queen's hand — Norfolk and Pembroke, and behind them was a great mass of the people. Indignation against Lord Robert was blazing out, fanned by such screaming preachers as Lever, who, from the London pulpits, denounced the projected marriage, hinting darkly at the truth of Amy Dudley's death.

What was hinted at home was openly expressed abroad, and in Paris Mary Stuart ventured a cruel witticism that Elizabeth was to conserve in her memory: "The Queen of England," she said, "is about to marry her horsekeeper, who has killed his wife to make a place for her."

Yet Elizabeth persisted in her intent to marry Dudley, until the sober Cecil conveyed to her towards the end of that month of September some notion of the rebellion that was smouldering.

She flared out at him, of course. But he stood his ground.

"There is," he reminded her, "this unfortunate matter of a prophecy, as the Bishop of Aquila persists in calling it."

"God's Body! Is the rogue blabbing?"

"What else did Your Majesty expect from a man smarting under a sense of injury? He has published it broadcast that on the day before Lady Robert broke her neck, you told him that she was dead or nearly so.

And he argues from it a guilty foreknowledge on Your Majesty's part of what was planned."

"A guilty foreknowledge!" She almost choked in rage, and then fell to swearing as furiously in that moment as old King Harry at his worst.

"Madame!" he cried, shaken by her vehemence. "I but report the phrase he uses. It is not mine."

"Do you believe it?"

"I do not, Madame. If I did I should not be here at present."

"Does any subject of mine believe it?"

"They suspend their judgment. They wait to learn the truth from the sequel."

"You mean?"

"That if your motive prove to be such as de Quadra and others allege, they will be in danger of believing."

"Be plain, man, in God's name. What exactly is alleged?"

He obeyed her very fully.

"That my lord contrived the killing of his wife so that he might have liberty to marry Your Majesty, and that Your Majesty was privy to the deed." He spoke out boldly, and hurried on before she could let loose her wrath. "It is still in your power, Madame, to save your honour, which is now in peril. But there is only one way in which you can accomplish it. If you put from you all thought of marrying Lord Robert, England will believe that de Quadra and those others lied. If you persist and carry out your intention, you proclaim the truth of his report; and you see what must inevitably follow."

She saw, indeed, and, seeing, was afraid.

Within a few hours of that interview she delivered her answer to Cecil, which was that she had no intention of marrying Dudley.

Because of her fear she saved her honour by sacrificing her heart, by renouncing marriage with the only man she could have taken for her mate of all who had wooed her. Yet the wound of that renunciation was slow to heal. She trifled with the notion of other marriages, but ever and anon, in her despair, perhaps, we see her turning longing eyes towards the handsome Lord Robert, later made Earl of Leicester. Once, indeed, some six years after Amy's death, there was again some talk of her marrying him, which was quickly quelled by a reopening of the question of how Amy died. Between these two, between the fulfilment of her desire and his ambition, stood the irreconcilable ghost of his poor murdered wife.

Perhaps it was some thought of this that found expression in her passionate outburst when she learnt of the birth of Mary Stuart's child: "The Queen of Scots is lighter of a fair son; and I am but a barren stock."

VII

SIR JUDAS

THE BETRAYAL OF SIR WALTER RALEGH

SIR WALTER was met on landing at Plymouth from his ill-starred voyage to El Dorado by Sir Lewis Stukeley, which was but natural, seeing that Sir Lewis was not only Vice-Admiral of Devon, but also Sir Walter's very good friend and kinsman.

If Sir Walter doubted whether it was in his quality as kinsman or as Vice-Admiral that Sir Lewis met him, the cordiality of the latter's embrace and the noble entertainment following at the house of Sir Christopher Hare, near the port, whither Sir Lewis conducted him, set this doubt at rest and relighted the lamp of hope in the despairing soul of our adventurer. In Sir Lewis he saw only his kinsman — his very good friend and kinsman, to insist upon Stukeley's own description of himself — at a time when of all others in his crowded life he needed the support of a kinsman and the guidance of a friend.

You know the story of this Sir Walter, who had been one of the brightest ornaments of the reign of Queen Elizabeth, and might have added lustre to that of King James, had not his Sowship — to employ the title bestowed upon that prince by his own queen — been too mean of soul to appreciate the man's great worth. Courtier, philosopher, soldier, man of letters and man of action alike, Ralegh was at once the greatest prose-writer, and one of the greatest captains of his age, the last survivor of that glorious company — whose other members were Drake and Frobisher and Hawkins — that had given England supremacy upon the seas, that had broken the power and lowered the pride of Spain.

His was a name that had resounded, to the honour and glory of England, throughout the world, a name that, like Drake's, was a thing of hate and terror to King Philip and his Spaniards; yet the King of Scots, unclean of body and of mind, who had succeeded to the throne of Elizabeth, must affect ignorance of that great name which shall never die while England lives.

When the splendid courtier stood before him — for at fifty Sir Walter was still handsome of person and magnificent of apparel — James looked him over and inquired who he might be. When they had told him:

"I've *rawly* heard of thee," quoth the royal punster, who sought by such atrocities of speech to be acclaimed a wit.

It was ominous of what must follow, and soon thereafter you see this great and gallant gentleman arrested on a trumped-up charge of high treason, bullied, vituperated, and insulted by venal, peddling lawyers, and, finally, although his wit and sincerity had shattered every fragment of evidence brought against him, sentenced to death. Thus far James went; but he hesitated to go further, hesitated to carry out the sentence. Sir Walter had too many friends in England then; the memory of his glorious deeds was still too fresh in the public mind, and execution might have been attended by serious consequences for King James. Besides, one at least of the main objects was achieved. Sir Walter's broad acres were confiscate by virtue of that sentence, and King James wanted the land — filched thus from one who was England's pride — to bestow it upon one of those golden calves of his who were England's shame.

"I maun hae the land for Carr. I maun hae it," was his brazen and peevish answer to an appeal against the confiscation.

For thirteen years Sir Walter lay in the Tower, under that sentence of death passed in 1603, enjoying after a season a certain liberty, visited there by his dear lady and his friends, among whom was Henry, Prince of Wales, who did not hesitate to publish that no man but his father — whom he detested — would keep such a bird in a cage. He beguiled the time in literary and scientific pursuits, distilling his essences and writing that stupendous work of his, "The History of the World." Thus old age crept upon him; but far from quenching the fires of enterprise within his adventurer's soul, it brought a restlessness that urged him at last to make a bid for liberty. Despairing of winning it from the clemency of James, he applied his wits to extracting it from the King's cupidity.

Throughout his life, since the day when first he had brought himself to the notice of a queen by making of his cloak a carpet for her feet, he had retained, side by side with the dignity of the sage and the greatness of the hero, the craft and opportunism of the adventurer. His opportunity now was the straitened condition of the royal treasury, a hint of which had been let fall by Winwood, the Secretary of State. He announced at once that he knew of a gold mine in Guiana, the El Dorado of the Spaniards.

On his return from a voyage to Guiana in 1595, he had written of it thus:

There the common soldier shall fight for gold instead of pence, pay himself with plates half a foot broad, whereas he breaks his bones in other wars for provant and penury. Those commanders and chieftains that shoot at honour and abundance shall find here more rich and beautiful cities, more temples adorned with golden images, more sepulchres filled with treasure than either Cortez found in Mexico or Pizarro in Peru.

Winwood now reminded him that as a consequence many expeditions had gone out, but failed to discover any of these things.

"That," said Ralegh, "is because those adventurers were ignorant alike of the country and of the art of conciliating its inhabitants. Were I permitted to go, I would make Guiana to England what Peru has been to Spain."

That statement, reported to James in his need, was enough to fire his cupidity, and when Ralegh had further added that he would guarantee to the Crown one-fifth of the treasure without asking any contribution towards the adventure either in money or in ships, he was permitted to come forth and prepare for the expedition.

His friends came to his assistance, and in March of 1617 he set sail for El Dorado with a well-manned and well-equipped fleet of fourteen ships, the Earls of Arundel and Pembroke standing sureties for his return.

From the outset the fates were unpropitious. Disaster closed the adventure. Gondomar, the Ambassador of Spain at Whitehall, too well-informed of what was afoot, had warned his master. Spanish ships waited to frustrate Sir Walter, who was under pledge to avoid all conflict with the forces of King Philip. But conflict there was, and bloodshed in plenty, about the city of Manoa, which the Spaniards held as the key to the country into which the English adventurers sought to penetrate. Among the slain were the Governor of Manoa, who was Gondomar's own brother, and Sir Walter's eldest son.

To Ralegh, waiting at the mouth of the Orinoco, came his beaten forces in retreat, with the terrible news of a happening that meant his ruin. Half-maddened, his anguish increased by the loss of his boy, he upbraided them so fiercely that Keymis, who had been in charge of the expedition, shut himself up in his cabin and shot himself with a pocket-pistol. Mutiny followed, and Whitney — most trusted of Sir Walter's captains — set sail for England, being followed by six other ships of that fleet, which meanwhile had been reduced to twelve. With the remaining five the stricken Sir Walter had followed more at leisure. What need to hurry? Disgrace, and perhaps death, awaited him in England. He knew the power of Spain with James, who was so set upon a Spanish marriage for his heir, knew Spain's hatred of himself, and what eloquence it would gather in the mouth of Gondomar, intent upon avenging his brother's death.

He feared the worst, and so was glad upon landing to have by him a kinsman upon whom he could lean for counsel and guidance in this the darkest hour of all his life. Sitting late that night in the library of Sir Christopher Hare's house, Sir Walter told his cousin in detail the story of his misadventure, and confessed to his misgivings.

"My brains are broken," was his cry.

Stukeley combed his beard in thought. He had little comfort to offer.

"It was not expected," said he, "that you would return."

"Not expected?" Sir Walter's bowed white head was suddenly flung back. Indignation blazed in the eyes that age had left undimmed. "What act in all my life justified the belief I should be false to honour? My danger here was made quite plain, and Captain King would have had me steer a course for France, where I had found a welcome and a harbour. But to consent I must have been false to my Lords of Arundel and Pembroke, who were sureties to the King for my return. Life is still sweet to me, despite my threescore years and more, but honour is sweeter still."

And then, because life was sweet, he bluntly asked his cousin: "What is the King's intent by me?"

"Nay, now," said Stukeley, "who shall know what passes in the King's mind? From the signs, I judge your case to be none so desperate. You have good friends in plenty, among whom, although the poorest, count myself the first. Anon, when you are rested, we'll to London by easy stages, baiting at the houses of your friends, and enlisting their good offices on your behalf."

Ralegh took counsel on the matter with Captain King, a bluff, tawny-bearded seaman, who was devoted to him body and soul.

"Sir Lewis proposes it, eh?" quoth the hardy seaman. "And Sir Lewis is Vice-Admiral of Devon? He is not by chance bidden to escort you to London?"

The captain, clearly, had escaped the spell of Stukeley's affability. Sir Walter was indignant. He had never held his kinsman in great esteem, and had never been on the best of terms with him in the past. Nevertheless, he was very far from suspecting him of what King implied. To convince him that he did Sir Lewis an injustice, Ralegh put the blunt question to his kinsman in King's presence.

"Nay," said Sir Lewis, "I am not yet bidden to escort you. But as Vice-Admiral of Devon I may at any moment be so bidden. It were wiser, I hold, not to await such an order. Though even if it come," he made haste to add, "you may still count upon my friendship. I am your kinsman first, and Vice-Admiral after."

With a smile that irradiated his handsome, virile countenance, Sir Walter held out his hand to clasp his cousin's in token of appreciation. Captain King expressed no opinion save what might be conveyed in a grunt and a shrug.

Guided now unreservedly by his cousin's counsel, Sir Walter set out with him upon that journey to London. Captain King went with them, as well as Sir Walter's body-servant, Cotterell, and a Frenchman named Manourie, who had made his first appearance in the Plymouth household on the previous day. Stukeley explained the fellow as a gifted man of medicine, whom he had sent for to cure him of a trivial but inconvenient ailment by which he was afflicted.

Journeying by slow stages, as Sir Lewis had

directed, they came at last to Brentford. Sir Walter, had he followed his own bent, would have journeyed more slowly still, for in a measure, as he neared London, apprehensions of what might await him there grew ever darker. He spoke of them to King, and the blunt captain said nothing to dispel them.

"You are being led like a sheep to the shambles," he declared, "and you go like a sheep. You should have landed in France, where you have friends. Even now it is not too late. A ship could be procured . . ."

"And my honour could be sunk at sea," Sir Walter harshly concluded, in reproof of such counsel.

But at the inn at Brentford he was sought out by a visitor, who brought him the like advice in rather different terms. This was De Chesne, the secretary of the French envoy, Le Clerc. Cordially welcomed by Ralegh, the Frenchman expressed his deep concern to see Sir Walter under arrest.

"You conclude too hastily," laughed Sir Walter.

"Monsieur, I do not conclude. I speak of what I am inform'."

"Misinformed, sir. I am not a prisoner — at least, not yet," he added, with a sigh. "I travel of my own free will to London with my good friend and kinsman Stukeley, to lay the account of my voyage before the King."

"Of your own free will? You travel of your own free will? And you are not a prisoner? Ha!" There was bitter mockery in De Chesne's short laugh. "*C'est bien drôle!*" And he explained: "Milord the Duke of Buckingham, he has write in his master's name to the ambassador Gondomar that you are taken and held at the disposal of the King of Spain. Gondomar is to inform him whether King Philip wish that you be sent to Spain to essay the justice of His Catholic Majesty, or that you suffer here. Meanwhile your quarters are being made ready in the Tower. Yet you tell me you are not prisoner! You go of your own free will to London. Sir Walter, do not be deceive'. If you reach London, you are lost."

Now here was news to shatter Sir Walter's last illusion. Yet desperately he clung to the fragments of it. The envoy's secretary must be at fault.

" 'Tis yourself are at fault, Sir Walter, in that you trust those about you," the Frenchman insisted.

Sir Walter stared at him, frowning. "D'ye mean Stukeley?" quoth he, half-indignant already at the mere suggestion.

"Sir Lewis, he is your kinsman." De Chesne shrugged. "You should know your family better than I. But who is this Manourie who accompanies you? Where is he come from? What you know of him?"

Sir Walter confessed that he knew nothing.

"But I know much. He is a fellow of evil reputation. A spy who does not scruple to sell his own people. And I know that letters of commission from the Privy Council for your arrest were give' to him in London ten days ago. Whether those letters were to himself, or he was just the messenger to another, imports nothing. The fact is everything. The warrant against you exists, and it is in the hands of one or another of those that accompany you. I say no more. As I have tol' you, you should know your own family. But of this be sure, they mean that you go to the Tower, and so to your death. And now, Sir Walter, if

I show you the disease I also bring the remedy. I am command' by my master to offer you a French barque which is in the Thames, and a safe conduct to the Governor of Calais. In France you will find safety and honour, as your worth deserve'."

Up sprang Sir Walter from his chair, and flung off the cloak of thought in which he had been mantled.

"Impossible!" he said. "Impossible! There is my plighted word to return, and there are my Lords of Arundel and Pembroke, who are sureties for me. I cannot leave them to suffer by my default."

"They will not suffer at all," De Chesne assured him. He was very well informed. "King James has yielded to Spain partly because he fears, partly because he will have a Spanish marriage for Prince Charles, and will do nothing to trouble his good relations with King Philip. But, after all, you have friends, whom His Majesty also fears. If you escape' you would resolve all his perplexities. I do not believe that any obstacle will be offer' to your escape — else why they permit you to travel thus without any guard, and to retain your sword?"

· Half distracted as he was by what he had learnt, yet Sir Walter clung stoutly and obstinately to what he believed to be the only course for a man of honour. And so he dismissed De Chesne with messages of gratitude but refusal to his master, and sent for Captain King. Together they considered all that the secretary had stated, and King agreed with De Chesne's implied opinion that it was Sir Lewis himself who held the warrant.

They sent for him at once, and Ralegh straightly taxed him with it. Sir Lewis as straightly admitted it, and when King thereupon charged him with deceit he showed no anger, but only the profoundest grief. He sank into a chair, and took his head in his hands.

"What could I do? What could I do?" he cried. "The warrant came in the very moment we were setting out. At first I thought of telling you; and then I bethought me that to do so would be but to trouble your mind, without being able to offer you help."

Sir Walter understood what was implied. "Did you not say," he asked, "that you were my kinsman first and Vice-Admiral of Devon after?"

"Aye — and so I am. Though I must lose my office of Vice-Admiral, which has cost me six hundred pounds, if I suffer you to escape, I'd never hesitate if it were not for Manourie, who watches me as closely as he watches you, and would baulk us at the last. And that is why I have held my peace on the score of this warrant. What can it help that I should trouble you with the matter until at the same time I can offer you some way out?"

"The Frenchman has a throat, and throats can be slit," said the downright King.

"So they can; and men can be hanged for slitting them," returned Sir Lewis and thereafter resumed and elaborated his first argument, using now such forceful logic and obvious sincerity that Sir Walter was convinced. He was no less convinced, too, of the peril in which he stood. He plied those wits of his, which had rarely failed him in an extremity. Manourie was the difficulty. But in his time he had known many of these agents who, without sentimental interest and purely for the sake of gold, were ready to play such parts; and never yet had he known one who was not to be corrupted. So that evening he desired Manourie's company in the room above stairs that had been set apart for Sir Walter's use. Facing him across the table at which both were seated, Sir Walter thrust his clenched fist upon the board, and, suddenly opening it, dazzled the Frenchman's beady eyes with the jewel sparkling in his palm.

"Tell me, Manourie, are you paid as much as that to betray me?"

Manourie paled a little under his tan. He was a swarthy, sharp-featured fellow, slight and wiry. He looked into Sir Walter's grimly smiling eyes, then again at the white diamond, from which the candle-light was striking every colour of the rainbow. He made a shrewd estimate of its price, and shook his black head. He had quite recovered from the shock of Sir Walter's question.

"Not half as much," he confessed, with impudence.

"Then you might find it more remunerative to serve me," said the knight. "This jewel is to be earned."

The agent's eyes flickered; he passed his tongue over his lips. "As how?" quoth he.

"Briefly thus: I have but learnt of the trammel in which I am taken. I must have time to concert my measures of escape, and time is almost at an end. You are skilled in drugs, so my kinsman tells me. Can you so drug me as to deceive physicians that I am *in extremis?*"

Manourie considered awhile.

"I . . . I think I could," he answered presently.

"And keep faith with me in this, at the price of, say — two such stones?"

The venal knave gasped in amazement. This was not generosity; it was prodigality. He recovered again, and swore himself Sir Walter's.

"About it, then." Sir Walter rolled the gem across the board into the clutch of the spy, which pounced to meet it. "Keep that in earnest. The other will follow when we have cozened them."

Next morning Sir Walter could not resume the journey. When Cotterell went to dress him he found his master taken with vomits, and reeling like a drunkard. The valet ran to fetch Sir Lewis, and when they returned together they found Sir Walter on all fours gnawing the rushes of the floor, his face livid and horribly distorted, his brow glistening with sweat.

Stukeley, in alarm, ordered Cotterell to get his master back to bed and to foment him, which was done. But on the next day there was no improvement, and on the third things were in far more serious case. The skin of his brow and arms and breast was inflamed, and covered with horrible purple blotches — the result of an otherwise harmless ointment with which the French empiric had supplied him.

When Stukeley beheld him thus disfigured, and lying apparently inert and but half-conscious upon his bed, he backed away in terror. The Vice-Admiral had seen aforetime the horrible manifestations of the plague, and could not be mistaken here. He fled from the infected air of his kinsman's chamber, and summoned what physicians were available to pronounce and prescribe. The physicians came — three in number — but manifested no eagerness to approach the patient closely. The mere sight of him was enough to lead them to the decision that he was afflicted with the plague in a singularly virulent form.

Presently one of them plucked up courage so far as to feel the pulse of the apparently delirious patient. Its feebleness confirmed his diagnosis; moreover, the hand he held was cold and turgid. He was not to know that Sir Walter had tightly wrapped about his upper arm the ribbon from his poniard, and so he was entirely deceived.

The physicians withdrew, and delivered their verdict, whereupon Sir Lewis at once sent word of it to the Privy Council.

That afternoon the faithful Captain King, sorely afflicted by the news, came to visit his master, and was introduced to Sir Walter's chamber by Manɔurie, who was in attendance upon him. To the seaman's amazement he found Sir Walter sitting up in bed, surveying in a hand-mirror a face that was horrible beyond description with the complacent smile of one who takes satisfaction in his appearance. Yet there was no fevered madness in the smiling eyes. They were alive with intelligence, amounting, indeed, to craft.

"Ah, King!" was the glad welcome. "The prophet David did make himself a fool, and suffered spittle to fall upon his beard, to escape from the hands of his enemies. And there was Brutus, aye, and others as memorable who have descended to such artifice."

Though he laughed, it is clear that he was seeking to excuse an unworthiness of which he was conscious.

"Artifice?" quoth King, aghast. "Is this artifice?"

"Aye — a hedge against my enemies, who will be afraid to approach me."

King sat himself down by his master's bed. "A

better hedge against your enemies, Sir Walter, would have been the strip of sea 'twixt here and France. Would to Heaven you had done as I advised ere you set foot in this ungrateful land."

"The omission may be repaired," said Sir Walter.

Before the imminence of his peril, as now disclosed to him, Sir Walter had been reconsidering De Chesne's assurance touching my Lords of Arundel and Pembroke, and he had come to conclude — the more readily, perhaps, because it was as he would have it — that De Chesne was right; that to break faith with them were no such great matter after all, nor one for which they would be called upon to suffer. And so, now, when it was all but too late, he yielded to the insistence of Captain King, and consented to save himself by flight to France. King was to go about the business of procuring a ship without loss of time. Yet there was no need of desperate haste, as was shown when presently orders came to Brentford for the disposal of the prisoner. The King, who was at Salisbury, desired that Sir Walter should be conveyed to his own house in London. Stukeley reported this to him, proclaiming it a sign of royal favour. Sir Walter was not deceived. He knew the reason to be fear lest he should infect the Tower with the plague by which he was reported stricken.

So the journey was resumed, and Sir Walter was brought to London, and safely bestowed in his own house, but ever in the care of his loving friend and kinsman. Manourie's part being fulfilled and the aim accomplished, Sir Walter completed the promised payment by bestowing upon him the second diamond — a form of eminently portable currency with which

the knight was well supplied. On the morrow Manourie was gone, dismissed as a consequence of the
part he had played.

It was Stukeley who told Sir Walter this — a very
well-informed and injured Stukeley, who asked to
know what he had done to forfeit the knight's confidence that behind his back Sir Walter secretly concerted means of escape. Had his cousin ceased to
trust him?

Sir Walter wondered. Looking into that lean,
crafty face, he considered King's unquenchable mistrust of the man, bethought him of his kinsman's
general neediness, remembered past events that shed
light upon his ways and nature, and began now at last
to have a sense of the man's hypocrisy and double-
dealing. Yet he reasoned in regard to him precisely
as he had reasoned in regard to Manourie. The
fellow was acquisitive, and therefore corruptible.
If, indeed, he was so base that he had been bought to
betray Sir Walter, then he could be bought again to
betray those who had so bought him.

"Nay, nay," said Sir Walter easily. "It is not
lack of trust in you, my good friend. But you are the
holder of an office, and knowing as I do the upright
honesty of your character, I feared to embarrass you
with things whose very knowledge must give you the
parlous choice of being false to that office or false to
me."

Stukeley broke forth into imprecations. He was,
he vowed, the most accursed and miserable of men
that such a task as this should have fallen to his
lot. And he was a poor man, too, he would have his
cousin remember. It was unthinkable that he should

use the knowledge he had gained to attempt to frustrate Sir Walter's plans of escape to France. And this notwithstanding that if Sir Walter escaped, it is certain he would lose his office of Vice-Admiral and the six hundred pounds he had paid for it.

"As to that, you shall be at no loss," Sir Walter assured him. "I could not suffer it. I pledge you my honour, Lewis, that you shall have a thousand pounds from my wife on the day that I am safely landed in France or Holland. Meanwhile, in earnest of what is to come, here is a toy of value for you." And he presented Sir Lewis with a jewel of price, a great ruby encrusted in diamonds.

Thus reassured that he would be immune from pecuniary loss, Sir Lewis was ready to throw himself whole-heartedly into Sir Walter's plans, and to render him all possible assistance. True, this assistance was a costly matter; there was this person to be bought and that one; there were expenses here and expenses there, incurred by Sir Lewis on his kinsman's behalf; and there were odd presents, too, which Stukeley seemed to expect and which Sir Walter could not deny him. He had no illusions now that King had been right; that here he was dealing with a rogue who would exact the uttermost farthing for his services, but he was gratified at the shrewdness with which he had taken his cousin's measure, and did not grudge the bribes by which he was to escape the scaffold.

De Chesne came again to the house in London, to renew his master's offer of a ship to carry Sir Walter overseas, and such other assistance as Sir Walter might require. But by now the knight's arrangements were complete. His servant Cotterell had come to inform him that his own boatswain, now in London, was the owner of a ketch, at present lying at Tilbury, admirably suited for the enterprise and entirely at Sir Walter's disposal. It had been decided, then, with the agreement of Captain King, that they should avail themselves of this; and accordingly Cotterell was bidden desire the boatswain to have the craft made ready for sea at once. In view of this, and anxious to avoid unnecessarily compromising the French envoy, Sir Walter gratefully declined the latter's offer.

And so we come at last to that July evening appointed for the flight. Ralegh, who, having for some time discarded the use of Manourie's ointment, had practically recovered his normal appearance, covering his long white hair under a Spanish hat, and muffling the half of his face in the folds of a cloak, came to Wapping Stairs — that ill-omened place of execution of pirates and sea-rovers — accompanied by Cotterell, who carried the knight's cloak-bag, and by Sir Lewis and Sir Lewis's son. Out of solicitude for their dear friend and kinsman, the Stukeleys could not part from him until he was safely launched upon his voyage. At the head of the stairs they were met by Captain King; at the foot of them a boat was waiting, as concerted, the boatswain at the tiller.

King greeted them with an air of obvious relief.

"You feared perhaps we should not come," said Stukeley, with a sneer at the captain's avowed mistrust of him. "Yet now, I trust, you'll do me the justice to admit that I have shown myself an honest man."

The uncompromising King looked at him and frowned, misliking the words.

"I hope that you'll continue so," he answered stiffly.

They went down the slippery steps to the boat, and then the shore glided slowly past them as they pushed off into the stream of the ebbing tide.

A moment later, King, whose suspicious eyes kept a sharp lookout, observed another boat put off some two hundred yards higher up the river. At first he saw it breast the stream as if proceeding towards London Bridge, then abruptly swing about and follow them. Instantly he drew the attention of Sir Walter to that pursuing wherry.

"What's this?" quoth Sir Walter harshly. "Are we betrayed?"

The watermen, taking fright at the words, hung now upon their oars.

"Put back," Sir Walter bade them. "I'll not betray my friends to no purpose. Put back, and let us home again."

"Nay, now," said Stukeley gravely, himself watching the wherry. "We are more than a match for them in oars, even if their purpose be such as you suspect — for which suspicion, when all is said, there is no ground. On then!" He addressed himself to the watermen, whipping out a pistol, and growing truculent in mien and voice. "To your oars! Row, you dogs, or I'll pistol you where you sit."

The men bent their backs forthwith, and the boat swept on. But Sir Walter was still full of apprehensions, still questioning the wisdom of keeping to their down-stream course if they were being followed.

"But are we followed?" cried the impatient Sir Lewis. "'Sdeath, cousin, is not the river a highway for all the world to use, and must every wherry that chances to go our way be in pursuit of us? If you are to halt at every shadow, faith, you'll never accomplish anything. I vow I am unfortunate in having a friend whom I would save so full of doubts and fears."

Sir Walter gave him reason, and even King came to conclude that he had suspected him unjustly, whilst the rowers, under Stukeley's suasion, now threw themselves heartily into their task, and onward sped the boat through the deepening night, taking but little account of that other wherry that hung ever in their wake. In this wise they came at length to Greenwich on the last of the ebb. But here finding the water beginning to grow against them, and wearied by the exertion into which Stukeley's enthusiasm had flogged them, the watermen paused again, declaring that they could not reach Gravesend before morning.

Followed a brief discussion, at the end of which Sir Walter bade them put him ashore at Purfleet.

"And that's the soundest counsel," quoth the boatswain. "For at Purfleet we can get horses on to Tilbury."

Stukeley was of the same opinion; but not so the more practical Captain King.

"'Tis useless," he declared to them. "At this hour how shall you get horses to go by land?"

And now, Sir Walter, looking over his shoulder, saw the other wherry bearing down upon them through the faintly opalescent mists of dawn. A hail came to them across the water.

"Oh, 'Sdeath! We are betrayed!" cried Ralegh

bitterly, and Stukeley swore more fiercely still. Sir Walter turned to him. "Put ashore," he said shortly, "and let us home."

"Aye, perhaps 'twere best. For to-night there's an end to the enterprise, and if I am taken in your company now, what shall be said to me for this active assistance in your escape?" His voice was gloomy, his face drawn and white.

"Could you not plead that you had but pretended to go with me to seize on my private papers?" suggested the ingenious mind of Ralegh.

"I could. But shall I be believed? Shall I?" His gloom was deepening to despair.

Ralegh was stricken almost with remorse on his cousin's account. His generous heart was now more concerned with the harm to his friends than with his own doom. He desired to make amends to Stukeley, but had no means save such as lay in the power of that currency he used. Having naught else to give, he must give that. He plunged his hand into an inner pocket, and brought forth a handful of jewels, which he thrust upon his kinsman.

"Courage," he urged him. "Up, now, and we may yet win out and home, so that all will be well with you at least, and you shall not suffer for your friendship to me."

Stukeley embraced him then, protesting his love and desire to serve him.

They came to land at last, just below Greenwich bridge, and almost at the same moment the other wherry grounded immediately above them. Men sprang from her, with the obvious intent of cutting off their retreat.

"Too late!" said Ralegh, and sighed, entirely without passion now that the dice had fallen and showed
that the game was lost. "You must act on my suggestion to explain your presence, Lewis."

"Indeed, there is no other course," Sir Lewis
agreed. "And you are in the same case, Captain
King. You must confess that you joined with me but
to betray Sir Walter. I'll bear you out. Thus, each
supporting the other . . ."

"I'll roast in hell before I brand myself a traitor,"
roared the captain furiously. "And were you an honest man, Sir Lewis, you'ld understand my meaning."

"So, so?" said Stukeley, in a quiet, wicked voice.
And it was observed that his son and one or two of the
watermen had taken their stand beside him as if in
readiness for action. "Why, then, since you will have
it so, Captain, I arrest you, in the King's name, on a
charge of abetting treason."

The captain fell back a step, stricken a moment by
sheer amazement. Then he groped for a pistol to do
at last what he realized he should have done long
since. Instantly he was overpowered. It was only
then that Sir Walter understood the thing that had
happened, and with understanding came fury. The
old adventurer flung back his cloak, and snatched at
his rapier to put it through the vitals of his dear
friend and kinsman. But he was too late. Hands
seized upon him, and he found himself held by the
men from the wherry, confronted by a Mr. William
Herbert, whom he knew for Stukeley's cousin, and he
heard Mr. Herbert formally asking him for the surrender of his sword.

Instantly he governed himself, repressed his fury.

He looked coldly at his kinsman, whose face showed white and evil in the growing light of the early summer dawn. "Sir Lewis," was all he said, "these actions will not turn out to your credit."

He had no illusion left. His understanding was now a very full one. His dear friend and kinsman had played him false throughout, intending first to drain him of his resources before finally flinging the empty husk to the executioner. Manourie had been in the plot; he had run with the hare and hunted with the hounds; and Sir Walter's own servant Cotterell had done no less. Amongst them they had "cozened the great cozener"—to use Stukeley's own cynical expression. Even so, it was only on his trial that Sir Walter plumbed the full depth of Stukeley's baseness; for it was only then he learnt that his kinsman had been armed by a warrant of immunity to assist his projects of escape, so that he might the more effectively incriminate and betray him; and Sir Walter discovered also that the ship in which he had landed, and other matters, were to provide additional Judas fees to this acquisitive betrayer.

If to escape his enemies Sir Walter had had recourse to artifices unworthy the great hero that he was, now that all hope was lost he conducted himself with a dignity and cheerfulness beyond equal. So calm and self-possessed and masterly was his defence from the charge of piracy preferred at the request of Spain, and so shrewd in its inflaming appeal to public opinion, that his judges were constrained to abandon that line of prosecution, and could discover no way of giving his head to King James save by falling back upon the thirteen-year-old sentence of death against him. Of this they now ordered execution.

Never a man who loved his life as dearly as Sir Walter loved it met death as blithely. He dressed himself for the scaffold with that elegance and richness which all his life he had observed. He wore a ruff band and black velvet wrought nightgown over a doublet of hair-coloured satin, a black wrought waistcoat, black cut taffety breeches and ash-coloured silk stockings. Under his plumed hat he covered his white locks with a wrought nightcap. This last he bestowed on his way to the scaffold upon a bald-headed old man who had come to take a last look of him, with the observation that he was more in need of it than himself. When he had removed it, it was observed that his hair was not curled as usual. This was a matter that had fretted his barber Peter in the prison of the Gatehouse at Westminster that morning. But Sir Walter had put him off with a laugh and a jest.

"Let them comb it that shall have it," he had said of his own head.

Having taken his leave of the friends who had flocked about him with the observation that he had a long journey before him, he called for the axe, and, when presented to him, ran his fingers along the edge, and smiled.

"Sharp medicine," quoth he, "but a sound cure for all diseases."

When presently the executioner bade him turn his head to the east: "It is no great matter which way a man's head stands, so that his heart lies right," he said.

Thus passed one of England's greatest heroes, indeed, one of the very makers of this England, and than his death there is no more shameful blot upon the shameful reign of that pusillanimous James, unclean of body and of soul, who sacrificed him to the King of Spain.

A spectator of his death, who suffered for his words — as men must ever suffer for the regardless utterance of Truth — declared that England had not such another head to cut off.

As for Stukeley, the acquisitiveness which had made a Judas of him was destined, by a poetic justice, ever desired but rarely forthcoming for knaves, soon to be his ruin. He was caught diminishing the gold coin of the realm by the operation known to-day as "clipping," and with him was taken his creature Manourie, who, to save himself, turned chief witness against Stukeley. Sir Lewis was sentenced to death, but saved himself by purchasing his pardon at the cost of every ill-gotten shilling he possessed, and he lived thereafter as bankrupt of means as he was of honour.

Yet before all this happened, Sir Lewis had for his part in Sir Walter Ralegh's death come to be an object of execration throughout the land, and to be commonly known as "Sir Judas." At Whitehall he suffered rebuffs and insults that found a climax in the words addressed to him by the Lord Admiral, to whom he went to give an account of his office.

"Base fellow, darest thou who art the contempt and scorn of men offer thyself in my presence?"

For a man of honour there was but one course. Sir Judas was not a man of honour. He carried his grievance to the King.

James leered at him. "What wouldst thou have me do? Wouldst thou have me hang him? On my soul, if I should hang all that speak ill of thee, all the trees of the country would not suffice, so great is the number."

VIII

HIS INSOLENCE OF BUCKINGHAM

GEORGE VILLIERS' COURTSHIP OF ANNE OF AUSTRIA

HE was Insolence incarnate.

Since the day when, a mere country lad, his singular good looks had attracted the attention of King James — notoriously partial to good-looking lads — and had earned him the office of cup-bearer to His Majesty, the career of George Villiers is to be read in a series of acts of violent and ever-increasing arrogance, expressing the vanity and levity inherent in his nature. Scarcely was he established in the royal favour than he distinguished himself by striking an offending gentleman in the very presence of his sovereign — an act of such gross disrespect to royalty that his hand would have paid forfeit, as by law demanded, had not the maudlin king deemed him too lovely a fellow to be so cruelly maimed.

Over the mind and will of King Charles his ascendancy became even greater than it had been over that of King James; and it were easy to show that the acts of George Villiers's life supplied the main planks of that scaffold in Whitehall whereupon Charles Stuart came to lose his head. Charles was indeed a martyr; a martyr chiefly to the reckless, insolent, irresponsible vanity of this Villiers, who, from a simple country squire with nothing but personal beauty to recommend him, had risen to be, as Duke of Buckingham, the first gentleman in England.

The heady wine of power had gone to his brain, and so addled it that, as John Chamberlain tells us, there was presently a touch of craziness in him — of the variety, no doubt, known to modern psychologists as megalomania. He lost the sense of proportion, and was without respect for anybody or anything. The Commons of England and the immensely dignified Court of Spain — during that disgraceful, pseudo-romantic adventure at Madrid — were alike the butts of this parvenu's unmeasured arrogance. But the crowning insolence of his career was that tragi-comedy the second act of which was played on a June evening in an Amiens garden on the banks of the river Somme.

Three weeks ago — on the 14th May, 1625, to be precise — Buckingham had arrived in Paris as ambassador extraordinary, charged with the task of conducting to England the King of France's sister, Henrietta Maria, who three days earlier had been married by proxy to King Charles.

The occasion enabled Buckingham to fling the reins on to the neck of his mad vanity, to indulge to the very fullest his crazy passion for ostentation and magnificence. Because the Court of France was proverbially renowned for splendour and luxury, Buckingham felt it due to himself to extinguish its brilliance by his own. On his first coming to the Louvre he literally blazed. He wore a suit of white satin velvet with a short cloak in the Spanish fashion, the whole powdered over with diamonds to the value of some ten thousand pounds. An enormous diamond clasped the heron's plume in his hat; diamonds flashed in the hilt of his sword; diamonds studded his very spurs, which were of beaten gold; the highest orders of England, Spain, and France flamed on his breast. On the occasion of his second visit he wore a suit of purple satin, of intent so lightly sewn with pearls that as he moved he shook them off like raindrops, and left them to lie where they fell, as largesse for pages and the lesser fry of the Court.

His equipages and retinue were of a kind to match his personal effulgence. His coaches were lined with velvet and covered with cloth of gold, and some seven hundred people made up his train. There were musicians, watermen, grooms of the chamber, thirty chief yeomen, a score of cooks, as many grooms, a dozen pages, two dozen footmen, six outriders, and twenty gentlemen, each with his own attendants, all arrayed as became the satellites of a star of such great magnitude.

Buckingham succeeded in his ambition. Paris, that hitherto had set the fashion to the world, stared mouth-agape, dazzled by the splendour of this superb and scintillating ambassador.

Another, by betraying consciousness of the figure that he cut, might have made himself ridiculous. But Buckingham's insolent assurance was proof against that peril. Supremely self-satisfied, he was conscious only that what he did could not be better done, and he ruffled it with an air of easy insouciance, as if in all this costly display there was nothing that was not normal. He treated with princes, and even with the gloomy Louis XIII, as with equals; and, becoming more and more intoxicated with his very obvious success, he condescended to observe approvingly the fresh beauty of the young Queen.

Anne of Austria, then in her twenty-fourth year, was said to be one of the most beautiful women in Europe. She was of a good height and carriage, slight, and very gracefully built, of a ravishing fairness of skin and hair, whilst a look of wistfulness had come to invest with an indefinable tenderness her splendid eyes. Her childless marriage to the young King of France, which had endured now for ten years, had hardly been successful. Gloomy, taciturn, easily moved to suspicion, and difficult to convince of error, Louis XIII held his wife aloof, throwing up between himself and her a wall of coldness, almost of dislike.

There is a story — and Tallemant des Réaux gives credit to it — that, in the early days of her reign as Queen of France, Richelieu had fallen deeply in love with her, and that she, with the mischief of an irresponsible young girl, had encouraged him, merely to betray him to a ridicule which his proud spirit had never been able to forgive. Be that or another the reason, the fact that Richelieu hated her, and subjected her to his vindictive persecution, is beyond dispute. And it was he who by a hundred suggestions poisoned against her the King's mind, and thus kept ever open the gulf between the two.

The eyes of that neglected young wife dilated a little, and admiration kindled in them, when they rested upon the dazzling figure of my Lord of Buckingham. He must have seemed to her a figure of romance, a prince out of a fairy-tale.

That betraying glance he caught, and it inflamed at

once his monstrous arrogance. To the scalps already
adorning the belt of his vanity he would add that of
the love of a beautiful young queen. Perhaps he was
thrilled in his madness by the thought of the peril
that would spice such an adventure. Into that adventure he plunged forthwith. He wooed her during the
eight days that he abode in Paris, flagrantly, openly,
contemptuous of courtiers and of the very King himself. At the Louvre, at the Hôtel de Chevreuse, at the
Luxembourg, where the Queen-Mother held her
Court, at the Hôtel de Guise, and elsewhere he was
ever at the Queen's side.

Richelieu, whose hard pride and self-love had been
wounded by the Duke's cavalier behaviour, who despised the fellow for an upstart, and may even have
resented that so shallow a man should have been sent
to treat with a statesman of his own calibre — for
other business besides the marriage had brought
Buckingham to Paris — suggested to the King that
the Duke's manner in approaching the Queen lacked
a proper deference, and the Queen's manner of receiving him a proper circumspection. Therefore the
King's long face became longer, his gloomy eyes
gloomier, as he looked on. Far, however, from acting
as a deterrent, the royal scowl was mere incense to the
vanity of Buckingham, a spur to goad him on to
greater daring.

On the 2d of June a splendid company of some four
thousand French nobles and ladies, besides Buckingham and his retinue, quitted Paris to accompany
Henrietta Maria, now Queen of England, on the first
stage of her journey to her new home. The King was
not of the party. He had gone with Richelieu to

Fontainebleau, leaving it to the Queen and the Queen-Mother to accompany his sister.

Buckingham missed no chance upon that journey of pressing his attentions upon Anne of Austria. Duty dictated that his place should be beside the carriage of Henrietta Maria. But duty did not apply to His Insolence of Buckingham, so indifferent of whom he might slight or offend. And then the devil took a hand in the game.

At Amiens, the Queen-Mother fell ill, so that the Court was compelled to halt there for a few days to give Her Majesty the repose she required. Whilst Amiens was thus honoured by the presence of three queens at one and the same time within its walls, the Duc de Chaulnes gave an entertainment in the Citadel. Buckingham attended this, and in the dance that followed the banquet it was Buckingham who led out the Queen.

Thereafter the royal party had returned to the Bishop's Palace, where it was lodged, and a small company went out to take the evening cool in the Bishop's fragrant gardens on the Somme, Buckingham ever at the Queen's side. Anne of Austria was attended by her Mistress of the Household, the beautiful, witty Marie de Rohan, Duchess of Chevreuse, and by her equerry, Monsieur de Putange. Madame de Chevreuse had for cavalier that handsome coxcomb, Lord Holland, who was one of Buckingham's creatures, between whom and herself a certain transient tenderness had sprung up. Monsieur de Putange was accompanied by Madame de Vernet, with whom at the time he was over head and ears in love. Elsewhere about the spacious gardens other courtiers sauntered.

Now either Madame de Chevreuse and Monsieur de Putange were too deeply engrossed in their respective companions, or else the state of their own hearts and the tepid, languorous eventide disposed them complacently towards the affair of gallantry upon which their mistress almost seemed to wish to be embarked. They forgot, it would seem, that she was a queen, and remembered sympathetically that she was a woman, and that she had for companion the most splendid cavalier in all the world. Thus they committed the unpardonable fault of lagging behind, and allowing her to pass out of their sight round the bend of an avenue by the water.

No sooner did Buckingham realize that he was alone with the Queen, that the friendly dusk and a screen of trees secured them from observation, than, piling audacity upon audacity, he determined to accomplish here and now the conquest of this lovely lady who had used him so graciously and received his advances with such manifest pleasure.

"How soft the night! How exquisite!" he sighed.

"Indeed," she agreed. "And how still but for the gentle murmur of the river."

"The river!" he cried, on a new note. "That is no gentle murmur. The river laughs, maliciously mocking. The river is evil."

"Evil?" quoth she.

He had checked in his step, and they stood now side by side.

"Evil," he repeated. "Evil and cruel. It goes to swell the sea that soon shall divide me from you, and it mocks me, rejoicing wickedly in the pain that will presently be mine."

It took her aback. She laughed, a little breath-lessly, to hide her discomposure, and scarce knew how to answer him, scarce knew whether she took pleasure or offence in his daring encroachment upon that royal aloofness in which she dwelt, and in which her Spanish rearing had taught her she must ever dwell.

"Oh, but Monsieur l'Ambassadeur, you will be with us again, perhaps before so very long."

His answer came in a swift, throbbing question, his lips so near her face that she could feel his breath hot upon her cheek.

"Do you wish it, Madame? Do you wish it? I im-plore you, of your pity, say but that you wish it, and I will come, though I tear down half a world to reach you."

She recoiled in affright and displeasure before a wooing so impetuous and violently outspoken; though the displeasure was perhaps but a passing emotion, the result of early training. Yet she contrived to an-swer him with the proper icy dignity due to her posi-tion as a princess of Spain, now Queen of France.

"Monsieur, you forget yourself. The Queen of France does not listen to such words. You are mad, I think."

"Yes, I am mad," he flung back. "Mad with love — so mad that I have forgot that you are a queen and I an ambassador. Under the ambassador there is a man, under the queen a woman — our real selves, not the titles with which Fate seeks to dissemble our true natures. And with the whole strength of my true na-ture do I love you, so potently, so overwhelmingly that I will not believe you sensible of no response."

Thus torrentially he delivered himself, and swept

her a little off her feet. She was a woman, as he said; a queen, it is true; but also a neglected, coldly used wife; and no one had ever addressed her in anything approaching this manner, no one had ever so much as suggested that her existence could matter greatly, that in her woman's nature there was the magic power of awakening passion and devotion. He was so splendidly magnificent, so masterful and unrivalled, and he came thus to lay his being, as it were, in homage at her feet. It touched her a little, who knew so little of the real man. It cost her an effort to repulse him, and the effort was not very convincing.

"Hush, monsieur, for pity's sake! You must not talk so to me. It . . . it hurts."

O fatal word! She meant that it was her dignity as Queen he wounded, for she clung to that as to the anchor of salvation. But he in his egregious vanity must of course misunderstand.

"Hurts!" he cried, and the rapture in his accents should have warned her. "Because you resist it, because you fight against the commands of your true self. Anne!" He seized her, and crushed her to him. "Anne!"

Wild terror gripped her at that almost brutal contact, and anger, too, her dignity surging up in violent outraged rebellion. A scream, loud and piercing, broke from her, and rang through the still garden. It brought him to his senses. It was as if he had been lifted up into the air, and then suddenly allowed to fall.

He sprang away from her, an incoherent exclamation on his lips, and when an instant later Monsieur de Putange came running up in alarm, his hand upon his sword, those two stood with the width of the avenue between them, Buckingham erect and defiant, the Queen breathing hard and trembling, a hand upon her heaving breast as if to repress its tumult.

"Madame! Madame!" had been Putange's cry, as he sprang forward in alarm and self-reproach.

He stood now almost between them, looking from one to the other in bewilderment. Neither spoke.

"You cried out, Madame," Monsieur de Putange reminded her, and Buckingham may well have wondered whether presently he would be receiving Monsieur de Putange's sword in his vitals. He must have known that his life now hung upon her answer.

"I called you, that was all," said the Queen, in a voice that she strove to render calm. "I confess that I was startled to find myself alone with Monsieur l'Ambassadeur. Do not let it occur again, Monsieur de Putange!"

The equerry bowed in silence. His itching fingers fell away from his sword-hilt, and he breathed more freely. He had no illusions as to what must have happened. But he was relieved there were to be no complications. The others now coming up with them, the party thereafter kept together until presently Buckingham and Lord Holland took their leave.

On the morrow the last stage of the escorting journey was accomplished. A little way beyond Amiens the Court took its leave of Henrietta Maria, entrusting her now to Buckingham and his followers, who were to convey her safely to Charles.

It was a very contrite and downcast Buckingham who came now to Anne of Austria as she sat in her coach with the Princesse de Conti for only companion.

"Madame," he said, "I am come to take my leave."

"Fare you well, Monsieur l'Ambassadeur," she said, and her voice was warm and gentle, as if to show him that she bore no malice.

"I am come to ask your pardon, Madame," he said, in a low voice.

"Oh, monsieur — no more, I beg you." She looked down; her hands were trembling, her cheeks going red and white by turns.

He put his head behind the curtains of the coach, so that none might see him from outside, and looking at him now, she beheld tears in his eyes.

"Do not misunderstand me, Madame. I ask your pardon only for having discomposed you, startled you. As for what I said, it were idle to ask pardon, since I could no more help saying it than I can help drawing breath. I obeyed an instinct stronger than the will to live. I gave expression to something that dominates my whole being, and will ever dominate it as long as I have life. Adieu, Madame! At need you know where a servant who will gladly die for you is to be found." He kissed the hem of her robe, dashed the back of his hand across his eyes, and was gone before she could say a word in answer.

She sat pale, and very thoughtful, and the Princesse de Conti, watching her furtively, observed that her eyes were moist.

"I will answer for the Queen's virtue," she stated afterwards, "but I cannot speak so positively for the hardness of her heart, since without doubt the Duke's tears affected her spirits."

But it was not yet the end. As Buckingham was

nearing Calais, he was met by a courier from White-hall, with instructions for him regarding the negotia-tions he had been empowered to carry out with France in the matter of an alliance against Spain — negotia-tions which had not thriven with Louis and Richelieu, possibly because the ambassador was ill-chosen. The instructions came too late to be of use, but in time to serve as a pretext for Buckingham's return to Amiens. There he sought an audience of the Queen-Mother, and delivered himself to her of a futile message for the King. This chimerical business — as Madame de Motteville shrewdly calls it — being accomplished, he came to the real matter which had prompted him to use that pretext for his return, and sought audience of Anne of Austria.

It was early morning, and the Queen was not yet risen. But the levées at the Court of France were pre-cisely what the word implies, and they were held by royalty whilst still abed. It was not, therefore, amaz-ing that he should have been admitted to her pres-ence. She was alone save for her lady-in-waiting, Madame de Lannoi, who was, we are told, aged, pru-dent, and virtuous. Conceive, therefore, the out-raged feelings of this lady upon seeing the English duke precipitate himself wildly into the room, and on his knees at the royal bedside seize the coverlet and bear it to his lips.

Whilst the young Queen looked confused and agi-tated, Madame de Lannoi became a pillar of icy dig-nity.

"Monsieur le Duc," said she, "it is not customary in France to kneel when speaking to the Queen."

"I care nothing for the customs of France, Madame," he answered rudely. "I am not a French-man."

"That is too obvious, Monsieur," snapped the elderly, prudent, and virtuous Countess. "Nevertheless, whilst in France perhaps Monsieur will perceive the convenience of conforming to French customs. Let me call for a chair for Monsieur le Duc."

"I do not want a chair, Madame."

The Countess cast her eyes to Heaven, as if to say, "I suppose one cannot expect anything else in a foreigner," and let him kneel as he insisted, placing herself, however, protectingly at the Queen's pillow.

Nevertheless, entirely unabashed, heeding Madame de Lannoi's presence no more than if she had been part of the room's furniture, the Duke delivered himself freely of what was in his mind. He had been obliged to return to Amiens on a matter of State. It was unthinkable that he should be so near to Her Majesty and not hasten to cast himself at her feet; and whilst gladdening the eyes of his body with the sight of her matchless perfection, the image of which was ever before the eyes of his soul, allow himself the only felicity life now held for him — that of protesting himself her utter slave. This, and much more of the kind, did he pour out, what time the Queen, embarrassed and annoyed beyond utterance, could only stare at him in silence.

Apart from the matchless impudence of it, it was also of a rashness beyond pardon. Unless Madame de Lannoi were the most circumspect of women, here was a fine tale for Court gossips, and for the King's ears, a tale that must hopelessly compromise the Queen. For that, Buckingham, in his self-sufficiency and arrogance, appears to have cared nothing. One suspects that it would have pleased his vanity to have his name linked with the Queen's by the lips of scandal.

She found her tongue at last.

"Monsieur le Duc," she said in her confusion, "it was not necessary, it was not worth while, to have asked audience of me for this. You have leave to go."

He looked up in doubt, and saw only confusion; attributed it, perhaps, to the presence of that third party to which himself he had been so indifferent. He kissed the coverlet again, stumbled to his feet, and reached the door. Thence he sent her a flaming glance of his bold eyes, and hand on heart —

"Adieu, Madame!" said he in tragic tones, and so departed.

Madame de Lannoi was discreet, and related at the time nothing of what had passed at that interview. But that the interview itself had taken place under such conditions was enough to set the tongue of gossip wagging. An echo of it reached the King, together with the story of that other business in the garden, and he was glad to know that the Duke of Buckingham was back in London. Richelieu, to vent his own malice against the Queen, sought to feed the King's suspicions.

"Why did she cry out, Sire?" he will have asked. "What did Monsieur de Buckingham do to make her cry out?"

"I don't know. But whatever it was, she was no party to it since she did cry out."

Richelieu did not pursue the matter just then. But neither did he abandon it. He had his agents in Lon-

don and elsewhere, and he desired of them a close report upon the Duke of Buckingham's movements,
and the fullest particulars of his private life.

Meanwhile, Buckingham had left behind him in
France two faithful agents of his own, with instructions to keep his memory green with the Queen. For
he intended to return upon one pretext or another before very long, and complete the conquest. Those
agents of his were Lord Holland and the artist Bal-
thazar Gerbier. It is to be presumed that they served
the Duke's interests well, and it is no less to be presumed from that which followed that they found Her
Majesty willing enough to hear news of that amazingly
romantic fellow who had flashed across the path of
her grey life, touching it for a moment with his own
flaming radiance. In her loneliness she came to think
of him with tenderness and pity, in which pity for herself and her dull lot was also blent. He was away,
overseas; she might never see him again; therefore
there could be little harm in indulging the romantic
tenderness he had inspired.

So one day, many months after his departure, she
begged Gerbier — as La Rochefoucauld tells us — to
journey to London and bear the Duke a trifling memento of her — a set of diamond studs. That love-
token — for it amounted to no less — Gerbier conveyed to England, and delivered to the Duke.

Buckingham's head was so completely turned by
the event, and his desire to see Anne of Austria again
became thereupon so overmastering, that he at once
communicated to France that he was coming over as
the ambassador of the King of England to treat of
certain matters connected with Spain. But Richelieu

had heard from the French ambassador in London that portraits of the Queen of France were excessively abundant at York House, the Duke's residence, and he had considered it his duty to inform the King. Louis was angry, but not with the Queen. To have believed her guilty of any indiscretion would have hurt his gloomy pride too deeply. All that he believed was that this was merely an expression of Buckingham's fanfaronading, thrasonical disposition, a form of vain, empty boasting peculiar to megalomaniacs.

As a consequence, the King of England was informed that the Duke of Buckingham, for reasons well known to himself, would not be agreeable as Charles's ambassador to His Most Christian Majesty. Upon learning this, the vainglorious Buckingham was loud in proclaiming the reason ("well known to himself") and in protesting that he would go to France to see the Queen with the French King's consent or without it. This was duly reported to Richelieu, and by Richelieu to King Louis. But His Most Christian Majesty merely sneered, accounted it more empty boasting on the part of the parvenu, and dismissed it from his mind.

Richelieu found this attitude singularly exasperating in a King who was temperamentally suspicious. It so piqued and annoyed him that, when considered in addition to his undying rancour against Anne of Austria, it is easily believed he spared no pains to obtain something in the nature of a proof that the Queen was not as innocent as Louis insisted upon believing.

Now it happened that one of his London agents informed him, among other matters connected with the Duke's private life, that he had a bitter and secret enemy in the Countess of Carlisle, between whom and himself there had been a passage of some tenderness too abruptly ended by the Duke. Richelieu, acting upon this information, contrived to enter into correspondence with Lady Carlisle, and in the course of this correspondence he managed her so craftily — says La Rochefoucauld — that very soon she was, whilst hardly realizing it, his eminence's most valuable spy near Buckingham. Richelieu informed her that he was mainly concerned with information that would throw light upon the real relations of Buckingham and the Queen of France, and he persuaded her that nothing was too insignificant to be communicated. Her resentment of the treatment she had received from Buckingham, a resentment the more bitter for being stifled — since for her reputation's sake she dared not have given it expression — made her a very ready instrument in Richelieu's hands, and there was no scrap of gossip she did not carefully gather up and dispatch to him. But all was naught until one day at last she was able to tell him something that set his pulses beating more quickly than their habit.

She had it upon the best authority that a set of diamond studs constantly worn of late by the Duke was a love-token from the Queen of France sent over to Buckingham by a messenger of her own. Here, indeed, was news. Here was a weapon by which the Queen might be destroyed. Richelieu considered. If he could but obtain possession of the studs, the rest would be easy. There would be an end — and such an end! — to the King's obstinate, indolent faith in his wife's indifference to that boastful, flamboyant English upstart. Richelieu held his peace for the time being, and wrote to the Countess.

Some little time thereafter there was a sumptuous ball given at York House, graced by the presence of King Charles and his young French Queen. Lady Carlisle was present, and in the course of the evening Buckingham danced with her. She was a very beautiful, accomplished, and ready-witted woman, and tonight his grace found her charms so alluring that he was almost disposed to blame himself for having perhaps treated her too lightly. Yet she seemed at pains to show him that it was his to take up again the affair at the point at which it had been dropped. She was gay, arch, provoking, and irresistible. So irresistible that presently, yielding to the lure of her, the Duke slipped away from his guests with the lady on his arm, and they found themselves at the foot of the garden in the shadow of the water-gate that Inigo Jones had just completed for him. My lady languished at his side, permitted him to encircle her with a protecting arm, and for a moment lay heavily against him. He caught her violently to him, and now her ladyship, hitherto so yielding, with true feminine contrariness set herself to resist him. A scuffle ensued between them. She broke from him at last, and sped swift as a doe across the lawn towards the lights of the great house, his grace in pursuit between vexation and amusement.

But he did not overtake her, and it was with a sense of having been fooled that he rejoined his guests. His questing eyes could discern her nowhere. Presently he made inquiries, to be told that she had desired her carriage to be called, and had left York House immediately upon coming in from the garden.

He concluded that she was gone off in a pet. It was very odd. It was, in fact, most flagrantly contradictory that she should have taken offence at that which she had so obviously invited. But then she always had been a perverse and provoking jade. With that reflection he put her from his mind.

But anon, when his guests had departed, and the lights in the great house were extinguished, Buckingham thought of the incident again. Cogitating it, he sat in his room, his fingers combing his fine, pointed, auburn beard. At last, with a shrug and a half-laugh, he rose to undress for bed. And then a cry escaped him, and brought in his valet from an adjoining room. The riband of diamond studs was gone.

Reckless and indifferent as he was, a sense of evil took him in the moment of his discovery of that loss, so that he stood there pale, staring, and moist of brow. It was no ordinary theft. There were upon his person a dozen ornaments of greater value, any one of which could have been more easily detached. This was the work of some French agent. He had made no secret of whence those studs had come to him.

There his thoughts checked on a sudden. As in a flash of revelation, he saw the meaning of Lady Carlisle's oddly contradictory behaviour. The jade had fooled him. It was she who had stolen the riband. He sat down again, his head in his hands, and swiftly, link by link, he pieced together a complete chain.

Almost as swiftly he decided upon the course of action which he must adopt so as to protect the Queen of France's honour. He was virtually the ruler of England, master in these islands of an almost boundless power. That power he would exert to the full this very night to thwart those enemies of his own and of the Queen's, who worked so subtly in concert. Many would be wronged, much harm would be done, the liberties of some thousands of freeborn Englishmen would be trampled underfoot. What did it matter? It was necessary that his grace of Buckingham should cover up an indiscretion.

"Set ink and paper yonder," he bade his gaping valet. "Then go call Monsieur Gerbier. Rouse Lacy and Thom, and send them to me at once, and leave word that I shall require a score of couriers to be in the saddle and ready to set out in half an hour."

Bewildered, the valet went off upon his errand. The Duke sat down to write. And next morning English merchants learnt that the ports of England were closed by the King's express command — delivered by his minister, the Duke of Buckingham — that measures were being taken — were already taken in all southern ports — so that no vessel of any kind should leave the island until the King's further pleasure were made known. Startled, the people wondered was this enactment the forerunner of war. Had they known the truth, they might have been more startled still, though in a different manner. As swiftly as couriers could travel — and certainly well ahead of any messenger seeking escape overseas — did this blockade spread, until the gates of England were tight-locked against the outgoing of those diamond studs which meant the honour of the Queen of France.

And meanwhile a diamond-cutter was replacing the purloined stones by others, matching them so closely that no man should be able to say which were the originals and which the copies. Buckingham and Gerbier between them guided the work. Soon it was accomplished, and a vessel slipped down the Thames, al-

lowed to pass by those who kept close watch to enforce the royal decree, and made sail for Calais, which
was beginning to manifest surprise at this entire cessa-
tion of traffic from England. From that vessel landed
Gerbier, and rode straight to Paris, carrying the
Queen of France the duplicate studs, which were to
replace those which she had sent to Buckingham.

Twenty-four hours later the ports of England were
unsealed, and commerce was free and unhampered
once more. But it was twenty-four hours too late for
Richelieu and his agent, the Countess of Carlisle.
His eminence deplored a fine chance lost through the
excessive power that was wielded in England by the
parvenu.

Yet that is not quite the end of the story. Buckingham's inflamed and reckless mind would stop at
nothing now to achieve the object of his desires — to
go to France and see the Queen. Since the country
was closed to him, he would force a way into it, the
red way of war. Blood should flow, ruin and misery
desolate the land, but in the end he would go to Paris
to negotiate a peace, and that should be his opportunity. Other reasons there may have been, but none so
dominant, none that could not have been removed by
negotiation. The pretexted *casus belli* was the matter
of the Protestants of La Rochelle, who were in rebellion against their king.

To their aid sailed Buckingham with an English expedition. Disaster and defeat awaited it. Its shattered remnant crept back in disgrace to England, and
the Duke found himself more detested by the people
than he had been already — which is saying much.

He went off to seek comfort at the hands of the two persons who really loved him — his doting King and his splendid wife.

But the defeat had neither lessened his resolve nor chastened his insolence. He prepared a second expedition in the very teeth of a long-suffering nation's hostility, indifferent to the mutinies and mutterings about him. What signified to him the will of a nation? He desired to win to the woman whom he loved, and to accomplish that he nothing recked that he should set Europe in a blaze, nothing recked what blood should be poured out, what treasure dissipated.

Hatred of him by now was so widespread and vocal that his friends, fearing that soon it would pass from words to deeds, urged him to take precautions, advised the wearing of a shirt of mail for greater safety.

But he laughed sneeringly, ever arrogant and scornful.

"It needs not. There are no Roman spirits left," was his contemptuous answer.

He was mistaken. One morning after breakfast, as he was leaving the house in the High Street, Portsmouth, where he lodged whilst superintending the final preparations for that unpopular expedition, John Felton, a self-appointed instrument of national vengeance, drove a knife to the hilt into the Duke's breast.

"May the Lord have mercy on your soul!" was the pious exclamation with which the slayer struck home. And, in all the circumstances, there seems to have been occasion for the prayer.

IX

THE PATH OF EXILE

THE FALL OF LORD CLARENDON

TIGHT-WRAPPED in his cloak against the icy whips of the black winter's night, a portly gentleman, well advanced in years, picked his way carefully down the wet, slippery steps of the jetty by the light of a lanthorn, whose rays gleamed lividly on crushed brown seaweed and trailing green sea slime. Leaning heavily upon the arm which a sailor held out to his assistance, he stepped into the waiting boat that rose and fell on the heaving black waters. A boathook scraped against the stones, and the frail craft was pushed off.

The oars dipped, and the boat slipped away through the darkness, steering a course for the two great poop lanterns that were swinging rhythmically high up against the black background of the night. The elderly gentleman, huddled now in the stern-sheets, looked behind him — to look his last upon the England he had loved and served and ruled. The lanthorn, shedding its wheel of yellow light upon the jetty steps, was all of it that he could now see.

He sighed, and settled down again to face the poop lights, dancing there above the invisible hull of the ship that was to carry Edward Hyde, Earl of Clarendon, lately Lord Chancellor of England, into exile.

As a dying man looks down the foreshortened vista

of his active life, so may Edward Hyde — whose career had reached a finality but one degree removed from the finality of death — have reviewed in that moment those thirty years of sincere endeavour and high achievement since he had been a law student in the Temple when Charles I was king.

That king he had served faithfully, so faithfully that when the desperate fortunes of the Royalist party made it necessary to place the Prince of Wales beyond the reach of Cromwell, it was in Sir Edward Hyde's care that the boy was sent upon his travels. The present was not to be Hyde's first experience of exile. He had known it, and of a bitter sort, in those impecunious days when the Second Charles, whose steps he guided, was a needy, homeless outcast. A man less staunch and loyal might have thrown over so profitless a service. He had talents that would have commanded a price in the Roundhead market. Yet staunchly adhering to the Stuart fortunes, labouring ceaselessly and shrewdly in the Stuart interest, employing his great ability and statecraft, he achieved at length the restoration of the Stuarts to the throne of England. And for all those loyal, self-denying labours in exile on the Stuart behalf, all the reward he had at the time was that James Stuart, Duke of York, debauched his daughter.

Nor did Hyde's labours cease when he had made possible the Restoration; it was Hyde who, when that Restoration was accomplished, took in hand and carried out the difficult task of welding together the old and the new conditions of political affairs. And it was Hyde who was the scapegoat when things did not run the course that Englishmen desired. As the head of the administration he was held responsible even for those acts which he had strongly but vainly reprobated in Council. It was Hyde who was blamed when Charles sold Dunkirk to the French, and spent the money in harlotry; it was Hyde who was blamed because the Queen was childless.

The reason for this last lay in the fact that the wrong done to Hyde's daughter Anne had now been righted by marriage with the Duke of York. Now the Duke of York was the heir-apparent, and the people, ever ready to attach most credit to that which is most incredible and fantastic, believed that to ensure the succession of his own grandchildren Hyde had deliberately provided Charles with a barren wife.

When the Dutch, sailing up the Thames, had burnt the ships of war at Chatham, and Londoners heard the thunder of enemy guns, Hyde was openly denounced as a traitor by a people stricken with terror and seeking a victim in the blind, unreasoning way of public feeling. They broke his windows, ravaged his garden, and erected a gibbet before the gates of his superb mansion on the north side of Piccadilly.

Edward Hyde, Earl of Clarendon, and Lord Chancellor of England, commanded the love of his intimates, but did not possess those qualities of cheap glitter that make for popularity with the masses. Nor did he court popularity elsewhere. Because he was austere in his morals, grave and sober in his conduct, he was hated by those who made up the debauched court of his prince. Because he was deeply religious in his principles, the Puritans mistrusted him for a bigot. Because he was autocratic in his policy, he was detested by the Commons, the day of autocracy being done.

Yet might he have weathered the general hostility had Charles been half as loyal to him as he had ever been loyal to Charles. For a time, it is true, the King stood his friend, and might so have continued to the end had not the women become mixed up in the business. As Evelyn, the diarist, puts it, this great man's fall was the work of "the buffoones and ladys of pleasure."

It really is a very tangled story — this inner history of the fall of Clarendon, with which the school-books are not concerned. In a sense, it is also the story of the King's marriage and of Catherine of Braganza, his unfortunate little ugly Queen, who must have suffered as much as any woman wedded to a sultan in any country where the seraglio is not a natural and proper institution.

If Clarendon could not be said to have brought about the marriage, at least he had given it his suffrages when proposed by Portugal, which was anxious to establish an alliance with England as some protection against the predatory designs of Spain. He had been influenced by the dowry offered — five hundred thousand pounds in money, Tangier, which would give England a commanding position on the Mediterranean, and the Island of Bombay. Without yet foreseeing that the possession of Bombay, and the freedom to trade in the East Indies — which Portugal had hitherto kept jealously to herself — were to enable England to build up her great Indian Empire, yet the commercial advantages alone were obvious enough to make the match desirable.

Catherine of Braganza sailed for England, and on the 19th of May, 1662, Charles, attended by a splendid following, went to meet his bride at Portsmouth. He was himself a very personable man, tall — he stood a full six feet high — lean and elegantly vigorous. The ugliness of his drawn, harsh-featured face was mitigated by the glory of full, low-lidded, dark eyes, and his smile could be irresistibly captivating. He was as graceful in manner as in person, felicitous of speech, and of an indolent good temper that found expression in a charming urbanity.

Good temper and urbanity alike suffered rudely when he beheld the wife brought him. Catherine, who was in her twenty-fifth year, was of an absurdly low stature, so long in the body and short in the legs that, dressed as she was in an outlandish, full-skirted farthingale, she had the appearance of being on her knees when she stood before him. Her complexion was sallow, and though her eyes, like his own, were fine, they were not fine enough to redeem the dull plainness of her face. Her black hair was grotesquely dressed, with a long fore-top and two great ribbon bows standing out, one on each side of her head, like a pair of miniature wings.

It is little wonder that the Merry Monarch, the fastidious voluptuary, with his nice discernment in women, should have checked in his long stride, and halted a moment in consternation.

"Lord!" was his wry comment to Etheredge, who was beside him. "They've brought me a bat, not a woman."

But if she lacked beauty, she was well dowered, and Charles was in desperate need of money.

"I suppose," he told Clarendon anon, "I must swallow this black draught to get the jam that goes with it."

The Chancellor's grave eyes considered him almost sternly what time he coldly recited the advantages of this marriage. If he did not presume to rebuke the ribaldry of his master, neither would he condescend to smile at it. He was too honest ever to be a sycophant.

Catherine was immediately attended — in the words of Grammont — by six frights who called themselves maids-of-honour, and a governess who was a monster. With this retinue she repaired to Hampton Court, where the honeymoon was spent, and where for a brief season the poor woman — entirely enamoured of the graceful, long-legged rake she had married — lived in a fool's paradise.

Disillusion was to follow soon enough. She might be, by the grace of her dowry, Queen of England, but she was soon to discover that to King Charles she was no more than a wife *de jure*. With wives *de facto* Charles would people his seraglio as fancy moved him; and the present wife *de facto*, the mistress of his heart, the first lady of his harem, was that beautiful termagant, Barbara Villiers, wife of the accommodating Roger Palmer, Earl of Castlemaine.

There was no lack — there never is in such cases — of those who out of concern and love for the happily deluded wife lifted the veil for her, and made her aware of the facts of His Majesty's association with my Lady Castlemaine — an association dating back to the time when he was still a homeless wanderer. The knowledge would appear to have troubled the poor soul profoundly; but the climax of her distress was reached when, on her coming to Whitehall, she found at the head of the list of ladies-in-waiting assigned to her the name of my Lady Castlemaine.

The forlorn little woman's pride rose up before this outrage. She struck out that offending name, and gave orders that the favourite was not to be admitted to her presence.

But she reckoned without Charles. For all his urbane, good-tempered, debonair ways, there was an ugly cynical streak in his nature, manifested now in the manner in which he dealt with this situation. Himself he led his boldly handsome favourite by the hand into his wife's presence, before the whole Court assembled, and himself presented her to Catherine, what time that Court, dissolute and profligate as it was, looked on in amazement at so outrageous a slight to the dignity of a queen.

What followed may well have exceeded all expectations. Catherine stiffened as if the blow dealt her had been physical. Gradually her face paled until it was grey and drawn; tears of outraged pride and mortification flooded her eyes. And then, as if something snapped within her brain under this stress of bitter emotion, blood gushed from her nostrils, and she sank back in a swoon into the arms of her Portuguese ladies.

Confusion followed, and under cover of it Charles and his light of love withdrew, realizing that if he lingered not all his easy skill in handling delicate situations could avail him to save his royal dignity.

Naturally the experiment was not to be repeated. But since it was his wish that the Countess of Castlemaine should be established as one of the Queen's ladies — or, rather, since it was her ladyship's wish, and since Charles was as wax in her ladyship's hands — it became necessary to have the Queen instructed in what was, in her husband's view, fitting. For this task he selected Clarendon. But the Chancellor, who had so long and loyally played Mentor to Charles's Telemachus, sought now to guide him in matters moral as he had hitherto guided him in matters political.

Clarendon declined the office of mediator, and even expostulated with Charles upon the unseemliness of the course upon which His Majesty was bent.

"Surely, Sire, it is for Her Majesty to say who shall and who shall not be the ladies of her bedchamber. And I nothing marvel at her decision in this instance."

"Yet I tell you, my lord, that it is a decision that shall be revoked."

"By whom, Sire?" the Chancellor asked him gravely.

"By Her Majesty, of course."

"Under coercion, of which you ask me to be the instrument," said Clarendon, in the tutorly manner he had used with the King from the latter's boyhood. "Yourself, Sire, at a time when your own wishes did not warp your judgment, have condemned the very thing that now you are urging. Yourself, Sire, hotly blamed your cousin, King Louis, for thrusting Mademoiselle de Vallière upon his queen. You will not have forgotten the things you said then of King Louis."

Charles remembered those unflattering criticisms which he was now invited to apply to his own case. He bit his lip, admitting himself in check.

But anon — no doubt in obedience to the overbearing suasion of my Lady Castlemaine — he returned to the attack, and sent the Chancellor his orders in a letter demanding unquestioning obedience.

"Use your best endeavours," wrote Charles, "to facilitate what I am sure my honour is so much concerned in. And whosoever I find to be my Lady Castlemaine's enemy in this matter, I do promise upon my word to be his enemy so long as I live."

My Lord Clarendon had few illusions on the score of mankind. He knew his world from froth to dregs — having studied it under a variety of conditions. Yet that letter from his king was a bitter draught. All that Charles possessed and was he owed to Clarendon. Yet in such a contest as this, Charles did not hesitate to pen that bitter, threatening line: "Whosoever I find to be my Lady Castlemaine's enemy in this matter, I do promise upon my word to be his enemy so long as I live."

All that Clarendon had done in the past was to count for nothing unless he also did the unworthy thing that Charles now demanded. All that he had accomplished in the service of his king was to be swept into oblivion by the breath of a spiteful wanton.

Clarendon swallowed the draught and sought the Queen, upon that odious embassy with whose ends he was so entirely out of sympathy. He used arguments whose hollowness was not more obvious to the Queen than to himself.

That industrious and entertaining chronicler of trifles, Mr. Pepys, tells us, scandalized, in his diary that on the following day the talk of the Court was all upon a midnight scene between the royal couple in the privacy of their own apartments, so stormy that the sounds of it were plainly to be heard in the neighbouring chambers.

You conceive the poor little woman, smarting under the insult of Charles's proposal by the mouth of Clarendon, assailing her royal husband, and fiercely upbraiding him with his lack, not merely of affection, but even of the respect that was her absolute due. And Charles, his purpose set, urged to it by the handsome termagant whom he dared not refuse, stirred out of his indolent good-nature, turning upon her, storming back, and finally threatening her with the greater disgrace of seeing herself packed home to Portugal, unless she would submit to the lesser disgrace he thrust upon her here.

Whether by these or by other arguments he made his will prevail, prevail it did. Catherine of Braganza swallowed her pride and submitted. And a very complete submission it was. Lady Castlemaine was not only installed as a lady of the bedchamber, but very soon we find the Queen treating her with a friendliness that provoked comment and amazement.

The favourite's triumph was complete, and marked by an increasing insolence, most marked in her demeanour towards the Chancellor, of whose views on the subject, as expressed to the King, she was aware. Consequently she hated him with all the spiteful bitterness that is inseparable from the nature of such women. And she hated him the more because, wrapped in his cold contempt, he moved in utter unconcern of her hostility. In this hatred she certainly did not lack for allies, members of that licentious Court whose hostility towards the austere Chancellor was begotten of his own scorn of them. Among them they worked to pull him down.

The attempt to undermine his influence with the

King proving vain — for Charles was as well aware of its inspiration as of the Chancellor's value to him — that crew of rakes went laboriously and insidiously to work upon the public mind, which is to say the public ignorance — most fruitful soil for scandal against the great. Who shall say how far my lady and the Court were responsible for the lampoon affixed one day to my Lord Clarendon's gatepost:

> *Three sights to be seen:*
> *Dunkirk, Tangier, and a barren queen.*

Her ladyship might well have considered the unpopularity of the Chancellor as the crown of her triumph, had this triumph been as stable as she could have wished. But, Charles being what he was, it follows that her ladyship had frequent, if transient, anxious jealousies to mar the perfection of her existence, to remind her how insecure is the tenure of positions such as hers, ever at the mercy of the very caprice to which they owe their existence.

And then, at long length, there came a day of horrid dread for her, a day when she found herself bereft of her influence with her royal lover, when pleadings and railings failed alike to sway him. In part she owed it to an indiscretion of her own, but in far greater measure to a child of sixteen, of a golden-headed, fresh, youthful loveliness, and a nature that still found pleasure in dolls and kindred childish things, yet of a quick and lively wit, and a clear, intelligent mind, untroubled either by the assiduity of the royal attentions or the fact that she was become the toast of the day.

This was Miss Frances Stewart, the daughter of

Lord Blantyre, newly come to Court as a lady-in-waiting to Her Majesty. How profound an impression her beauty made upon the admittedly impressionable old Pepys you may study in his diary. He had a glimpse of her one day riding in the Park with the King, and a troop of ladies, among whom my Lady Castlemaine, looking, as he tells us, "mighty out of humour." There was a moment when Miss Stewart came very near to becoming Queen of England, and although she never reached that eminence, yet her effigy not only found its way into the coinage, but abides there to this day (more perdurable than that of any actual queen) in the figure of Britannia, for which she was the model.

Charles wooed her openly. It was never his way to study appearances in these matters. He was so assiduous that it became customary in that winter of 1666 for those seeking the King at Whitehall to inquire whether he were above or below — "below" meaning Miss Stewart's apartments on the ground-floor of the palace, in which apartments His Majesty was a constant visitor. And since where the King goes the Court follows, and where the King smiles there the Court fawns, it resulted that this child now found herself queening it over a court that flocked to her apartments. Gallants and ladies came there to flirt and to gossip, to gamble and to pay homage.

About a great table in her splendid salon, a company of rustling, iridescent fops in satin and heavy periwigs, and of ladies with curled head-dresses and bare shoulders, played at basset one night in January. Conversation rippled, breaking here and there into laughter, white, jewelled hands reached out for cards, or for a share of the heaps of gold that swept this way and that with the varying fortunes of the game.

My Lady Castlemaine, seated between Etheredge and Rochester, played in silence, with lips tight-set and brooding eyes. She had lost, it is true, some fifteen hundred pounds that night; yet, a prodigal gamester, and one who came easily by money, she had been known to lose ten times that sum and yet preserve her smile. The source of her ill-humour was not the game. She played recklessly, her attention wandering; those handsome, brooding eyes of hers were intent upon watching what went on at the other end of the long room. There, at a smaller table, sat Miss Stewart, half a dozen gallants hovering near her, engaged upon a game of cards of a vastly different sort. Miss Stewart did not gamble. The only purpose she could find for cards was to build castles; and here she was building one with the assistance of her gallants, and under the superintendence of his grace of Buckingham, who was as skilled in this as in other equally unstable forms of architecture.

Apart, over by the fire, in a great chair of gilt leather, lounged the King, languidly observing this smaller party, a faint, indolent smile on his swarthy, saturnine countenance. Absently, with one hand he stroked a little spaniel that was curled in his lap. A black boy in a gorgeous, plumed turban and a long, crimson surcoat arabesqued in gold — there were three or four such attendants about the room — proffered him a cup of posset on a golden salver.

The King rose, thrust aside the little blackamoor, and with his spaniel under his arm, sauntered across to Miss Stewart's table. Soon he found himself alone with her — the others having removed themselves on his approach, as jackals fall back before the coming of the lion. The last to go, and with signs of obvious reluctance, was his grace of Richmond, a delicately built, uncomely, but very glittering gentleman.

Charles faced her across the table, the tall house of cards standing between them.

Miss invited His Majesty's admiration for my Lord of Buckingham's architecture. Pouf! His Majesty blew, and the edifice rustled down to a mere heap of cards again.

"Symbol of kingly power," said Miss, pertly. "You demolish better than you build, Sire."

"Oddsfish! If you challenge me, it were easy to prove you wrong," quoth he.

"Pray do. The cards are here."

"Cards! Pooh! Card castles are well enough for Buckingham. But such is not the castle I'll build you if you command me."

"I command the King's Majesty? Mon Dieu! But it would be treason surely."

"Not greater treason than to have enslaved me." His fine eyes were oddly ardent. "Shall I build you this castle, child?"

Miss looked at him, and looked away. Her eyelids fluttered distractingly. She fetched a sigh.

"The castle that Your Majesty would build for any but your Queen must prove a prison."

She rose, and, looking across the room, she met the handsome, scowling eyes of the neglected favourite. "My Lady Castlemaine looks as if she feared that Fortune were not favouring her." She was so artless that Charles could not be sure there was a double meaning to her speech. "Shall we go see how she is faring?" she added, with a disregard for etiquette, whose artlessness he also doubted.

He yielded, of course. That was his way with beauty, especially with beauty not yet reduced into possession. But the characteristic urbanity with which he sauntered beside her across the room was no more than a mask upon his chagrin. It was always thus that pretty Frances Stewart used him. She always knew how to elude him and, always with that cursed air of artlessness, uttered seemingly simple sentences that clung to his mind to tantalize him.

"The castle Your Majesty would build for any but your Queen must prove a prison." What had she meant by that? Must he take her to queen before she would allow him to build a castle for her?

It was an insistent, haunting thought, racking his mind. He knew there was a party hostile to the Duke of York and Clarendon, which, fearing the succession of the former, and, so, of the grandchildren of the latter, as a result of Catherine of Braganza's childlessness, strongly favoured the King's divorce.

It was a singular irony that my Lady Castlemaine should be largely responsible for the existence of that party. In her hatred for Clarendon, and her blind search for weapons that would slay the Chancellor, she had, if not actually invented, at least helped to give currency to the silly slander that Clarendon had deliberately chosen for Charles a barren queen, so as to ensure the ultimate succession of his own daughter's children. But she had never thought to see that slander recoil upon her as it now did; she had never thought that a party would come to rise up in conse-

quence that would urge divorce upon the King at the
very moment when he was consumed by passion for
the unattainable, artlessly artful Frances Stewart.

It was Buckingham, greatly daring, who slyly made
himself that party's mouthpiece. The suggestion
startled Charles, voicing, as perhaps it did, the temptation by which he was secretly assailed. He looked
at Buckingham, frowning.

"I verily believe you are the wickedest dog in England."

The impudent gallant made a leg. "For a subject,
Sire, I believe I am."

Charles — with whom the amusing word seems
ever to have been more compelling than the serious
— laughed his soft, mellow laugh. Then he sighed,
and the frown of thought returned.

"It would be a wicked thing to make a poor lady
miserable only because she is my wife, and has no
children by me, which is no fault of hers."

He was a thoroughly bad husband, but his indolent
good-nature shrank from purchasing his desires at the
price of so much ignominy to the Queen. Before that
could come to pass it would be necessary to give the
screw of temptation another turn or two. And it was
Miss Stewart herself who — in all innocence — supplied what was required in that direction. Driven to
bay by the importunities of Charles, she announced
at last that it was her intention to retire from Court,
so as to preserve herself from the temptations by
which she was beset, and to determine the uneasiness
which, through no fault of her own, her presence was
occasioning the Queen; and she announced further,
that, so desperate had she been rendered that she

would marry any gentleman of fifteen hundred pounds a year who would have her in honour.

You behold Charles reduced to a state of panic. He sought to bribe her with offers of any settlements she chose to name, or any title she coveted, offering her these things at the nation's expense as freely and lightly as the jewels he had tossed into her lap, or the collar of pearls worth sixteen hundred pounds he had put about her neck. The offers were ineffectual, and Charles, driven almost to distraction by such invulnerable virtue, might now have yielded to the insidious whispers of divorce and remarriage had not my Lady Castlemaine taken a hand in the game.

Her ladyship, dwelling already, as a consequence of that royal infatuation for Miss Stewart, in the cold, rarefied atmosphere of a neglect that amounted almost to disgrace, may have considered with bitterness how her attempt to exploit her hatred of the Chancellor had recoiled upon herself.

In the blackest hour of her despair, when hope seemed almost dead, she made a discovery — or, rather, the King's page, the ineffable Chiffinch, Lord Keeper of the Back Stairs and Grand Eunuch of the Royal Seraglio, who was her ladyship's friend, made it and communicated it to her.

There had been one ardent respondent in the Duke of Richmond to that proclamation of Miss Stewart's that she would marry any gentleman of fifteen hundred pounds a year. Long enamoured of her, his grace saw here his opportunity, and he seized it. Consequently he was now in constant attendance upon her, but very secretly, since he feared the King's displeasure.

My Lady Castlemaine, having discovered this, and being well served in the matter by Chiffinch, spied her opportunity. It came one cold night towards the end of February of that year 1667. Charles, going below at a late hour to visit Miss Stewart, when he judged that she would be alone, was informed by her maid that Miss was not receiving, a headache compelling her to keep her room.

His Majesty returned above in a very ill-humour, to find himself confronted in his own apartments by my Lady Castlemaine. Chiffinch had introduced her by the back-stairs entrance. Charles stiffened at sight of her.

"I hope I may be allowed to pay my homage," says she, on a note of irony, "although the angelic Stewart has forbid you to see me at my own house. I come to condole with you upon the affliction and grief into which the new-fashioned chastity of the inhuman Stewart has reduced Your Majesty."

"You are pleased to be amused, ma'am," says Charles frostily.

"I will not," she returned him, "make use of reproaches which would disgrace myself; still less will I endeavour to excuse frailties in myself which nothing can justify, since your constancy for me deprives me of all defence." Her ladyship, you see, had a considerable gift of sarcasm.

"In that case, may I ask you why you have come?"

"To open your eyes. Because I cannot bear that you should be made the jest of your own Court."

"Madam!"

"Ah! You didn't know, of course, that you are being laughed at for the gross manner in which you are being imposed upon by the Stewart's affectations, any more than you know that whilst you are denied admittance to her apartments, under the pretence of some indisposition, the Duke of Richmond is with her now."

"That is false," he was beginning, very indignantly.

"I do not desire you to take my word for it. If you will follow me, you will no longer be the dupe of a false prude, who makes you act so ridiculous a part."

She took him, still half-resisting, by the hand, and in silence led him, despite his reluctance, back by the way he had so lately come. Outside her rival's door she left him, but she paused at the end of the gallery to make sure that he had entered.

Within he found himself confronted by several of Miss Stewart's chambermaids, who respectfully barred his way, one of them informing him scarcely above a whisper that her mistress had been very ill since His Majesty left, but that, being gone to bed, she was, God be thanked, in a very fine sleep.

"That I must see," said the King. And, since one of the women placed herself before the door of the inner room, His Majesty unceremoniously took her by the shoulders and put her aside.

He thrust open the door, and stepped without further ceremony into the well-lighted bedroom. Miss Stewart occupied the handsome, canopied bed. But far from being, as he had been told, in "a very fine sleep," she was sitting up; and far from presenting an ailing appearance, she looked radiantly well and very lovely in her diaphanous sleeping toilet, with golden ringlets in distracting disarray. Nor was she alone.

By her pillow sat one who, if at first to be presumed her physician, proved upon scrutiny to be the Duke of Richmond.

The King's swarthy face turned a variety of colours, his languid eyes lost all trace of languor. Those who knew his nature might have expected that he would now deliver himself with that sneering sarcasm, that indolent cynicism, which he used upon occasion. But he was too deeply stirred for acting. His self-control deserted him entirely. Exactly what he said has not been preserved for us. All that we are told is that he signified his resentment in such terms as he had never before used; and that his grace, almost petrified by the King's most royal rage, uttered never a word in answer. The windows of the room overlooked the Thames. The King's eyes strayed towards them. Richmond was slight of build, Charles vigorous and athletic. His grace took the door betimes, lest the window should occur to His Majesty, and so he left the lady alone with the outraged monarch.

Thereafter Charles did not have it all quite his own way. Miss Stewart faced him in an indignation nothing less than his own, and she was very far from attempting any such justification of herself, or her conduct, as he may have expected.

"Will Your Majesty be more precise as to the grounds of your complaint?" she invited him challengingly.

That checked his wildness. It brought him up with a round turn. His jaw fell, and he stared at her, lost now for words. Of this she took the fullest advantage.

"If I am not allowed to receive visits from a man of the Duke of Richmond's rank, who comes with honourable intentions, then I am a slave in a free country. I know of no engagement that should prevent me from disposing of my hand as I think fit. But if this is not permitted me in Your Majesty's dominions, I do not believe there is any power on earth can prevent me going back to France, and throwing myself into a convent, there to enjoy the peace denied me at this Court."

With that she melted into tears, and his discomfiture was complete. On his knees he begged her forgiveness for the injury he had done her. But Miss was not in a forgiving humour.

"If Your Majesty would graciously consent to leave me now in peace," said she, "you would avoid offending by a longer visit those who accompanied or conducted you to my apartments."

She had drawn a bow at a venture, but shrewdly, and the shaft went home. Charles rose, red in the face. Swearing he would never speak to her again, he stalked out.

Later, however, he considered. If he felt bitterly aggrieved, he must also have realized that he had no just grounds for this, and that in his conduct in Miss Stewart's room he had been entirely ridiculous. She was rightly resolved against being lightly worn by any man. If anything, the reflection must have fanned his passion. It was impossible, he thought, that she should love that knock-kneed fellow, Richmond, who had no graces either of body or of mind, and if she suffered the man's suit, it must be, as she had all but said, so that she might be delivered from the persecution to which His Majesty had submitted her. The thought of her marrying Richmond, or, indeed, anybody, was unbearable to Charles, and it may have stifled his last scruple in the matter of the divorce.

His first measure next morning was to banish Richmond from the Court. But Richmond had not stayed for the order to quit. The King's messenger found him gone already.

Then Charles took counsel in the matter with the Chancellor. Clarendon's habitual gravity was increased to sternness. He spoke to the King — taking the fullest advantage of the tutelary position in which for the last twenty-five years he had stood to him — much as he had spoken when Charles had proposed to make Barbara Palmer a lady of the Queen's bedchamber, saving that he was now even more uncompromising. The King was not pleased with him. But just as he had had his way, despite the Chancellor, in that other matter, so he would have his way despite him now.

This time, however, the Chancellor took no risks. He feared too much the consequences for Charles, and he determined to spare no effort to avoid a scandal, and to save the already deeply injured Queen. So he went secretly to work to outwit the King. He made himself the protector of those lovers, the Duke of Richmond and Miss Stewart, with the result that one dark night, a week or two later, the lady stole away from the Palace of Whitehall, and made her way to the Bear Tavern, at the Bridgefoot, Westminster, where Richmond awaited her with a coach. And so, by the secret favour of the Lord Chancellor, they stole away to Kent and matrimony.

That was checkmate, indeed, to Charles, who swore all manner of things in his mortification. But it was not until some six weeks later that he learnt by whose agency the thing had been accomplished. He learnt it, not a doubt, from my Lady Castlemaine.

The estrangement between her ladyship and the King, which dated back to the time of his desperate courtship of Miss Stewart, was at last made up; and once again we see her ladyship triumphant, and firmly established in the amorous King's affections. She had cause to be grateful to the Chancellor for this. But her vindictive nature remembered only the earlier injury still unavenged. Here at last was her chance to pay off that score. Clarendon, beset by enemies on every hand, yet trusting in the King whom he had served so well, stood his ground unintimidated and unmoved — an oak that had weathered mightier storms than this. He did not dream that he was in the power of an evil woman. And that woman used her power. When all else failed, she told the King of Clarendon's part in the flight of Miss Stewart, and lest the King should be disposed to pardon the Chancellor out of consideration for his motives, represented him as a self-seeker, and charged him with having acted thus so as to make sure of keeping his daughter's children by the Duke of York in the succession.

That was the end. Charles withdrew his protection, threw Clarendon to the wolves. He sent the Duke of Albemarle to him with a command that he should surrender his seals of office. The proud old man refused to yield his seals to any but the King himself. He may have hoped that the memory of all that lay between them would rise up once more when they were face to face. So he came in person to Whitehall to make surrender. He walked deliberately, firmly, and with

head erect, through the hostile throng of courtiers —
"especially the buffoones and ladys of pleasure," as
Evelyn says.

Of his departure thence, his disgrace now consum-
mated, Pepys has left us a vivid picture:

"When he went from the King on Monday morning
my Lady Castlemaine was in bed (though about
twelve o'clock), and ran out in her smock into her
aviary looking into Whitehall Gardens; and thither
her woman brought her her nightgown; and she stood,
blessing herself at the old man's going away; and several of the gallants of Whitehall — of which there
were many staying to see the Chancellor's return —
did talk to her in her birdcage; among others Bland-
ford, telling her she was the bird of passage."

Clarendon lingered, melancholy and disillusioned,
at his fine house in Piccadilly until, impeached by
Parliament, he remembered Strafford's fate, and set
out to tread once more and for the remainder of his
days the path of exile.

Time avenged him. Two of his granddaughters —
Mary and Anne — reigned successively as queens in
England.

X

THE TRAGEDY OF HERRENHAUSEN

COUNT PHILIP KÖNIGSMARK AND THE PRINCESS SOPHIA DOROTHEA

HE was accounted something of a scamp throughout Europe, and particularly in England, where he had been associated with his brother in the killing of Mr. Thynne. But the seventeenth century did not look for excessively nice scruples in a soldier of fortune; and so it condoned the lack of virtue in Count Philip Christof Königsmark for the sake of his personal beauty, his elegance, his ready wit, and his magnificent address. The Court of Hanover made him warmly welcome, counting itself the richer for his presence; whilst he, on his side, was retained there by the colonelcy in the Electoral Guard to which he had been appointed, and by his deep and ill-starred affection for the Princess Sophia Dorothea, the wife of the Electoral Prince, who later was to reign in England as King George I.

His acquaintance with her dated back to childhood, for they had been playmates at her father's ducal Court of Zell, where Königsmark had been brought up. With adolescence he had gone out into the world to seek the broader education which it offered to men of quality and spirit. He had fought bulls in Madrid, and the infidel overseas; he had wooed adventure wherever it was to be met, until romance hung about him like an aura. Thus Sophia met him again, a dazzling personality, whose effulgence shone the more brightly against the dull background of that gross Hanoverian Court; an accomplished, graceful, self-reliant man of the world, in whom she scarcely recognized her sometime playmate.

The change he found in her was no less marked, though of a different kind. The sweet child he had known — she had been married in 1682, at the age of sixteen — had come in her ten years of wedded life to the fulfilment of the handsome promise of her maidenhood. But her beauty was spiritualized by a certain wistfulness that had not been there before, that should not have been there now had all been well. The sprightliness inherent in her had not abated, but it had assumed a certain warp of bitterness; humour, which is of the heart, had given place in her to wit, which is of the mind, and this wit was barbed, and a little reckless of how or where it offended.

Königsmark observed these changes that the years had wrought, and knew enough of her story to account for them. He knew of her thwarted love for her cousin, the Duke of Wolfenbüttel, thwarted for the sake of dynastic ambition, to the end that by marrying her to the Electoral Prince George the whole of the Duchy of Lüneberg might be united. Thus, for political reasons, she had been thrust into a union that was mutually loveless; for Prince George had as little affection to bring to it as herself. Yet for a prince the door to compensations is ever open. Prince George's taste, as is notorious, was ever for ugly women, and this taste he indulged so freely, openly, and grossly that the coldness towards him with which Sophia had entered the alliance was eventually converted into disgust and contempt.

Thus matters stood between that ill-matched couple; contempt on her side, cold dislike on his, a dislike that was fully shared by his father, the Elector, Ernest Augustus, and encouraged in the latter by the Countess von Platen.

Madame von Platen, the wife of the Elector's chief minister of state, was — with the connivance of her despicable husband, who saw therein the means to his own advancement — the acknowledged mistress of Ernest Augustus. She was a fleshy, gauche, vain, and ill-favoured woman. Malevolence sat in the creases of her painted face, and peered from her mean eyes. Yet, such as she was, the Elector Ernest loved her. His son's taste for ugly women would appear to have been hereditary.

Between the Countess and Sophia there was a deadly feud. The Princess had mortally offended her father-in-law's favourite. Not only had she never troubled to dissemble the loathing which that detestable woman inspired in her, but she had actually given it such free and stinging expression as had provoked against Madame von Platen the derision of the Court, a derision so ill-concealed that echoes of it had reached its object, and made her aware of the source from whence it sprang.

It was into this atmosphere of hostility that the advent of the elegant, romantic Königsmark took place. He found the stage set for comedy of a grim and bitter kind, which he was himself, by his recklessness, to convert into tragedy.

It began by the Countess von Platen's falling in

love with him. It was some time before he suspected it, though Heaven knows he did not lack for self-esteem. Perhaps it was this very self-esteem that blinded him here to the appalling truth. Yet in the end understanding came to him. When the precise significance of the fond leer of that painted harridan's repellent coquetry was borne in upon him, he felt the skin of his body creep and roughen. But he dissembled craftily. He was a venal scamp, after all, and in the Court of Hanover he saw opportunities to employ his gifts and his knowledge of the great world in such a way as to win to eminence. He saw that the Elector's favourite could be of use to him; and it is not your adventurer's way to look too closely into the nature of the ladder by which he has the chance to climb.

Skilfully, craftily, then, he played the enamoured Countess so long as her fondness for him might be useful, her hostility detrimental. But once the colonelcy of the Electoral Guard was firmly in his grasp, and an intimate friendship had ripened between himself and Prince Charles — the Elector's younger son — sufficiently to ensure his future, he plucked off the mask and allied himself with Sophia in her hostility towards Madame von Platen. He did worse. Some little time thereafter, whilst on a visit to the Court of Poland, he made one night in his cups a droll story of the amorous persecution which he had suffered at Madame von Platen's hands.

It was a tale that set the profligate company in a roar. But there was one present who afterwards sent a report of it to the Countess, and you conceive the nature of the emotions it aroused in her. Her rage was the greater for being stifled. It was obviously impossible for her to appeal to her lover, the Elector, to avenge her. From the Elector, above all others, must the matter be kept concealed. But not on that account would she forgo the vengeance due. She would present a reckoning in full ere all was done, and bitterly should the presumptuous young adventurer who had flouted her be made to pay.

The opportunity was very soon to be afforded her. It arose more or less directly out of an act in which she indulged her spite against Sophia. This lay in throwing Melusina Schulemberg into the arms of the Electoral Prince. Melusina, who was years afterwards to be created Duchess of Kendal, had not yet attained to that completeness of lank, bony hideousness that was later to distinguish her in England. But even in youth she could boast of little attraction. Prince George, however, was easily attracted. A dull, undignified libertine, addicted to over-eating, heavy drinking, and low conversation, he found in Melusina von Schulemberg an ideal mate. Her installation as maîtresse-en-titre took place publicly at a ball given by Prince George at Herrenhausen, a ball at which the Princess Sophia was present.

Accustomed, inured, as she was to the coarse profligacy of her dullard husband, and indifferent to his philandering as her contempt of him now left her, yet, in the affront thus publicly offered her, she felt that the limit of endurance had been reached. Next day it was found that she had disappeared from Herrenhausen. She had fled to her father's Court at Zell.

But her father received her coldly; lectured her upon the freedom and levity of her manners, which he condemned as unbecoming the dignity of her rank; recommended her to use in future greater prudence, and a proper, wifely submission; and, the homily delivered, packed her back to her husband at Herrenhausen.

George's reception of her on her return was bitterly hostile. She had been guilty of a more than usual, of an unpardonable want of respect for him. She must learn what was due to her station, and to her husband. He would thank her to instruct herself in these matters against his return from Berlin, whither he was about to journey, and he warned her that he would suffer no more tantrums of that kind.

Thus he delivered himself, with cold hate in his white, flabby, frog-face and in the very poise of his squat, ungainly figure.

Thereafter he departed for Berlin, bearing hate of her with him, and leaving hate and despair behind.

It was then, in this despair, that Sophia looked about her for a true friend to lend her the aid she so urgently required; to rescue her from her intolerable, soul-destroying fate. And at her elbow, against this dreadful need, Destiny had placed her sometime playmate, her most devoted friend — as she accounted him, and as, indeed, he was — the elegant, reckless Königsmark, with his beautiful face, his golden mane, and his unfathomable blue eyes.

Walking with him one summer day between clipped hedges in the formal gardens of Herrenhausen — that palace as squat and ungraceful as those who had built and who inhabited it — she opened her heart to him very fully, allowed him, in her overwhelming need of sympathy, to see things which for very shame she had hitherto veiled from all other eyes. She kept nothing back; she dwelt upon her unhappiness with her boorish husband, told him of slights and indignities innumerable, whose pain she had hitherto so bravely dissembled, confessed, even, that he had beaten her upon occasion.

Königsmark went red and white by turns, with the violent surge of his emotions, and the deep sapphire eyes blazed with wrath when she came at last to the culminating horror of blows endured.

"It is enough, Madame," he cried. "I swear to you, as Heaven hears me, that he shall be punished."

"Punished?" she echoed, checking in her stride, and looked at him with a smile of sad incredulity. "It is not his punishment I seek, my friend, but my own salvation."

"The one can be accomplished with the other," he answered hotly, and struck the cut-steel hilt of his sword. "You shall be rid of this lout as soon as ever I can come to him. I go after him to Berlin to-night."

The colour all faded from her cheeks, her sensitive lips fell apart, as she looked at him aghast.

"Why, what would you do? What do you mean?" she asked him.

"I will send him the length of my sword, and so make a widow of you, Madame."

She shook her head. "Princes do not fight," she said, on a note of contempt.

"I shall so shame him that he will have no alternative — unless, indeed, he is shameless. I will choose my occasion shrewdly, put an affront on him one evening in his cups, when drink shall have made him valiant enough to commit himself to a meeting. If

even that will not answer, and he still shields himself behind his rank — why, there are other ways
to serve him." He was thinking, perhaps, of Mr.
Thynne.

The heat of so much reckless, romantic fury on her
behalf warmed the poor lady, who had so long been
chilled for want of sympathy, and starved of love.
Impulsively she caught his hand in hers.

"My friend, my friend!" she cried, on a note that
quivered and broke, "you are mad — wonderfully,
beautifully mad, but mad. What would become of
you if you did this?"

He swept the consideration aside by a contemptuous, almost angry gesture. "Does that matter? I am
concerned with what is to become of you. I was born
for your service, my Princess, and the service being
rendered . . ." He shrugged and smiled, threw out his
hands and let them fall again to his sides in an eloquent
gesture. He was the complete courtier, the knight-
errant, the romantic preux-chevalier all in one.

She drew closer to him, took the blue lapels of his
military coat in her white hands, and looked patheti-
cally up into his beautiful face. If ever she wanted to
kiss a man, she surely wanted to kiss Königsmark in
that moment, but as she might have kissed a loving
brother, in token of her deep gratitude for his devotion to her who had known so little true devotion.

"If you knew," she said, "what balsam this proof
of your friendship has poured upon the wounds of my
soul, you would understand my utter lack of words
in which to thank you. You dumbfound me, my
friend; I can find no expression for my gratitude."

"I ask no gratitude," quoth he. "I am all gratitude

myself that you should have come to me in the hour of your need. I but ask your leave to serve you in my own way."

She shook her head. She saw his blue eyes grow troubled. He was about to speak, to protest, but she hurried on. "Serve me if you will — God knows I need the service of a loyal friend — but serve me as I shall myself decide — no other way."

"But what alternative service can exist?" he asked, almost impatiently.

"I have it in mind to escape from this horrible place — to quit Hanover, never to return."

"But to go whither?"

"Does it matter? Anywhere away from this hateful Court, and this hateful life; anywhere, since my father will not let me find shelter at Zell, as I had hoped. Had it not been for the thought of my children, I should have fled long ago. For the sake of those two little ones I have suffered patiently through all these years. But the limit of endurance has been reached and passed. Take me away, Königsmark!" She was clutching his lapels again. "If you would really serve me, help me to escape."

His hands descended upon hers, and held them prisoned against his breast. A flush crept into his fair cheeks, there was a sudden kindling of the eyes that looked down into her own piteous ones. These sensitive, romantic natures are quickly stirred to passion, ever ready to yield to the adventure of it.

"My Princess," he said, "you may count upon your Königsmark while he has life." Disengaging her hands from his lapels, but still holding them, he bowed low over them, so low that his heavy golden mane tumbled forward on either side of his handsome head to form a screen under cover of which he pressed his lips upon her fingers.

She let him have his will with her hands. It was little enough reward for so much devotion.

"I thank you again," she breathed. "And now I must think — I must consider where I can count upon finding refuge."

That cooled his ardour a little. His own high romantic notion was, no doubt, to fling her there and then upon the withers of his horse, and so ride out into the wide world to carve a kingdom for her with his sword. Her sober words dispelled the dream, revealed to him that it was not quite intended he should hereafter be her custodian. And there for the moment the matter was suspended.

Both had behaved quite recklessly. Each should have remembered that an Electoral Princess is not wise to grant a protracted interview, accompanied by lapel-holding, hand-holding, and hand-kissings, within sight of the windows of a palace. And, as it happened, behind one of those windows lurked the Countess von Platen, watching them jealously, and without any disposition to construe the meeting innocently. Was she not the deadly enemy of both? Had not the Princess whetted satire upon her, and had not Königsmark scorned the love she proffered him, and then unpardonably published it in a ribald story to excite the mirth of profligates?

That evening the Countess purposefully sought her lover, the Elector.

"Your son is away in Prussia," quoth she. "Who guards his honour in his absence?"

"George's honour?" quoth the Elector, bulging eyes staring at the Countess. He did not laugh, as might have been expected at the notion of guarding something whose existence was not easily discerned. He had no sense of humour, as his appearance suggested. He was a short, fat man with a face shaped like a pear — narrow in the brow and heavy in the jowl. "What the devil do you mean?" he asked.

"I mean that this foreign adventurer, Königsmark, and Sophia grow too intimate."

"Sophia!" Thick eyebrows were raised until they almost met the line of his ponderous peruke. His face broke into malevolent creases expressive of contempt.

"That white-faced ninny! Bah!" Her very virtue was matter for his scorn.

"It is these white-faced ninnies can be most sly," replied the Countess, out of her worldly wisdom. "Listen a moment now." And she related, with interest rather than discount, you may be sure, what she had witnessed that afternoon.

The malevolence deepened in his face. He had never loved Sophia, and he felt none the kinder towards her for her recent trip to Zell. Then, too, being a libertine, and the father of a libertine, it logically followed that unchastity in his women-folk was in his eyes the unpardonable sin.

He heaved himself out of his deep chair. "How far has this gone?" he demanded.

Prudence restrained the Countess from any overstatement that might afterwards be disproved. Besides, there was not the need, if she could trust her senses. Patience and vigilance would presently afford her all the evidence required to damn the pair. She said as much, and promised the Elector that she would exercise herself the latter quality in his son's service. Again the Elector did not find it grotesque that his mistress should appoint herself the guardian of his son's honour.

The Countess went about that congenial task with zeal — though George's honour was the least thing that concerned her. What concerned her was the dishonour of Sophia, and the ruin of Königsmark. So she watched assiduously, and set others, too, to watch for her and to report. And almost daily now she had for the Elector a tale of whisperings and hand-pressings, and secret stolen meetings between the guilty twain. The Elector raged, and would have taken action, but that the guileful Countess curbed him. All this was not enough. An accusation that could not be substantiated would ruin all chance of punishing the offenders, might recoil, indeed, upon the accusers by bringing the Duke of Zell to his daughter's aid. So they must wait yet awhile until they held more absolute proof of this intrigue.

And then at last one day the Countess sped in haste to the Elector with word that Königsmark and the Princess had shut themselves up together in the garden pavilion. Let him come at once, and he should so discover them for himself, and thus at last be able to take action. The Countess was flushed with triumph. Be that meeting never so innocent — and Madame von Platen could not, being what she was, and having seen what she had seen, conceive it innocent — it was in an Electoral Princess an unforgivable indiscretion, to take the most charitable view, which none would dream of taking. So the Elector, fiercely red in the face, hurried off to the pavilion with Madame von Platen following. He came too late, despite the diligence of his spy.

Sophia had been there, but her interview with the Count had been a brief one. She had to tell him that at last she was resolved in all particulars. She would seek a refuge at the Court of her cousin, the Duke of Wolfenbüttel, who, she was sure — for the sake of what once had lain between them — would not now refuse to shelter and protect her. Of Königsmark she desired that he should act as her escort to her cousin's Court.

Königsmark was ready, eager. In Hanover he would leave nothing that he regretted. At Wolfenbüttel, having served Sophia faithfully, his ever-growing, romantic passion for her might find expression. She would make all dispositions, and advise him when she was ready to set out. But they must use caution, for they were being spied upon. Madame von Platen's over-eagerness had in part betrayed her. It was, indeed, their consciousness of espionage which had led to this dangerous meeting in the seclusion of the pavilion, and which urged him to linger after Sophia had left him. They were not to be seen to emerge together.

The young Dane sat alone on the window-seat, his chin in his hands, his eyes dreamy, a faint smile on his shapely lips, when Ernest Augustus burst furiously in, the Countess von Platen lingering just beyond the threshold. The Elector's face was apoplectically purple from rage and haste, his breath came in wheezing gasps. His bulging eyes swept round the chamber, and fastened finally, glaring, upon the startled Königsmark.

"Where is the Princess?" he blurted out.

The Count espied Madame von Platen in the background, and had the scent of mischief very strong. But he preserved an air of innocent mystification. He rose and answered with courteous ease:

"Your Highness is seeking her? Shall I ascertain for you?"

At a loss, Ernest Augustus stared a moment, then flung a glance over his shoulder at the Countess.

"I was told that Her Highness was here," he said.

"Plainly," said Königsmark, with perfect calm, "you have been misinformed." And his quiet glance and gesture invited the Elector to look round for himself.

"How long have you been here yourself?" Feeling at a disadvantage, the Elector avoided the direct question that was in his mind.

"Half an hour at least."

"And in that time you have not seen the Princess?"

"Seen the Princess?" Königsmark's brows were knit perplexedly. "I scarcely understand Your Highness."

The Elector moved a step and trod on a soft substance. He looked down, then stooped, and rose again, holding in his hand a woman's glove.

"What's this?" quoth he. "Whose glove is this?"

If Königsmark's heart missed a beat — as well it may have done — he did not betray it outwardly. He smiled; indeed, he almost laughed.

"Your Highness is amusing himself at my expense by asking me questions that only a seer could answer."

The Elector was still considering him with his ponderously suspicious glance, when quick steps approached. A serving-maid, one of Sophia's women, appeared in the doorway of the pavilion.

"What do you want?" the Elector snapped at her.

"A glove Her Highness lately dropped here," was the timid answer, innocently precipitating the very discovery which the woman had been too hastily dispatched to avert.

The Elector flung the glove at her, and there was a creak of evil laughter from him. When she had departed, he turned again to Königsmark.

"You fence skilfully," said he, sneering, "too skilfully for an honest man. Will you now tell me without any more of this, precisely what the Princess Sophia was doing here with you?"

Königsmark drew himself stiffly up, looking squarely into the furnace of the Elector's face.

"Your Highness assumes that the Princess was here with me, and a prince is not to be contradicted, even when he insults a lady whose spotless purity is beyond his understanding. But Your Highness can hardly expect me to become in never so slight a degree a party to that insult by vouchsafing any answer to your question."

"That is your last word, sir?" The Elector shook with suppressed anger.

"Your Highness cannot think that words are necessary?"

The bulging eyes grew narrow, the heavy nether lip was thrust forth in scorn and menace.

"You are relieved, sir, of your duties in the Electoral Guard, and as that is the only tie binding you to

Hanover, we see no reason why your sojourn here should be protracted."

Königsmark bowed stiffly, formally. "It shall end, Your Highness, as soon as I can make the necessary arrangements for my departure — in a week at most."

"You are accorded three days, sir." The Elector turned, and waddled out, leaving Königsmark to breathe freely again. The three days should suffice for the Princess also. It was very well.

The Elector, too, thought that it was very well. He had given this troublesome fellow his dismissal, averted a scandal, and placed his daughter-in-law out of the reach of harm. Madame von Platen was the only one concerned who thought that it was not well at all, the consummation being far from that which she had desired. She had dreamt of a flaming scandal, that should utterly consume her two enemies, Sophia and Königsmark. Instead, she saw them both escaping, and the fact that she was — as she may have supposed — effectively separating two loving hearts could be no sort of adequate satisfaction for such bitter spite as hers. Therefore she plied her wicked wits to force an issue more germane to her desires.

The course she took was fraught with a certain peril. Yet confident that at worst she could justify it, and little fearing that the worst would happen, she boldly went to work. She forged next day a brief note in which the Princess Sophia urgently bade Königsmark to come to her at ten o'clock that night in her own apartments, and with threat and bribe induced the waiting woman of the glove to bear that letter.

Now it so happened that Königsmark, through the

kind offices of Sophia's maid-of-honour, Mademoiselle
de Knesebeck, who was in the secret of their intentions, had sent the Princess a note that morning,
briefly stating the urgency of departure, and begging
her so to arrange that she could leave Herrenhausen
with him on the morrow. He imagined the note now
brought him to be in answer to that appeal of his.
Its genuineness he never doubted, being unacquainted
with Sophia's writing. He was aghast at the rashness
which dictated such an assignation, yet never hesitated as to keeping it. It was not his way to hesitate.
He trusted to the gods who watch over the destinies
of the bold.

And meanwhile Madame von Platen was reproaching her lover with having dealt too softly with the
Dane.

"Bah!" said the Elector. "To-morrow he goes his
ways, and we are rid of him. Is not that enough?"

"Enough, if, soon as he goes, he goes not too late
already," quoth she.

"Now what will you be hinting?" he asked her
peevishly.

"I'll be more plain. I will tell you what I know.
It is this. Königsmark has an assignation with the
Princess Sophia this very night at ten o'clock — and
where do you suppose? In Her Highness's own apartments."

The Elector came to his feet with an oath. "That
is not true!" he cried. "It cannot be!"

"Then I'll say no more," quoth Jezebel, and
snapped her thin lips.

"Ah, but you shall. How do you know this?"

"That I cannot tell you without betraying a confidence. Let it suffice you that I do know it. Consider now whether in banishing this profligate you have sufficiently avenged the honour of your son."

"My God, if I thought this were true . . ." He choked with rage, stood shaking a moment, then strode to the door, calling.

"The truth is easily ascertained," said Madame. "Conceal yourself in the Rittersaal, and await his coming forth. But you had best go attended, for it is a very reckless rogue, and he has been known aforetime to practise murder."

Whilst the Elector, acting upon this advice, was getting his men together, Königsmark was wasting precious moments in Sophia's ante-chamber, whilst Mademoiselle de Knesebeck apprised Her Highness of his visit. Sophia had already retired to bed, and the amazing announcement of the Count's presence there startled her into a fear of untoward happenings. She was overwhelmed, too, by the rashness of this step of his, coming after the events of yesterday. If it should be known that he had visited her thus, terrible consequences might ensue. She rose, and with Mademoiselle de Knesebeck's aid made ready to receive him. Yet for all that she made haste, the precious irreclaimable moments sped.

She came to him at last, Mademoiselle de Knesebeck following, for propriety's sake.

"What is it?" she asked him breathlessly. "What brings you here at such an hour?"

"What brings me?" quoth he, surprised at that reception. "Why, your commands — your letter."

"My letter? What letter?"

A sense of doom, of being trapped, suddenly awoke

in him. He plucked forth the treacherous note, and proffered it.

"Why, what does this mean?" She swept a white hand over her eyes and brows, as if to brush away something that obscured her vision. "That is not mine. I never wrote it. How could you dream I should be so imprudent as to bid you hither, and at such an hour? How could you dream it?"

"You are right," said he, and laughed, perhaps to ease her alarm, perhaps in sheer bitter mirth. "It will be, no doubt, the work of our friend, Madame von Platen. I had best begone. For the rest, my traveling-chaise will wait from noon until sunset to-morrow by the Markt Kirck in Hanover, and I shall wait within it. I shall hope to conduct you safely to Wolfenbüttel."

"I will come, I will come. But go now — oh, go!"

He looked very deeply into her eyes — a valedictory glance against the worst befalling him. Then he took her hand, bowed over it and kissed it, and so departed.

He crossed the outer ante-room, descended the short flight of stairs, and pushed open the heavy door of the Hall of Knights. He passed through, and thrust the door behind him, then stood a moment looking round the vast apartment. If he was too late to avoid the springs of the baited trap, it was here that they should snap upon him. Yet all was still. A single lamp on a table in the middle of the vast chamber shed a feeble, flickering light, yet sufficient to assure him that no one waited here. He sighed relief, wrapped his cloak about him, and set out swiftly to cross the hall.

But even as he passed, four shadows detached themselves from the tall stove, resolved themselves into armed men, and sprang after him.

He heard them, wheeled about, flung off his cloak, and disengaged his sword, all with the speed of lightning and the address of the man who for ten years had walked amid perils, and learned to depend upon his blade. That swift action sealed his doom. Their orders were to take him living or dead, and standing in awe of his repute, they were not the men to incur risks. Even as he came on guard, a partisan grazed his head, and another opened his breast.

He went down, coughing and gasping, blood dabbling his bright golden hair, and staining the priceless Mechlin at his throat, yet his right hand still desperately clutching his useless sword.

His assassins stood about him, their partisans levelled to strike again, and summoned him to yield. Then, beside one of them, he suddenly beheld the Countess von Platen materializing out of the surrounding shadows as it seemed, and behind her the squat, ungraceful figure of the Elector. He fought for breath.

"I am slain," he gasped, "and as I am to appear before my Maker I swear to you that the Princess Sophia is innocent. Spare her at least, Your Highness."

"Innocent!" said the Elector hoarsely. "Then what did you now in her apartments?"

"It was a trap set for us by this foul hag, who . . ."

The heel of the vindictive harridan ground viciously upon the lips of the dying man and choked his utterance. Thereafter the halberts finished him off, and he was buried there and then, in lime, under the floor of the Hall of Knights, under the very spot where he had fallen, which was long to remain imbrued with his blood.

Thus miserably perished the glittering Königsmark, a martyr to his own irrepressible romanticism.

As for Sophia, better might it have been for her had she shared his fate that night. She was placed under arrest next morning, and Prince George was summoned back from Berlin at once.

The evidence may have satisfied him that his honour had not suffered, for he was disposed to let the matter drop, content that they should remain in the forbidding relations which had existed between them before this happening. But Sophia was uncompromising in her demand for strict justice.

"If I am guilty, I am unworthy of you," she told him. "If innocent, you are unworthy of me."

There was no more to be said. A consistory court was assembled to divorce them. But since with the best intentions there was no faintest evidence of her adultery, this court had to be content to pronounce the divorce upon the ground of her desertion.

She protested against the iniquity of this. But she protested in vain. She was carried off into the grim captivity of a castle on the Ahlen, to drag out in that melancholy duress another thirty-two years of life.

Her death took place in November of 1726. And the story runs that on her death-bed she delivered to a person of trust a letter to her sometime husband, now King George I of England. Seven months later, as King George was on his way to his beloved Hanover, that letter was placed in his carriage as it crossed the frontier into Germany. It contained Sophia's dying declaration of innocence, and her solemn summons to King George to stand by her side before the judgment-seat of Heaven within a year, and there make answer in her presence for the wrongs he had done her, for her blighted life and her miserable death.

King George's answer to that summons was immediate. The reading of that letter brought on the apoplectic seizure of which he died in his carriage next day — the 9th of June, 1727 — on the road to Osnabrück.

XI

THE TYRANNICIDE

CHARLOTTE CORDAY AND JEAN PAUL MARAT

TYRANNICIDE was the term applied to her deed by Adam Lux, her lover in the sublimest and most spiritual sense of the word — for he never so much as spoke to her, and she never so much as knew of his existence.

The sudden spiritual passion which inflamed him when he beheld her in the tumbril on her way to the scaffold is a fitting corollary to her action. She in her way and he in his were alike sublime; her tranquil martyrdom upon the altar of Republicanism and his exultant martyrdom upon the altar of Love were alike splendidly futile.

It is surely the strangest love-story enshrined in history. It has its pathos, yet leaves no regrets behind, for there is no might-have-been which death had thwarted. Because she died, he loved her; because he loved her, he died. That is all but for the details which I am now to give you.

The convent-bred Marie Charlotte Corday d'Armont was the daughter of a landless squire of Normandy, a member of the chétive noblesse, a man of gentle birth, whose sadly reduced fortune may have predisposed him against the law of entail or primogeniture — the prime cause of the inequality out of which were sprung so many of the evils that afflicted France.

Like many of his order and condition he was among the earliest converts to republicanism — the pure, ideal republicanism, demanding constitutional government of the people by the people, holding monarchical and aristocratic rule an effete and parasitic anachronism.

From M. de Corday Charlotte absorbed the lofty Republican doctrines to which anon she was to sacrifice her life; and she rejoiced when the hour of awakening sounded and the children of France rose up and snapped the fetters in which they had been trammelled for centuries by an insolent minority of their fellow-countrymen.

In the early violence of the Revolution she thought she saw a transient phase — horrible, but inevitable in the dread convulsion of that awakening. Soon this would pass, and the sane, ideal government of her dreams would follow — must follow, since among the people's elected representatives was a goodly number of unselfish, single-minded men of her father's class of life; men of breeding and education, impelled by a lofty altruistic patriotism; men who gradually came to form a party presently to be known as the Girondins.

But the formation of one party argues the formation of at least another. And this other in the National Assembly was that of the Jacobins, less pure of motive, less restrained in deed, a party in which stood preëminent such ruthless, uncompromising men as Robespierre, Danton — and Marat.

Where the Girondins stood for Republicanism, the Jacobins stood for Anarchy. War was declared between the two. The Girondins arraigned Marat and Robespierre for complicity in the September massacres, and thereby precipitated their own fall. The triumphant acquittal of Marat was the prelude to the ruin of the Girondins, and the proscription of twenty-nine deputies followed at once as the first step. These fled into the country, hoping to raise an army that should yet save France, and several of the fugitives made their way to Caen. Thence by pamphlets and oratory they laboured to arouse true Republican enthusiasm. They were gifted, able men, eloquent speakers and skilled writers, and they might have succeeded but that in Paris sat another man no less gifted, and with surer knowledge of the temper of the proletariat, tirelessly wielding a vitriolic pen, skilled in the art of inflaming the passions of the mob.

That man was Jean Paul Marat, sometime medical practitioner, sometime professor of literature, a graduate of the Scottish University of Saint Andrews, author of some scientific and many sociological works, inveterate pamphleteer and Revolutionary journalist, proprietor and editor of "L'Ami du Peuple," and idol of the Parisian rabble, who had bestowed upon him the name borne by his gazette, so that he was known as "The People's Friend."

Such was the foe of the Girondins, and of the pure, altruistic, Utopian Republicanism for which they stood; and whilst he lived and laboured, their own endeavours to influence the people were all in vain. From his vile lodging in the rue de l'École de Médecine in Paris he span with his clever, wicked pen a web that paralyzed their high endeavours and threatened finally to choke them.

He was not alone, of course. He was one of the dread triumvirate in which Danton and Robespierre were his associates. But to the Girondins he appeared by far the most formidable and ruthless and implacable of the three, whilst to Charlotte Corday — the friend and associate now of the proscribed Girondins who had sought refuge in Caen — he loomed so vast and terrible as to eclipse his associates entirely. To her young mind, inflamed with enthusiasm for the religion of Liberty as preached by the Girondins, Marat was a loathly, dangerous heresiarch, threatening to corrupt that sublime new faith with false, anarchical doctrine, and to replace the tyranny that had been overthrown by a tyranny more odious still.

She witnessed in Caen the failure of the Girondin attempt to raise an army with which to deliver Paris from the foul clutches of the Jacobins. An anguished spectator of this failure, she saw in it a sign that Liberty was being strangled at its birth. On the lips of her friends the Girondins she caught again the name of Marat, the murderer of Liberty; and, brooding, she reached a conclusion embodied in a phrase of a letter which she wrote about that time:

As long as Marat lives there will never be any safety for the friends of law and humanity.

From that negative conclusion to its positive, logical equivalent it was but a step. That step she took. She may have considered awhile the proposition thus presented to her, or resolve may have come to her with realization. She understood that a great sacrifice was necessary; that who undertook to rid France of that unclean monster must go prepared for self-immolation. She counted the cost calmly and soberly — for calm and sober was now her every act.

She made her packages, and set out one morning by the Paris coach from Caen, leaving a note for her father, in which she had written:

I am going to England, because I do not believe that it will be possible for a long time to live happily and tranquilly in France. On leaving I post this letter to you. When you receive it I shall no longer be here. Heaven denied us the happiness of living together, as it has denied us other happinesses. May it show itself more clement to our country. Good-bye, dear Father. Embrace my sister for me, and do not forget me.

That was all. The fiction that she was going to England was intended to save him pain. For she had so laid her plans that her identity should remain undisclosed. She would seek Marat in the very Hall of the Convention, and publicly slay him in his seat. Thus Paris should behold Nemesis overtaking the false Republican in the very Assembly which he corrupted, and anon should adduce a moral from the spectacle of the monster's death. For herself she counted upon instant destruction at the hands of the furious spectators. Thus, thinking to die unidentified, she trusted that her father, hearing, as all France must hear, the great tidings that Marat was dead, would never connect her with the instrument of Fate shattered by the fury of the mob.

You realize, then, how great and how terrible was the purpose of this maid of twenty-five, who so demurely took her seat in the Paris diligence on that July morning of the Year 2 of the Republic — 1793, old style. She was becomingly dressed in brown cloth, a lace fichu folded across her well-developed breast, a conical hat above her light brown hair. She was of a good height and finely proportioned, and her carriage as full of dignity as of grace. Her skin was of such white loveliness that a contemporary compares it with the lily. Like Athene, she was grey-eyed, and, like Athene, noble-featured, the oval of her face squaring a little at the chin, in which there was a cleft. Calm was her habit, calm her slow-moving eyes, calm and deliberate her movements, and calm the mind reflected in all this.

And as the heavy diligence trundles out of Caen and takes the open country and the Paris road, not even the thought of the errand upon which she goes, of her death-dealing and death-receiving mission, can shake that normal calm. Here is no wild exaltation, no hysterical obedience to hotly conceived impulse. Here is purpose, as cold as it is lofty, to liberate France and pay with her life for the privilege of doing so.

That lover of hers, whom we are presently to see, has compared her ineptly with Joan of Arc, that other maid of France. But Joan moved with pomp in a gorgeous pageantry, amid acclamations, sustained by the heady wine of combat and of enthusiasm openly indulged, towards a goal of triumph. Charlotte travelled quietly in the stuffy diligence with the quiet conviction that her days were numbered.

So normal did she appear to her travelling companions, that one among them, with an eye for beauty, pestered her with amorous attentions, and actually proposed marriage to her before the coach had rolled over the bridge of Neuilly into Paris two days later.

She repaired to the Providence Inn in the rue des Vieux Augustins, where she engaged a room on the first floor, and then she set out in quest of the Deputy Duperret. She had a letter of introduction to him from the Girondin Barbaroux, with whom she had been on friendly terms at Caen. Duperret was to assist her to obtain an interview with the Minister of the Interior. She had undertaken to see the latter on the subject of certain papers relating to the affairs of a nun of Caen, an old convent friend of her own, and she was in haste to discharge this errand, so as to be free for the great task upon which she was come.

From inquiries that she made, she learnt at once that Marat was ill, and confined to his house. This rendered necessary a change of plans, and the relinquishing of her project of affording him a spectacular death in the crowded Hall of the Convention.

The next day, which was Friday, she devoted to furthering the business of her friend the nun. On Saturday morning she rose early, and by six o'clock she was walking in the cool gardens of the Palais Royal, considering with that almost unnatural calm of hers the ways and means of accomplishing her purpose in the unexpected conditions that she found.

Towards eight o'clock, when Paris was awakening to the business of the day and taking down its shutters, she entered a cutler's shop in the Palais Royal, and bought for two francs a stout kitchen knife in a shagreen case. She then returned to her hotel to breakfast, and afterwards, dressed in her brown travelling-gown and conical hat, she went forth again, and, hailing a hackney carriage, drove to Marat's house in the rue de l'École de Médecine.

But admittance to that squalid dwelling was denied her. The Citizen Marat was ill, she was told, and could receive no visitors. It was Simonne Evrard, the triumvir's mistress — later to be known as the Widow Marat — who barred her ingress with this message.

Checked, she drove back to the Providence Inn and wrote a letter to the triumvir:

PARIS, 13th *July*, *Year* 2 *of the Republic*

CITIZEN, — I have arrived from Caen. Your love for your country leads me to assume that you will be anxious to hear of the unfortunate events which are taking place in that part of the Republic. I shall therefore call upon you towards one o'clock. Have the kindness to receive me, and accord me a moment's audience. I shall put you in the way of rendering a great service to France.

MARIE CORDAY

Having dispatched that letter to Marat, she sat until late afternoon waiting vainly for an answer. Despairing at last of receiving any, she wrote a second note, more peremptory in tone:

I wrote to you this morning, Marat. Have you received my letter? May I hope for a moment's audience? If you have received my letter, I hope you will not refuse me, considering the importance of the matter. It should suffice for you that I am very unfortunate to give me the right to your protection.

Having changed into a grey-striped dimity gown — you observe this further manifestation of a calm so complete that it admits of no departure from the ordinary habits of life — she goes forth to deliver in person this second letter, the knife concealed in the folds of the muslin fichu crossed high upon her breast.

In a mean, brick-paved, ill-lighted, and almost unfurnished room of that house in the rue de l'École de Médecine, the People's Friend is seated in a bath. It is no instinct of cleanliness he is obeying, for in all France there is no man more filthy in his person and his habits than this triumvir. His bath is medicated. The horrible, loathsome disease that corrodes his flesh demands these long immersions to quiet the gnawing pains which distract his active, restless mind. In these baths he can benumb the torment of the body with which he is encumbered.

For Marat is an intellect, and nothing more — leastways, nothing more that matters. What else there is to him of trunk and limbs and organs he has neglected until it has all fallen into decay. His very lack of personal cleanliness, the squalor in which he lives, the insufficient sleep which he allows himself, his habit of careless feeding at irregular intervals, all have their source in his contempt for the physical part of him. This talented man of varied attainments, accomplished linguist, skilled physician, able naturalist and profound psychologist, lives in his intellect alone, impatient of all physical interruptions. If he consents to these immersions, if he spends whole days seated in this medicated bath, it is solely because it quenches or cools the fires that are devouring him, and thus permits him to bend his mind to the work that is his life. But his long-suffering body is avenging upon the mind the neglect to which it has been submitted. The morbid condition of the former is being communicated to the latter, whence results that disconcerting admixture of cold, cynical cruelty and exalted sensibility which marked his nature in the closing years of his life.

In his bath, then, sat the People's Friend on that

July evening, immersed to the hips, his head swathed in a filthy turban, his emaciated body cased in a sleeveless waistcoat. He is fifty years of age, dying of consumption and other things, so that, did Charlotte but know it, there is no need to murder him. Disease and Death have marked him for their own, and grow impatient.

A board covering the bath served him for writing-table; an empty wooden box at his side bore an ink-stand some pens, sheets of paper, and two or three copies of "L'Ami du Peuple." There was no sound in the room but the scratch and splutter of his quill. He was writing diligently, revising and editing a proof of the forthcoming issue of his paper.

A noise of voices raised in the outer room invaded the quiet in which he was at work, and gradually penetrated his absorption, until it disturbed and irri-tated him. He moved restlessly in his bath, listened a moment, then, with intent to make an end of the in-terruption, he raised a hoarse, croaking voice to in-quire what might be taking place.

The door opened, and Simonne, his mistress and household drudge, entered the room. She was fully twenty years younger than himself, and under the slat-tern appearance which life in that house had imposed upon her there were vestiges of a certain comeliness.

"There is a young woman here from Caen, who de-mands insistently to see you upon a matter of na-tional importance."

The dull eyes kindle at the mention of Caen; inter-est quickens in that leaden-hued countenance. Was it not in Caen that those old foes of his, the Girondins, were stirring up rebellion?

"She says," Simonne continued, "that she wrote a letter to you this morning, and she brings you a second note herself. I have told her that you will not receive any one, and . . ."

"Give me the note," he snapped. Setting down his pen, he thrust out an unclean paw to snatch the folded sheet from Simonne's hand. He spread it, and read, his bloodless lips compressed, his eyes narrowing to slits.

"Let her in," he commanded sharply, and Simonne obeyed him without more ado. She admitted Charlotte, and left them alone together — the avenger and her victim. For a moment each regarded the other. Marat beheld a handsome young woman, elegantly attired. But these things had no interest for the People's Friend. What to him was woman and the lure of beauty? Charlotte beheld a feeble man of a repulsive hideousness, and was full satisfied, for in this outward loathsomeness she imagined a confirmation of the vileness of the mind she was come to blot out.

Then Marat spoke. "So you are from Caen, child?" he said. "And what is doing in Caen that makes you so anxious to see me?"

She approached him.

"Rebellion is stirring there, Citizen Marat."

"Rebellion, ha!" It was a sound between a laugh and a croak. "Tell me what deputies are sheltered in Caen. Come, child, their names." He took up and dipped his quill, and drew a sheet of paper towards him.

She approached still nearer; she came to stand close beside him, erect and calm. She recited the names of her friends, the Girondins, whilst hunched there in his bath his pen scratched briskly.

"So many for the guillotine," he snarled, when it was done.

But whilst he was writing, she had drawn the knife from her fichu, and as he uttered those words of doom to others his own doom descended upon him in a lightning stroke. Straight driven by that strong young arm, the long, stout blade was buried to its black hilt in his breast.

He looked at her with eyes in which there was a faint surprise as he sank back. Then he raised his voice for the last time.

"Help, chère amie! Help!" he cried, and was forever silent.

The hand still grasping the pen trailed on the ground beside the bath at the end of his long, emaciated arm. His body sank sideways in the same direction, the head lolling nervelessly upon his right shoulder, whilst from the great rent in his breast the blood gushed forth, embruing the water of his bath, trickling to the brick-paved floor, bespattering — symbolically almost — a copy of "L'Ami du Peuple," the journal to which he had devoted so much of his uneasy life.

In answer to that cry of his came now Simonne in haste. A glance sufficed to reveal to her the horrible event, and, like a tigress, she sprang upon the unresisting slayer, seizing her by the head, and calling loudly the while for assistance. Came instantly from the ante-room Jeanne, the old cook, the portress of the house, and Laurent Basse, a folder of Marat's paper; and now Charlotte found herself confronted by four maddened, vociferous beings, at whose hands she may well have expected to receive the death for which she was prepared.

Laurent, indeed, snatched up a chair, and felled her by a blow of it across her head. He would, no doubt, have proceeded in his fury to have battered her to death, but for the arrival of gens d'armes and the police commissioner of the district, who took her in their protecting charge.

The soul of Paris was convulsed by the tragedy when it became known. All night terror and confusion were abroad. All night the Revolutionary rabble, in angry grief, surged about and kept watch upon the house wherein the People's Friend lay dead.

That night, and for two days and nights thereafter, Charlotte Corday lay in the Prison of the Abbaye, supporting with fortitude the indignities that for a woman were almost inseparable from Revolutionary incarceration. She preserved throughout her imperturbable calm, based now upon a state of mind content in the contemplation of accomplished purpose, duty done. She had saved France, she believed; saved Liberty, by slaying the man who would have strangled it. In that illusion she was content. Her own life was a small price to pay for the splendid achievement.

Some of her time of waiting she spent in writing letters to her friends, in which tranquilly and sanely she dwelt upon what she had done, expounding fully the motives that had impelled her, dwelling upon the details of the execution, and of all that had followed. Among the letters written by her during those "days of the preparation of peace" — as she calls that period, dating in such terms a long epistle to Barbaroux

— was one to the Committee of Public Safety, in which she begs that a miniature-painter may be sent to her to paint her portrait, so that she may leave this token of remembrance to her friends. It is only in this, as the end approaches, that we see in her conduct any thought for her own self, any suggestion that she is anything more than an instrument in the hands of Fate.

On the 15th, at eight o'clock in the morning, her trial began before the Revolutionary Tribunal. A murmur ran through the hall as she appeared in her gown of grey-striped dimity, composed and calm — always calm.

The trial opened with the examination of witnesses; into that of the cutler, who had sold her the knife, she broke impatiently.

"These details are a waste of time. It is I who killed Marat."

The audience gasped, and rumbled ominously. Montané turned to examine her.

"What was the object of your visit to Paris?" he asks.

"To kill Marat."

"What motives induced you to this horrible deed?"

"His many crimes."

"Of what crimes do you accuse him?"

"That he instigated the massacre of September; that he kept alive the fires of civil war, so that he might be elected dictator; that he sought to infringe upon the sovereignty of the People by causing the arrest and imprisonment of the deputies to the Convention on May 31st."

"What proof have you of this?"

"The future will afford the proof. Marat hid his designs behind a mask of patriotism."

Montané shifted the ground of his interrogatory.

"Who were your accomplices in this atrocious act?"

"I have none."

Montané shook his head. "You cannot convince any one that a person of your age and sex could have conceived such a crime unless instigated by some person or persons whom you are unwilling to name."

Charlotte almost smiled. "That shows but a poor knowledge of the human heart. It is easier to carry out such a project upon the strength of one's own hatred than upon that of others." And then, raising her voice, she proclaimed: "I killed one man to save a hundred thousand; I killed a villain to save innocents; I killed a savage wild beast to give repose to France. I was a Republican before the Revolution. I never lacked for energy."

What more was there to say? Her guilt was completely established. Her fearless self-possession was not to be ruffled. Yet Fouquier-Tinville, the dread prosecutor, made the attempt. Beholding her so virginal and fair and brave, feeling perhaps that the Tribunal had not had the best of it, he sought with a handful of Revolutionary filth to restore the balance. He rose slowly, his ferrety eyes upon her.

"How many children have you had?" he rasped, sardonic, his tone a slur, an insult.

Faintly her cheeks crimsoned. But her voice was composed, disdainful, as she answered coldly:

"Have I not stated that I am not married?"

A leer, a dry laugh, a shrug from Tinville to complete the impression he sought to convey, and he sat down again.

It was the turn of Chauveau de la Garde, the advocate instructed to defend her. But what defence was possible? And Chauveau had been intimidated. He had received a note from the jury ordering him to remain silent, another from the President bidding him declare her mad.

Yet Chauveau took a middle course. His brief speech is admirable; it satisfied his self-respect, without derogating from his client. It uttered the whole truth.

"The prisoner," he said, "confesses with calm the horrible crime she has committed; she confesses with calm its premeditation; she confesses its most dreadful details; in short, she confesses everything, and does not seek to justify herself. That, citizens of the jury, is her whole defence. This imperturbable calm, this utter abnegation of self, which displays no remorse even in the very presence of death, are contrary to nature. They can only be explained by the excitement of political fanaticism which armed her hand. It is for you, citizens of the jury, to judge what weight that moral consideration should have in the scales of justice."

The jury voted her guilty, and Tinville rose to demand the full sentence of the law.

It was the end. She was removed to the Conciergerie, the ante-chamber of the guillotine. A constitutional priest was sent to her, but she dismissed him with thanks, not requiring his ministrations. She preferred the painter Hauer, who had received the Revolutionary Tribunal's permission to paint her portrait in accordance with her request. And during the sitting, which lasted half an hour, she conversed with him quietly on ordinary topics, the tranquillity of her spirit unruffled by any fear of the death that was so swiftly approaching.

The door opened, and Sanson, the public executioner, came in. He carried the red smock worn by those convicted of assassination. She showed no dismay; no more, indeed, than a faint surprise that the time spent with Hauer should have gone so quickly. She begged for a few moments in which to write a note, and, the request being granted, acquitted herself briskly of that task; then announcing herself ready, she removed her cap that Sanson might cut her luxuriant hair. Yet first, taking his scissors, she herself cut off a lock and gave it to Hauer for remembrance. When Sanson would have bound her hands, she begged that she might be allowed to wear gloves, as her wrists were bruised and cut by the cord with which she had been pinioned in Marat's house. He answered that she might do so if she wished, but that it was unnecessary, as he could bind her without causing pain.

"To be sure," she said, "those others had not your experience," and she proffered her bare wrists to his cord without further demur. "If this toilet of death is performed by rude hands," she commented, "at least it leads to immortality."

She mounted the tumbril awaiting in the prison yard, and, disdaining the chair offered her by Sanson, remained standing, to show herself dauntless to the mob and brave its rage. And fierce was that rage, indeed. So densely thronged were the streets that the tumbril proceeded at a crawl, and the people surging about the cart screamed death and insult at the doomed woman. It took two hours to reach the Place de la Révolution, and meanwhile a terrific summer thunderstorm had broken over Paris, and a torrential rain had descended upon the densely packed streets. Charlotte's garments were soaked through and through, so that her red smock, becoming glued now to her body and fitting her like a skin, threw into relief its sculptural beauty, whilst a reflection of the vivid crimson of the garment faintly tinged her cheeks, and thus heightened her appearance of complete composure.

And it is now in the rue Saint-Honoré that at long last we reach the opening of our tragic love-story.

A tall, slim, fair young man, named Adam Lux — sent to Paris by the city of Mayence as Deputy Extraordinary to the National Convention — was standing there in the howling press of spectators. He was an accomplished, learned young gentleman, doctor at once of philosophy and of medicine, although in the latter capacity he had never practised owing to an extreme sensibility of nature, which rendered anatomical work repugnant to him. He was a man of a rather exalted imagination, unhappily married — the not uncommon fate of such delicate temperaments — and now living apart from his wife. He had heard, as all Paris had heard, every detail of the affair, and of the trial, and he waited there, curious to see this woman, with whose deed he was secretly in sympathy.

The tumbril slowly approached, the groans and execrations swelled up around him, and at last he beheld her — beautiful, serene, full of life, a still smile upon her lips. For a long moment he gazed upon her, standing as if stricken into stone. Then heedless of those about him, he bared his head, and thus silently saluted and paid homage to her. She did not see him. He had not thought that she would. He saluted her as the devout salute the unresponsive image of a saint. The tumbril crawled on. He turned his head, and followed her with his eyes for a while; then, driving his elbows into the ribs of those about him, he clove himself a passage through the throng, and so followed, bare-headed now, with fixed gaze, a man entranced.

He was at the foot of the scaffold when her head fell. To the last he had seen that noble countenance preserve its immutable calm, and in the hush that followed the sibilant fall of the great knife his voice suddenly rang out.

"She is greater than Brutus!" was his cry; and he added, addressing those who stared at him in stupefaction: "It were beautiful to have died with her!"

He was suffered to depart unmolested. Chiefly, perhaps, because at that moment the attention of the crowd was upon the executioner's attendant, who, in holding up Charlotte's truncated head, slapped the cheek with his hand. The story runs that the dead face reddened under the blow. Scientists of the day disputed over this, some arguing from it a proof that consciousness does not at once depart the brain upon decapitation.

That night, while Paris slept, its walls were secretly placarded with copies of a eulogy of Charlotte Corday, the martyr of Republicanism, the deliverer of France, in which occurs the comparison with Joan of

Arc, that other great heroine of France. This was the work of Adam Lux. He made no secret of it. The vision of her had so wrought upon the imagination of this susceptible dreamer, had fired his spirit with such enthusiasm, that he was utterly reckless in yielding to his emotions, in expressing the phrenetic, immaterial love with which in her last moments of life she had inspired him.

Two days after her execution he issued a long manifesto, in which he urged the purity of her motive as the fullest justification of her act, placed her on the level of Brutus and Cato, and passionately demanded for her the honour and veneration of posterity. It is in this manifesto that he applies euphemistically to her deed the term "tyrannicide." That document he boldly signed with his own name, realizing that he would pay for that temerity with his life.

He was arrested on the 24th of July — exactly a week from the day on which he had seen her die. He had powerful friends, and they exerted themselves to obtain for him a promise of pardon and release if he would publicly retract what he had written. But he laughed the proposal to scorn, ardently resolved to follow into death the woman who had aroused the hopeless, immaterial love that made his present torment.

Still his friends strove for him. His trial was put off. A doctor named Wetekind was found to testify that Adam Lux was mad, that the sight of Charlotte Corday had turned his head. He wrote a paper on this plea, recommending that clemency be shown to the young doctor on the score of his affliction, and that he should be sent to a hospital or to America. Adam Lux was angry when he heard of this, and protested indignantly against the allegations of Dr. Wetekind. He wrote to the "Journal de la Montagne," which published his declaration on the 26th of September, to the effect that he was not mad enough to desire to live, and that his anxiety to meet death halfway was a crowning proof of his sanity.

He languished on in the prison of La Force until the 10th of October, when at last he was brought to trial. He stood it joyously, in a mood of exultation at his approaching deliverance. He assured the court that he did not fear the guillotine, and that all ignominy had been removed from such a death by the pure blood of Charlotte.

They sentenced him to death, and he thanked them for the boon.

"Forgive me, sublime Charlotte," he exclaimed, "if I should find it impossible to exhibit at the last the courage and gentleness that were yours. I glory in your superiority, for it is right that the adored should be above the adorer."

Yet his courage did not fail him. Far from it, indeed; if hers had been a mood of gentle calm, his was one of ecstatic exaltation. At five o'clock that same afternoon he stepped from the tumbril under the gaunt shadow of the guillotine. He turned to the people, his eyes bright, a flush on his cheeks.

"At last I am to have the happiness of dying for Charlotte," he told them, and mounted the scaffold with the eager step of the bridegroom on his way to the nuptial altar.

THE HONOUR OF VARANO

CESARE BORGIA, Duke of Valentinois and Romagna, rose slowly from his chair, and slowly crossed to the window of that spacious chamber in the Rocca of Imola. He stood there in the autumn sunshine gazing down upon the tented meadow and the river beyond, and upon the long ribbon of road, the ancient Via Æmilia, stretching smooth and straight with never a crease until it was lost in the distant hazy pile that was Faenza.

That road which crosses Northern Italy diagonally — a line of almost unwavering straightness for a hundred miles from the ancient Rubicon to Piacenza — may well have been a source of pride to Marcus Æmilius Lepidus, some fifteen hundred years before; to Cesare Borgia, contemplating it upon that autumn day, it was no better than a source of vexation — a way north and south by which to his relief might march the troops he did not dare to summon.

From the road his eyes shifted again to the besieging camp in the meadows by the river. There all was bustle, an incessant movement of men and horses, industrious as a colony of ants. Yonder a group of engineers were mounting a park of artillery with which they hoped to smash a way into his stronghold. Farther off was a great coming-and-going of glittering armed figures about the large green tent that housed the too-daring Venanzio Varano. Away to the west a swarm of half-naked men laboured with picks and

spades at a ditch by which to deviate the water from
the river and so serve them as a rampart against any
sudden sortie of the besieged.

A faint hum of all this business reached the watcher
in his eyrie, and he cursed it between contempt and
anger; contempt, to think how the mere lifting of his
finger would scatter that presumptuous little army,
as a flock of sparrows scatters perceiving the hawk
poised above them in the blue; anger, to consider that
he dared not lift that same finger lest other and
greater plans, not yet mature, should suffer by this
too-early display of might; contempt again, of this
fool Varano, and his petty daring, to conceive that
Cesare Borgia was at the end of his resources and a
prey for such a handful of mercenaries — the very
sweepings of the martial market-place — as Varano
had assembled; anger again, that for a day, for an
hour, he must allow Varano to continue in that con-
ceit. With what a puffed-up arrogance would not this
fool of Camerino be ordering the business of the siege
against this Imola that gave no sign, against this
brown citadel drowsing unresponsive in the late
autumn sunshine under the Borgia banner with its
bull device that floated from the Maschio Tower!

A stealthy step in the room behind him went un-
heeded by the Duke. That it did so proved the extent
of his absorption, for there never lived a man of keener
senses; never a man who combined with an intellect
super-acute such splendid animal faculties as were his.
Merely to behold him was to perceive all this. He was
in the very flower of his youth; some seven and twenty
years of age; tall, straight, and lithe as steel. His
father, Pope Alexander VI, had been accounted in

early life the handsomest man of his day; of a beauty
of countenance, it was said, that acted upon women
as the lodestone upon iron — which had by no means
helped him to the virtuous course that should be
looked for in a churchman. That beauty Cesare had
inherited, but refined and glorified by the graces of
Madonna Vanozza de' Catanei, the Roman lady who
had been his mother. If there was sensuality in the
full lips of the red mouth, half-hidden by the silky
tawny beard, this was corrected by the loftiness of the
pale brow; the nose was delicately arched, the nostrils
sensitive, and the eyes — who shall describe the glory
of those hazel eyes? Who shall read their message,
who shall depict the will, the intellect, the dreamy
wistfulness, the impassiveness that looks out of
them?

He was dressed from head to foot in black; but
through the slashings of his velvet doublet gleamed
the rich yellow of an undervest of cloth of gold; a
ruby-studded girdle gripped his loins, and on his hip
hung a heavy gold-hilted Pistoja dagger in a golden
sheath of cunning workmanship. His tawny head was
bare.

Again came never so faintly the creak of that
stealthy footstep behind him, and again it went un-
perceived. Nor yet did Cesare move when another
and heavier tread rang on the staircase mounting to
his room. Absorbed he continued his survey of
Varano's camp.

The door was opened and reclosed. Some one had
entered and was approaching him. Still he did not
stir; yet without stirring he spoke, addressing the
newcomer by name.

"And so, Agabito," said he, "you have sent my summons to Varano?"

To another less accustomed than his secretary, Agabito Gherardi, to Cesare's ways, this might have seemed almost uncanny. But Agabito was familiar with that super-acuteness of his master, whose perceptions were keen as a blind man's and who could recognize a step where another would have needed to behold the face.

He bowed as Cesare turned to him. He was a man of middle height, well-nourished, with a mobile, humorous mouth and keen dark eyes. His age may have been forty, and, as became his clerkly station, he wore a black surcoat that descended to his knees.

"It has gone, Highness," he answered. "But I doubt the gentleman of Camerino will decline the invitation."

Agabito observed the Duke's glance to stray past and beyond him. Musing and idle seemed his eyes to Agabito — which but serves to show that, intimately though the secretary accounted that he knew his master, yet he had not fathomed the inscrutability of Cesare's glance. For the eyes which looked dreamy were alert and watchful, and the brain behind them was working swiftly to conclusions. The arras over beyond the great carved writing-table was quivering never so faintly. This Cesare was observing — seeming to muse — and he was considering that the air was still and that no draught could account for that phenomenon. Yet, when presently he spoke, he betrayed nothing of observation or conclusion.

"Art ever a pessimist, Agabito," said he.

"True-sighted, my lord," amended the secretary,

with the easy familiarity Cesare conceded him. "For the rest, what does it matter, whether he comes or not?" And he smiled, a thousand wrinkles gathering about his eyes. "There is always the back door."

"It is your cursed pessimism again to remind me that there is that and naught but that."

Agabito spread his hands, his countenance a grimace of deprecation.

"Who cares to open that back door?" quoth the Duke. "Why, man, if I make the allies aware of its existence, if I so much as lift the latch, the click of it will so scare them that they'll every one escape me. The back door, you say! You are growing old, Agabito. Show me the way to drive off that shallow fool with such means as I dispose of here."

"Alas!" sighed the secretary, hopelessly.

"Alas, indeed!" snapped the Duke, and strode past him into the room. There he paced a while, considering the position, Agabito observing him.

To a more vexatious pass than this matters could not have come. It was the season of the league against him formed by the Orsini in alliance with his own revolted captains Vitelli and Baglioni. These rebels stood in arms a full ten thousand strong, determined upon his destruction, having sworn his death. Cunningly they spread their net to hem him in, believing that they had him safe and that his strength was sapped. And he, the better to take them in the toils they were spinning for himself, had indulged them in their conviction that he was powerless and unprepared. Actively had he done so, deliberately dismissing three of his companies of French lances — the very backbone of his army — and putting it about

that they had left him of their own accord, led off by
their captains with whom he had quarrelled. Thus
had it seemed as if his knell had indeed sounded; already the allies accounted him their prey, for, without
the French lances, the forces of which he disposed
were of no account. But they knew nothing of the
Romagnuoli men-at-arms that Naldo had assembled
for him, still less of the Swiss foot and the Gascon
mercenaries whom his officers held ready for him in
Lombardy — nor should they know until the hour
was ripe. He had but to lift his finger, and there
would sprout up such an army as should make the
allies sick with misgivings. Meanwhile he desired that
they should bait their trap for him, lulled by their false
security. He would walk into it complacently enough;
but — by the Host! — what a surprising stir would
he not make within it. How the springs of that same
trap should take them on the recoil and crush them!

To have planned so well, so precisely to have
reckoned the moves that must enable him to cry
"Checkmate!" — and to find himself, instead, stale-
mated by the act of this rash fool of Camerino who
sat out there in egregious self-complacency, little
reckoning the volcano that was under him!

For here is what had happened. This Venanzio
Varano, one of the dethroned lords of Camerino, impatient at the sluggishness of the allies, and unable
to urge them into swifter action, had drawn off and
taken matters into his own hands. Gathering together
a desperate, out-at-elbow army of discredited mercenaries of all nations, numbering perhaps a thousand
strong, he had marched upon Imola, and there laid
siege to Cesare in his stronghold — cursed alike by

the allies and by Cesare for his interference in the plans of each.

"Perhaps," said Agabito presently, "if the allies observe the success that seems to attend Varano, they will join him here. Then would be your opportunity."

But Cesare waved a hand impatiently. "How can I put a net about them here?" he asked. "I could rout their army; but what of that? It is the brains of it I want — and at one blow. No, no," he ended. "Meanwhile, let us see what answer Varano makes to my invitation, and what comes of it."

"And if nothing comes, you'll strike?" said Agabito, as though he urged it.

Cesare pondered, his face clouding. "Not yet," said he. "I'll wait and hope for some chance. My luck — there is my luck, remember." He turned to the massive, richly wrought writing-table, and took up a packet. "Here is the letter for the Signory of Florence. I have signed it. Contrive to get it hence."

Agabito took the package. "It will tax my ingenuity," said he, and pursed his lips.

"Attend to it," said Cesare, and so dismissed him.

The door closed upon the secretary; his steps receded down the stone staircase, and the sound of them was lost. Then Cesare, standing in mid-apartment, faced the arras which had quivered on Agabito's entrance.

"Come forth, messer the spy," said he quite calmly.

He was prepared to see a man emerge in answer to that summons — and he had some notion of that man's identity — but he was quite unprepared for the manner in which his order was to be obeyed.

The arras was swept aside, and across the intervening space, it seemed to Cesare, was hurled as from a catapult a great, brown human shape with one arm raised to strike. The blow descended. The dagger took Cesare full in the breast, and there snapped suddenly. As the broken blade tinkled on the floor, the Duke's hands closed like manacles about the wrists of his assailant.

The wretch may never have seen Cesare snap a horseshoe in his fingers, nor yet seen Cesare decapitate a bull at one single stroke of a spadoon, but of the awful strength that could accomplish such feats as those he had now the fullest and most painful demonstration. This murderer was a big fellow, of stout thews and sinews, yet in the grip of that lithe young man his strength was all turned to water. He felt as if the iron pressure of Cesare's fingers were crushing his wrists to pulp, were twisting his elbows out of joint. He came howling to his knees, then caught his nether lip in his teeth to repress another howl. His right hand opened and released the hilt and stump of his poniard, which went to rejoin the blade upon the floor. He looked up with fearful eyes into the Duke's face, and found it calm — horribly, terrifically calm — betraying neither anger nor exertion.

"Messer Malipiero," said His Highness, "you should never have chanced a shirt of mail when there was my naked throat to offer you so fair a mark." And he smiled amiably — the very superlative of mockery — into the other's tortured countenance. Then he released him. "Get up!" he said more briskly. "We must talk."

"My lord! My lord!" whimpered the assassin, holding out his maimed wrists. "Forgive! Forgive!"

"Forgive?" echoed Cesare, halting as he moved away. "Forgive what?"

"My — the thing I did but now."

"Oh, that! Why, it is the manliest thing you have done since you came hither. Count it forgiven. But the rest, Malipiero — your offering your sword to me in a time of need, your lies to me, your gaining my confidence, and you the spy of Varano — must I forgive that too?"

"My lord!" groaned the abject Malipiero.

"And even if I forgive you all this, can you forgive yourself — you, a patrician — that you should have come to turn spy and assassin?"

"Not — not assassin, my lord. I had not meant that. It was in self-defence, seeing myself discovered and accounting myself lost. Oh, I was mad! Mad!"

The Duke moved away towards the table. "Well, well," said he, "it is over and done with." He took up a silver whistle, and blew a blast upon it. Malipiero, staggering to his feet, turned if possible a shade paler than he had been. But the Duke's next words reassured him. "And for my own part, since you lay such store by it — I forgive you."

"You forgive me?" Malipiero could not believe his ears.

"Why not? I am a good Christian, I hope; and I practice the Christian virtue of forgiveness; so much, indeed, that I deplore most deeply the necessity of hanging you none the less."

Malipiero flung wide his aching arms, and made a sound in his throat, terror staring from his protruding eyes.

"What choice have I?" quoth Cesare, in answer

to that incoherent cry. "There are the things you have overheard. It was unfortunate."

"Gesú!" cried the other, and advanced a step towards Cesare. "I swear that I'll be dumb."

"You shall," said Cesare.

Heavy steps approached. Malipiero gulped, then spoke quickly, with fearful earnestness.

"I swear no word of what I heard shall ever cross my lips — I swear it by all my hopes of heaven, by the Blessed Mother of God!"

"You shall not be forsworn," Cesare assured him. Then the door opened, and the officer of the guard stood at attention on the threshold.

Malipiero clutched at his breast, swung about this way and that in the frenzy of his despair, until his glance met Cesare's calm eyes and impassive countenance. Then his tongue was loosened. Imprecations, ordures of speech too horrible for chronicling, poured torrentially from his quivering lips, until a touch upon the shoulder struck him into a shuddering silence. Limply he surrendered himself to the officer who at a sign from Cesare had advanced.

"Let him be confined in solitude," said the Duke, "until I make known my pleasure."

Malipiero looked hopelessly at Cesare. "When — when is it to be?" he asked hoarsely.

"At dawn to-morrow," Cesare answered. "God rest your soul!"

A trumpet blared beneath the walls of Imola, and its brazen voice reached Cesare Borgia in that room in the Maschio Tower. He dropped his pen and lay back in his chair. Conjecturing what might hang upon that trumpet-blast, he smiled pensively at the groined ceiling that was painted blue and flecked with golden stars, and waited.

Presently came Messer Gherardi with news that an ambassador had arrived from Varano's camp, and Cesare ceased to smile.

"An ambassador?" he echoed, his brows knitting. "Does a servant come in response to the invitation I sent the master?"

Agabito's ready smile deprecated this vexation. "Is it really matter for wonder? These Varani are treacherous, bloody men. Venanzio fears that you might deal with him as he with you in the like circumstances. He knows that were he removed, his mercenaries would not avenge him, would not stand together for a day. You will see the ambassador, my lord? I can promise that you will find Varano's choice of messenger most interesting."

"How?" quoth Cesare shortly.

But the secretary's answer seemed almost an evasion. "There has been an arrest made since last I was here," said he. "I never trusted Gustavo Malipiero. How came he in this room, Highness?"

"That matters little. What he sought matters rather more. It was my life." And Cesare pointed to the pieces of the broken dagger, still lying where Malipiero had dropped them half an hour ago. "Pick it up, Agabito," said he.

On the point of obeying, Agabito checked, a queer smile twisting the corners of his mobile mouth. "You might presently wish that I had left it," said he "Let it lie there yet a while, my lord."

Cesare's eyes questioned the secretary.

"Shall I introduce the ambassador of Varano?" was Agabito's bland inquiry.

"Why — what has he to do with Malipiero's dagger?" quoth the Duke, perceiving that in Gherardi's mind some connection must exist.

"Perhaps nothing, perhaps much. Be Your Highness the judge."

Cesare waved a hand, assenting. Agabito crossed to the door, opened it and called; then leisurely returned to take his stand by the table at Cesare's elbow. Steps ascended the stairs. Two men-at-arms in morion and corselet clattered in and flanked the doorway, and between them entered, with clank and scabbard and ring of spurs, an elderly man of middle height, very splendid in purple velvet. In mid-apartment he checked with military abruptness, and bowed stiffly, yet profoundly, to the Duke. Then he came upright again, and out of a vulture face a pair of shifty eyes met Cesare's stern glance.

Whilst a man might count a dozen there was utter silence in the chamber, the ambassador waiting for the Duke to address him, the Duke seeming in no haste, but staring at the man and understanding what had been in Gherardi's mind when he had begged that the dagger should be let lie a while.

A bee sailed through the window and the hum of its wings was the only sound that disturbed a stillness that was becoming unnatural. At last Cesare spoke to the ambassador of Varano, to the father of the man who half an hour ago had sought to murder him.

"It is thou, Malipiero, eh?" said he, his face impassive as a mask, his brain a whirl of speculation, of considering and connecting.

The man bowed again. "Your servant always, Highness."

"Art the servant of the lord of Camerino?" the Duke amended. "Art the fox that waits upon the wolf?" And the evenness of his tones was marred by the faintest suspicion of a sneer. "I bade your master attend me that we might arrange the terms upon which he will consent to raise this siege. He sends you in his place. It is an affront — tell him — which I shall lay to his already very heavy score. Let him flout me while the little fleeting chance is his. But let him not cry out hereafter when I call the reckoning."

"My lord was afraid to come, Magnificent."

Cesare laughed shortly. "I nothing doubt it. But you — you, Malipiero?" And he leant forward, his tone of a sudden invested with a deadly menace. "Were you not afraid to take his place?"

Malipiero started, his natural pallor deepened, and the corners of his mouth were perceived by Agabito to quiver slightly.

But before he could answer, the Duke had sunk back into his chair again, and asked in normal tones: "Why have you come?"

"To treat in my lord's name."

Cesare considered him a moment in silence. "For that, and nothing else?" he inquired.

"What else, indeed, Highness?"

" 'Tis what I asked thee," said Cesare shortly.

"My lord," the other cried in quaking protest, "I come as an ambassador."

"Why, true. I was forgetting. Discharge your embassy. You know the thing that I would buy. Tell me the price this trader of Camerino asks."

Malipiero the elder drew himself erect, and formally performed his errand. As he spoke, his eyes strayed to the broken dagger lying almost at his feet, the gold hilt gleaming in a shaft of sunlight; but the weapon told him nothing, it was plain, for he never checked or faltered in the delivery of his message.

"My lord of Camerino," he announced, "will raise this siege and withdraw his army in return for your signed undertaking to recall your troops from Camerino, reinstating him in his lordship and leaving him to enjoy it unmolested."

Cesare stared in amazement at the effrontery of the demand. "Was he drunk, this lout of Camerino, when he sent that message?"

Malipiero quailed under the scorn of the Duke's eyes. "Magnificent," he said, "it may be that my Lord Venanzio seems arrogant to you. But you will find him firm in his resolve. He has you, he swears, in the hollow of his hand."

"Has he so? Body of God! Then he shall find that I am made of gunpowder, and when I burst, that same hand of his shall be blown to rags. Go tell him so."

"You'll not accept his terms?"

"Sooner will I sit in Imola until the Resurrection of the Flesh."

Malipiero paused a moment like a man undecided. His glance shifted to the shaven, humorous face of Agabito Gherardi; but he saw nothing there to embolden him. Nevertheless, like a good ambassador, he said what else he had been bidden say.

"Vitellozzo, the Orsini, and the Baglioni are coalescing."

"Do you give me news? And how shall that serve Varano? His subjects of Camerino loathe him for a bloody tyrant, and being once rid of him they'll never suffer his return."

"I am not sure . . ." began Malipiero.

"I know thou'rt not. But I, who am, tell thee." He pushed back his chair on that, and rose. "Agabito, let this ambassador of Varano be reconducted, and with courteous treatment."

And with that, as if dismissing the entire matter from his mind, he sauntered across the room, past Malipiero, towards the window; and as he went he drew from his pocket a little comfit-box in gold and blue enamel.

Agabito experienced a pang of disappointment. Not so, by much, had he pictured the conclusion of this interview. And yet, perhaps Cesare in his cunning and unfailing calculation counted upon something more. Even as he thought of it, he saw in Malipiero's attitude that it was so, indeed. For the ambassador made no shift to go. He stood there shuffling uneasily, his foxy old eyes roaming from the secretary to the young duke, and betraying the labour of his mind.

"Highness," he said at last, "may I speak with you alone?"

"We are alone," said Cesare over his shoulder. "What else have you to add?"

"Something that will make for the advancement of your interests."

Cesare turned his back to the window, and his beautiful eyes grew very narrow as they surveyed the bowing Malipiero. Then a faint smile hovered round his lips. He made a sign to the men-at-arms standing by the door. They turned and clattered out.

"Agabito remains. I have no secrets from my secretary. Speak out."

"Highness . . ." began the ambassador, and halted there. Then, under Cesare's impatient eye, "My Lord Varano is in earnest," he concluded lamely.

Cesare shrugged and raised the lid of his comfit-box. "So I had understood from you already. Is there nothing more?"

"You were pleased to correct me, Highness, when upon entering here I announced myself your servant."

"By what tortuous ways do you travel to your goal? Well, well! You were my servant once; now you are his. Would you be mine again? Is that your meaning?"

Malipiero bowed eloquently. The Duke considered him, shot a glance at Agabito, then with deliberation picked a coriander-seed. "The Lord of Camerino's fortunes, then, do not wear so very prosperous a look?" said he, between question and conclusion, and thereby set Malipiero infernally ill at ease.

The ambassador had looked for some eagerness on Cesare's part. This calm, half-mocking indifference chilled him. At last he took his courage in both hands. "It was I," he announced, "who made Varano afraid to come — to the end that he might send me."

The lid of the comfit-box snapped down. His Magnificence of Valentinois was interested at last, it seemed.

Encouraged, Malipiero went on. "I did this that I

might lay my poor services at your disposal; for at heart, Highness, I have ever been your most devoted. My only son is in your service."

"You lie, you foul, infernal traitor! You lie!" And Cesare advanced upon him as if to strike him into dust. Gone now was the impassive calm of his face; gone the inscrutable softness of his eyes; their glance enveloped Malipiero as in a flame — a flame that swept about his heart and left it ashes.

"My lord! My lord!" he babbled foolishly.

Cesare halted in his approach, and resumed his quiet manner as abruptly as he had cast it off.

"Look at that dagger at your feet," he said, and Malipiero obeyed him stupidly. "It was broken an hour ago against my breast. Can you guess whose the hand that wielded it? Your son's — this precious only son of yours, who is in my service."

Malipiero recoiled, bearing a hand to his throat as if something choked him.

"You came hither for such scraps of knowledge as that spy might have gleaned. My invitation to Varano was your opportunity. Without it you would still have come, bearing as spontaneous the offer that you brought as answer. The object of your spying you best know — you that never yet kept faith with any man. Oh! there is no doubt, Malipiero, that at heart you have ever been my devoted servants — you and your son."

"O God!" groaned the unhappy wretch.

"Your only son is to be hanged at daybreak to-morrow. It shall be from this window here, in sight of this Varano whom he served, in sight of you who have ever been my most devoted."

Malipiero cast himself upon his knees; he flung out his arms wildly. "My lord, I swear to you that I knew naught of any plot to — to hurt you."

"Why, I believe you for once. There may have been no such plot. But I caught your son in the act of spying, and so he took, perhaps, what seemed to him the only course. It makes no difference. He would have hanged without that."

Malipiero, on his knees, raised a livid face, his brow glistening with the sweat of the agony that racked him.

"Highness," he cried in a quavering voice, "I have it in my power to make amends for my son's folly. I can rid you of this bankrupt of Camerino. Shall it — shall it be a bargain between us? My son's life for the raising of this siege?"

Cesare smiled. "It was to make me some such proposal, I think, that you desired to speak with me alone. Nothing is altered but the price — for not a doubt but that you intended some other profit from the treachery you had conceived."

Malipiero flung dissimulation to the winds. What, indeed, could it avail him against one who looked so deep and unerringly into motives? The greed of gold which had made him a constant traitor to any whom he served had been his only stimulus in this fresh treachery. But now, the life of his boy was all the recompense he asked. He frankly said as much.

"I will not bargain with you," was Cesare's contemptuous answer.

Tears welled to the eyes of the distraught man and coursed down the furrows of the livid cheeks. Wildly he implored clemency and urged upon the Duke's attention the gain he stood to make.

"There is not in all Italy a knave with whom I would so scorn to deal as you, Malipiero. Man, you have steeped yourself in the filth of treachery until you stink of it. The very sight of you offends me."

"My lord," the wretch clamoured, "I can raise this siege as could no other man. Grant me Gustavo's life, and it shall be done to-morrow. I will draw Varano away — back to Camerino. What are his men without him? You know their worth, Highness — a parcel of hirelings with no heart in the business, who would never stay to oppose a sally if Varano were not at hand to urge them."

Cesare measured the man with a calculating eye. "What means have you to perform so much?"

At that suggestion that the Duke was inclined to treat with him, Malipiero rose. He shuffled a step nearer, licking his lips. "Varano loves his throne of Camerino dearly. But there is one thing he loves still more — his honour. Let it be whispered to him that the lady, his wife —" He leered horribly. "You understand, Magnificent? He would leave his camp out yonder and dash back to Camerino, where she bides, as fast as horse could bear him."

Cesare felt his soul revolt. The thing was vile, the fruit of a vile mind, uttered by a vile mouth; and, as he looked at the leering creature before him, a sense of nausea took him. But his face showed no sign of this; his beautiful passionless eyes betrayed none of the loathing with which this arch-traitor inspired him. Presently his lips parted in a smile; but what that smile portended Malipiero could not guess until he spoke.

"Possibly there is in Italy a viler thing than thou;

probably there is not. Still, it is for me to use thee, not convert thee. Do this thing, then, since you are assured it may be done."

Malipiero drew a deep breath of relief. Insults were of no account to him. "Grant me my son's life, and I undertake that by to-night Varano shall be in the saddle."

"I'll make no bargains with you," Cesare answered him.

"But if I do this thing you will be clement, you will be merciful, Highness?"

"Rest content. You shall not fail to find me just."

"I am content," said Malipiero. "I count upon that. And yet — and yet . . . Reassure me, Highness! I am a father. Promise me that, if I serve you in this, Gustavo shall not hang."

Cesare eyed him a moment and shrugged contemptuously. "He shall not hang. I have said that you shall find me just. And now to details." Cesare crossed briskly to the writing-table. "Have you power in Varano's name to grant a safe-conduct?"

"I have, Highness."

"Here is what you will need. Write, then — for twenty men from Imola."

Malipiero snatched a quill, and in a hand that shook, for all his efforts to steady it, he wrote and signed the order Cesare demanded. The Duke took the paper and sat down.

"How shall I have knowledge that Varano has departed?" he inquired.

Malipiero considered a moment. Then, "As soon as he goes to-night I will extinguish the cresset that burns outside his tent. You can see it from here."

Cesare nodded shortly, and blew upon his silver whistle. To the men-at-arms, reëntering in answer to that summons, he consigned the person of the ambassador, bidding them reconduct him to the gates.

When the door had closed again, Cesare turned to Agabito with a smile of grim contempt. "I had best served the world had I violated the sacredness of that ambassador's person, and held a family hanging in the morning. The toad! Madonna! The foul, crapulous toad! But there! Summon Corella, and bid them have young Malipiero at hand."

When, presently, Cesare's Venetian captain, whom so many supposed to be a Spaniard, stalked into the room — a tall, stately man, all steel and leather — the Duke tossed Malipiero's safe-conduct across to him, and gave his orders.

"You will watch to-night the cresset that burns outside Varano's tent. Ten minutes after it has been quenched, you will ride out with the twenty men you choose, and make for Camerino." Cesare unrolled a map and beckoned Corella to his side. "But not this way, Michele — not by Faenza and Forli. You shall take to the hills and thus outstrip another party going by the main road. Contrive that you reach Camerino in advance of it by at least six hours, and remember that those others will ride desperately. Agabito will instruct you later in what else you have to do. The manner of it shall be in your own hands."

Michele da Corella gasped. "They will set out before me," he said. "They will take the shorter road, and they will ride desperately. Yet I am to be in Camerino at least six hours ahead of them. In

short, I am to work a miracle, and I am just Michele
da Corella, a captain of horse."

Cesare looked up quietly. "Chucklehead!" said he.
"You will detach the two best-mounted men of your
company, and send them after the other party by the
Rimini road. Let them pass and precede them, and so
contrive with the relays to delay them upon the road
sufficiently to enable you to do as I command."

Corella flushed out of shame of wits that must
appear so dull.

"Now, go, Michele," the Duke bade him, "and
make ready."

As Corella was withdrawing, the Duke recalled
him. "I said twenty men. I should have said nineteen — counting yourself; the twentieth will be
Messer Gustavo Malipiero, who is to ride with you.
Bid them bring him in now."

Corella saluted and withdrew. Cesare sat back in
his great leathern chair and glanced at Agabito.
"Well?" he inquired. "Do you perceive what a web
of justice I am weaving?"

"Not yet, my lord," confessed Agabito.

"Not? I sometimes think you are as dull-witted as
Michele."

And Agabito kept it to himself that he sometimes
thought his master possessed all the guile and craft of
Satan.

As Malipiero the elder had undertaken, so did he
perform; though in the performance he went near to
being strangled by the powerful hands of Venanzio
Varano.

He repaired at nightfall to Venanzio's tent with his

foul invention, and at the first hint of his meaning the passionate lord of Camerino flung into a fury. He caught Malipiero by his scraggy throat, swung him off his feet, and went over with him in a dark corner of the tent. There he pinned him to the ground under a knee that seemed to be crushing every bone in the old traitor's breast.

"Dog!" he snarled, and Malipiero writhed and squirmed, half-dead from shock and fright, expecting to feel the other's teeth close on his windpipe, so brutal was Varano become in his great rage. "Do you proclaim my wife a trull?" he roared. "Say that you lied! Confound yourself, you rogue, or, by the Host! I'll wring your carrion neck."

Then Malipiero, coward though he was at heart, was fired with the courage of despair. "Fool!" he panted, struggling for breath. "Fool, I spoke out of love for you, and I can prove the thing I say."

"Prove it?" roared the infuriate Varano, and he heaved the wretch up to dash him down again. "Prove it? Can lies be proved?"

"No," said Malipiero. "But truth can."

It was a simple and very obvious retort. Yet it produced its effect upon Varano, and Malipiero was able to breathe more freely at last. Varano had released him; he had risen, and was bawling for lights. Malipiero sat up, nursing his bruises, making sure that no bones were broken, and breathing a prayer of thanksgiving to Our Lady of Loreto — who had ever been the object of a special devotion on his part — that he had had the wit to forge proofs betimes that should lend countenance to the foul charges he made against a pure lady's honour. He comforted himself,

too, with the reflection that those same proofs would
avenge the mishandling he had suffered, and that for
the bruises Varano had dealt his body he would presently deal such bruises to Varano's soul as should go
some way to make them quits.

Lights came, revealing the shrivelled, yellow-faced
man sitting there upon the floor, with tumbled hair
and rent garments and a very evil glimmer in his
rat's eyes, and the other — the great lumbering
Varano — standing over him, no less pale and evil to
behold.

"Now, dog, the proofs."

This was Malipiero's hour of vengeance. Slowly he
loosed the points of his purple doublet; slowly he
groped within the breast of it, and slowly he drew
forth a package tied with an orange ribbon. Slowly
he was proceeding to unfasten it, when Varano, with
an oath of impatience, stooped, snatched the package,
and tore away the ribbon. Then he strode to the table,
unfolded a letter, and spread it under his great hand.

Malipiero, watching him with fearful, unblinking
eyes, saw the great head slowly sink forward on to his
breast. But Varano rallied quickly. His faith in his
wife was no mere thistledown to be so lightly scat-
tered. He sank to a chair, and turned to Malipiero,
who had now risen.

"Tell me," he said, "tell me again, how came these
into your hands?" There was now no anger in his
voice. He spoke like a man who is struggling between
dark unconsciousness and painful consciousness.

"Madonna's chamberlain Fabio brought them an
hour ago during your absence. He dared not come
while you were here. Love of you made him traitor to

your lady. Fear of you kept him from delivering the letters to you himself. And no sooner had he said so much to me than he was gone again, leaving the cursed package in my hands."

"If — if they were false!" cried Varano, wrestling with that fierce natural jealousy of his upon which the cunning Malipiero had built his schemes.

The traitor's face grew long with simulated sorrow. "My lord," he murmured dolefully, "to bid you build on that were not to love you. What ends could Fabio wish to serve? And Fabio loves you. And Fabio, who purloined those letters from madonna's treasure casket, knew of their existence, else he had not sought them."

"Enough!" cried the wretched Varano — a cry of anguish. Then with an oath he opened out another letter. "Oh, vile!" he groaned. "Oh, worse and worse!" and he read the signature — "Galeotto" — then knit his brows. "But who is this Galeotto?"

On the livid face of the satyr behind his chair a faint smile was smeared. He had a sense of humour, this Malipiero, and in the fiction of that name, in the equivoque it covered, it had found a sly expression. Aloud he parodied a line of Dante's:

"Galeotto fu il nome, e chi lo scrisse!"

With a snort the lord of Camerino turned to a third letter. His hand clenched and unclenched as he read. Then he raised it, and smashed it down upon the table with a fearful oath. He came to his feet. "Oh, shameless!" he inveighed. "Adulteress! Trull! Oh, and yet — so fond to all seeming, and so foully false! God help me! Is it possible — is it —"

He checked, his blood-injected eyes fastened upon Malipiero, and Malipiero recoiled now in horror of the devil he had raised. He drew hastily aside, out of Varano's way, as the latter, moved by a sudden resolve, strode to the entrance of the tent, beating his hands together and calling.

"Saddle me three horses on the instant," he commanded, "and bid Gianpaolo make ready for a journey." Then, striding back into the tent, "The third horse is for you, Malipiero."

"For me?" clucked the traitor, in a greater fright than any that had yet touched him since embarking on this evil business.

"For thee," said Varano sternly. Then, towering above the shivering wretch, "Hast ever known torture, Malipiero?" he inquired. "Hast ever seen the hoist at work; or the rack disjointing bones and stretching sinews till they burst, till the patient screams for the mercy of a speedy death? If God in His great clemency should please that you have lied to me — as I pray He may — you shall make acquaintance with those horrors, Malipiero. Ah, it makes you faint to think on them," he gloated, for he was, as Cesare had said, a cruel, bloody man. Then suddenly, sternly, "Go, make you ready for this journey," he commanded, and Malipiero went.

Here was a tangle, a complication on which the astute Venetian — for this Malipiero hailed from Venice, the very home and source of craft — had failed to reckon. That Varano should still be suspicious amid all his passion of jealousy, and should wish to make sure of Malipiero against the chance of precisely some such situation as the existing one, was something that had never entered the traitor's calculations.

What was he to do? Mother of God, what was he to do?

As he stood in his own tent a sickness took him, a sickness that was physical as well as spiritual. Then he rallied, played the man a moment, and drew his sword. He ran his thumb along the edge of it to test its keenness; he set the hilt against the ground, and paused. He had but to place himself with his heart over the point — so — and drop forward. A Roman death was here — swift and painless. Surely he had reached the end, and if he took not this easy means of egress, there were the horrors Varano had promised him — the rack and the hoist.

Then he bethought him of his son. His son would hang at dawn unless Varano went. And if he killed himself now, Varano must guess the truth, and would remain. That, and the reflection that between Imola and Camerino much might betide, restrained him. He took up his sword again, and restored it to its sheath. Steps sounded without; a soldier stood at the entrance, with a summons from Varano. The traitor braced himself to go.

As they reached Varano's tent, he bethought him of one thing there was yet to do, and, turning to the mercenary who paced behind him,

"Quench me that cresset," he commanded shortly.

The fellow caught up a pail of water standing near, and flung the contents on the blaze, extinguishing it.

"Why, what is this?" asked Varano, stepping forth.

"There was too much light," said Malipiero glibly. "They can see us from the castle."

"What, then, man?"

"Would you have Cesare Borgia know that you ride forth?" cried Malipiero, with a very obvious sneer for the thing the other overlooked.

"Ah, true! You are a thoughtful knave. Come, now. To horse!"

As they mounted, and were ready to set out — Malipiero between Varano and Gianpaolo da Trani, his esquire — Schwarz, the captain of the mercenaries, came up. The rumour of Varano's departure running round the camp had reached the Swiss, and, incredulous, he came for orders.

"Plague me not," growled the Lord Venanzio in answer.

"But, Excellency," the man protested, "shall you be absent long?"

"As long as my business needs."

"Then, from whom shall I take orders in the mean time?" cried the condottiero, out of patience.

"From the Devil," said Varano, and gave his horse the spur.

All night they rode, and so desperately that by dawn they were in San Arcangelo, and Malipiero bethought him with a pang that here, under this bridge, which gave back a hollow echo of their horses' hoofs, flowed the ancient fateful Rubicon, which he was crossing figuratively as well as literally.

Varano, riding half a horse's length in advance of his companions, pushed on, his face set, his eyes ahead. A mile or so beyond Arcangelo they were overtaken and passed by two riders going at the gallop, who thundered away towards Rimini in a cloud of dust. They were the men despatched by Corella, and they had taken fresh horses at Cesena in the Duke's name, thus outstripping the weary cattle of the men of Camerino.

Varano watched their speed with eyes of furious envy, and cursed the spent condition of his own horse. So they pressed on towards Rimini, their pace slackening now with every mile and in spite of all their flogging. At last the town was reached, and at the "Three Kings" Varano bawled for fresh horses with never a thought for breakfast. But horses, the host regretfully informed them, there were none to be had that morning.

"Perhaps at Cattolica . . ." he suggested.

Varano never stayed to argue. He drank a cup of wine and ate a crust, then heaved himself back into the saddle and urged his companions on. He was to pay for this unreasoning haste; for it was a haste that did not make for speed in the end. It took them three hours to reach Cattolica — three weary men on three spent horses. And here again they were met by the same tale of no relays. There would be none until the evening.

"Until evening?" roared Varano hoarsely. "Why, 'tis not yet noon!"

Malipiero, utterly worn out, had sunk on to a stone bench in the innyard. "Horses or no horses," he groaned, "I can go no farther." His face was grey, his eyes encircled by black lines. Yet Varano observed nothing of this, as he turned upon the fellow in a fury of suspicion. Before he could speak, however, his esquire had come to Malipiero's rescue.

"Nor I, Body of God!" he swore. "Before I ride another mile I must eat and sleep. What odds, my lord?" he reasoned with the scowling Varano. "We'll sleep by day, and ride by night. When all is said, it is the speediest travelling."

"Sleep?" growled Varano. "I had not meant to sleep this side Camerino — perhaps, indeed, not then. But since I ride with women . . . Pshaw!"

Thus matters stood, then. They rested all that day in Cattolica, and what hopes of escaping Malipiero may have fostered were quenched entirely by the lack of means. They resumed their journey again at dusk, upon fresh horses then provided — indifferent beasts, however, and far from such as Varano's hot impatience craved. Again they rode all night, going westward by Urbino, which was in the hands of Cesare's revolted captains, then south to Pergola, where they came soon after daybreak on the morrow.

Thence to Camerino was little more than thirty miles, and Varano would have gone straight on, but that again the lack of fresh horses foiled his purpose. It was in vain he swore, besought, or threatened. The country was all topsy-turvy, he was answered, infested with men-at-arms, and horses were scarce. He must wait until his own were rested. Until noon, then, they abode there, and now it was that Malipiero had the inspiration to feign illness, since flight was impossible.

"My head swims," he had whimpered, "and my loins burn. I am an old man, my lord, unfit to ride as you have made me ride."

Varano's eyes, dull, aching and bloodshot from his sleeplessness, measured the other fiercely. "Shalt have a physician in Camerino," said he.

"But, my lord, it is my fear that I may never get so far."

"Dismiss the fear," Varano enjoined him. "For you shall be there this evening — living or dead." And he stalked out, leaving Malipiero cold with a great fear that already he was suspected. When the hour to resume the journey came, Malipiero renewed his protestations.

"Mount!" was all the answer Varano returned him, and Malipiero, resigning himself to the awful fate that awaited him, climbed painfully to the saddle. He was ill, indeed; between fear and saddle-weariness he was all but spent. Yet he sat his horse in a sort of desperation, and so came into Camerino at eventide between his companions.

The place was garrisoned by a small company of Borgia soldiers — nor were many needed, for had the Varani attempted to return, the whole State would have taken up arms to beat them off. Under cover of the dusk Venanzio led his companions to a mean hostelry in the borgo. There he left Malipiero with Gianpaolo — the latter virtually jailer to the former. Alone Varano went forth to seek for himself the truth of this vile tale that had been told him.

Meanwhile, Malipiero, wrapped in his cloak, lay stretched on a settle shivering with horrid anticipation of the hoist and the rack. Soon, soon now Varano would discover the treachery, and then — He groaned aloud, disturbing Gianpaolo, who sat at table eating.

"Do you suffer, sir?" quoth the esquire; not that he greatly cared, for he loved Malipiero little, but that it seemed an inquiry which courtesy demanded.

Malipiero groaned again for only answer, and the esquire, moved to pity, brought the unhappy man a cup of wine.

Malipiero gulped it down. It warmed him, he protested, and begged for more. Then having drained a second, and after that a third goblet, he relapsed into his forlorn attitude. But the wine creeping through his veins inspired him with new courage. He had been too fearful of consequences, he now perceived. He should have made a dash for it before this. Even now it might not be too late. There were Borgia troops in the town. He would find refuge at the citadel. He had but to inform the captain or the governor, or whoever might be in command, of Varano's whereabouts in the town, and he would find shelter and gratitude.

Fired by the notion, he flung off the cloak, and got briskly to his feet.

"I need air!" he cried.

"I'll open the window," said the too-obliging Gianpaolo.

"The window? Bah! This place is foul. I will take a turn outside."

Gianpaolo eyeing him curiously — and with good reason, for the man had lately sworn he could not move without pain — barred his way to the door.

"Best await my lord's return," said he.

"Why, I shall be back before then."

But Gianpaolo had his orders — that Malipiero was not to be allowed out of his sight. Moreover, there was this sudden vigour in one who so lately had been prostrate from exhaustion. Gianpaolo could not believe that wine alone had wrought a change so portentous.

"Why, if you will, you will," said he. "But in that case I'll with you," and he reached for his cap.

Malipiero's face fell at that. But his recovery was

swift. Let the fool come, by all means, if he insisted.
Malipiero would march him into a trap, and quickly.
And then, even as he was on the point of consenting,
the stairs groaned under a heavy step; the door was
flung open so violently that it struck against the wall,
and Venanzio Varano, with mad blazing eyes and a
brow of thunder, strode into the room.

Malipiero backed away in terror, with an inward
curse at his own tardiness in perceiving the obvious
way of escape. Now it was too late. Varano had
learnt the truth already, and again Malipiero bethought him of the rack; already in imagination he
felt his sinews cracking and the rude hands of the
executioner upon him.

And then, marvel of marvels, Varano dropped into
a chair, and took his great black head in his hands.
A while he remained thus, Gianpaolo and Malipiero
watching him — the traitor understanding nothing of
this bearing, unable to think what could have happened.

Presently Varano sat up, composed himself, and
looked sorrowfully at Malipiero.

"Malipiero," said he, "I have prayed God ever
since we left Imola that, for some reasons which
the rack should tear from you, you had lied to me.
But —" A sob cut his utterance. "Oh, there is no
more pity in heaven than on earth. This thing is
true, it seems — most vilely, hideously true."

True! Malipiero's senses reeled an instant under
the shock of it. Then a great warmth thawed his
terror-frozen veins; a great exultation sang within his
vile soul; a great thankfulness welled up from his

heart to heaven for this miraculous escape. His spirit capered and jested within him. He would set up for a diviner, a seer, after this.

Outwardly he remained a pale embodiment of sorrow. He licked his dry lips, his little eyes sought Varano's and fell away before the awful glance that met them. So may the damned look.

He wanted to question Varano, to ask how he had discovered this thing, that he might satisfy himself of the incredible truth of it; and yet he dared not. Nor was there the need; for presently Varano gave him the information that he craved.

"I was recognized in the street as I quitted the inn. A man who saw me come forth followed me, overtook me, and called to me by name. He had been my servant once, he said, and had ever loved me, wherefore he had meant this very night to ride forth in quest of me to tell me of the things that were happening in my absence.

"When I had heard this story, I would have gone at once to that accursed palace where by the Borgia clemency that vile adulteress is housed. But he stayed my impatience with his counsel. He bade me wait — wait until dead midnight, and so make certain. He himself — this good soul that loves me — will watch for me, and will be at hand when I arrive."

He rose violently. His grief and shame dropped from him, and were replaced by an anger dreadful to behold. Imprecations rained from his mouth, which was twisted like that of a man in physical suffering. A mirror hanging from a wall of that poor chamber caught his eye. He strode to it and scanned himself, rubbing his brow the while.

Then with his fist he shivered the thing to atoms. "It lied," he roared, and laughed most terribly. "It showed a fair smooth brow — no horns — no horns! I that am antlered like a stag!" And his awful laugh shook the windows in their crazy frames.

At midnight the Lord Venanzio rose from his chair where he had been sitting motionless for upwards of an hour. His face was haggard, his eyes stern and his mouth hard.

"Come," he said quietly, "it is the hour."

Gianpaolo, with a deep sorrow in his heart, and Malipiero, with an unholy glee in his, followed their lord down the narrow stairs, and out into the scented autumn night. They went up the steep street to the palace that crowned the hill. But passing the main doors they struck down a narrow lane and so came to a wicket in a high wall. A man rose up before them, seeming to materialize out of the gloom.

"He is within," he murmured to Varano. "He went the usual way, leaving the gate unlocked."

"That was considerate in him," said Varano heavily, and dropped a purse into the hands of the spy. Then he pushed the wicket till it opened, and beckoned his companions after him into a garden that was thick with shrubs. They came by an alley black as Erebus into a fair clearing under the stars; and here Varano checked, and gripped Malipiero's wrist.

"Yonder," he snarled. "That is her chamber." And with his other hand he pointed to a lighted window — the only window of the palace that still showed a light. "See with what a warmth it burns — a Vestal fire!" he sneered, and laughed softly.

Next he sped swiftly forward across the yielding turf, his companions following. Under her balcony he paused.

"See," he whispered back to them. "Is he not considerate, this gallant? Look!" And they saw dangling from the balcony a grey ladder of silken rope.

Had Varano still hoped against hope, still set his trust in his wife against the things he had been told, the letters he had seen, then must this last hope have foundered here.

He swarmed the ladder with the ease and speed of an ape. They saw him fling one leg over the stone parapet and then the other; there followed a crash and ring of shivered glass, as with his shoulder the infuriate husband smashed a way into the room.

He found his quarry standing in mid-apartment, startled by this terrific entrance — a fair young man, tall and comely, decked like a bridegroom all in white and gold, his discarded doublet still hanging in his hand.

Varano swooped upon him ere he could utter a word, locked an arm about his neck, wrenched him backward, and, dropping on one knee, caught him, as he fell, across the other. The wretch, half-strangled in that awful grip, saw a long dagger gleam above him, heard a terrific voice:

"Hound of hell, I am Venanzio Varano. Look on me and die!"

The dagger sank to the hilt; it was raised again, and yet again, to be replunged into the heart of this man who had dishonoured him. Then, by an arm, Varano dragged the warm, twitching body across the room towards the bed, leaving a great crimson smear in its wake along the mosaic floor.

"Shalt lie snug to-night," he sneered, "snug and warm, snug and warm. And this wanton —" He dropped his hold of the dead arm and turned to the bed, his thoughts running now directly upon his wife. Clutching his dagger firmly in one hand he swung aside the heavy curtains with the other.

"Now, harlot . . ." He checked. The bed was empty, undisturbed.

The door behind him opened suddenly. He swung about, a horrid, blood-spattered sight.

On the threshold stood a tall man with a grave dark countenance and a very martial bearing, a man whose fame was almost as well known to every soldier in Italy as was that of the Duke his master.

"Michele da Corella!" quoth Varano, thunder-struck. "You were in Imola. What make you here?" Then, his mind swinging back to the weightier matter that oppressed it. "My wife?" he cried. "Where is Madonna Eulalia?"

Corella advanced into the room. Behind him pressed a posse of javelin-men in the Borgia livery of red and yellow.

"Your wife, my lord, is in Bologna — safe," said he.

Varano, bewildered, stared at Cesare's captain. "Why — why — what treachery is here?" he mumbled thickly, like a drunkard.

"A very foul one, my lord — yet not one that touches you so nearly as that other. The traitor is that knave, that scavenger, Malipiero, a part of whose plot it was most vilely to slander the fair name of the spotless lady of Venanzio Varano."

"Slander?" echoed Varano, and "Spotless?" fastening upon those words amid all that Corella had spoken. "It is not true, then?" he cried.

"As Heaven hears me, it is not true," Corella answered. "The people of Camerino were venting upon Madonna Eulalia their resentment against your house, my lord; and so, a week ago, she sought shelter with her father in Bologna. No doubt her courier would reach your camp almost in the hour in which you left it."

A great sob broke from Varano; tears coursed down his war-worn cheeks. What signified to him that he had been betrayed in other matters? What signified losses and reverses so that his Eulalia was true and spotless?

Corella was speaking. Briefly he gave Varano the details of the treachery by which Malipiero had drawn him away from Imola, so that Cesare might rout the mercenary rabble that would never stand in its leader's absence. He had sought to bargain for the life of his son, who was to have hanged for spying and for attempting to murder the Duke. Cesare, loving the treason but loathing the traitor, had refused to make terms, promising Malipiero in return for the betrayal he proposed no more than justice.

"It was by Malipiero's contriving," he pursued, "that I left Imola, and did what else was necessary to accomplish my lord's wishes in this matter, even to housing comfortably in this chamber a person whom His Highness had entrusted to me. My thought was that he would attempt to escape by the ladder provided for the purpose and that you would take him as he came forth. Your impatience, my lord —"

"By the Host!" roared Varano, breaking in, "Cesare Borgia shall answer to me for having put upon me the slaying of an innocent man."

Corella looked at him a moment with lifted brows. "You have not understood," he said. He pointed to the corpse. "That carrion was Gustavo Malipiero."

Varano recoiled. "Gustavo Malipiero? His son?" And he jerked a thumb in the direction of the window.

"His son."

"My God!" said Varano hoarsely. "Is this the justice of your Duke?"

"Aye, my lord, upon the assassin there and the traitor outside; upon both at one blow — and that by the hand of yourself, whom Malipiero so foully abused, and through the very scheme that he invented. Such is the very perfect justice of my Duke."

Varano looked at Corella. "And incidentally his own purposes are served," he sneered.

Corella shrugged. But already Varano had turned from him. He took up the body in his powerful arms, and staggered with it to the shattered window. He heaved it over the balcony into the garden below.

"There, Malipiero," he cried, "is the price of your services to me. Take it, and begone."

THE LUST OF CONQUEST

THE hour of Cesare Borgia's power and glory was that of full noontide. He had made an end of the treacherous condottieri who had dared to rise against him and for a moment to hold him in check, threatened not only to arrest his conquering progress, but to undo all that he had done. He had limed a springe for them at Sinigaglia, and — in the words of the Florentine Secretary, Macchiavelli — he had lured them thither by the sweetness of his whistling. They came the more readily in that they mistook their rôles, conceiving themselves the fowlers, and him the victim. He quickly disabused their minds on that score; and having taken them, he wrung their necks with no more compunction than had they been so many capons. Their considerable forces he partly destroyed and partly dispersed, partly assimilated into his own vast army, whereafter he swept southward and homeward to Rome by way of Umbria.

In Perugia his sometime captain, Gianpaolo Baglioni, one of the more fortunate rebels who had escaped him, was arming to resist him, and making big talk of the reckoning he would present to Cesare Borgia. But when, from the high-perched eyrie of his ancient Etruscan stronghold, Gianpaolo caught afar the first gleam of arms in the white January sunshine, he talked no more. He packed instead, and fled discreetly, intent to reach Siena and take shelter with Petrucci.

And no sooner was he gone than Perugia — which

for generations had been weary of his blood-smeared
family — sent ambassadors with messages of welcome
to the Duke.

Gianpaolo heard of this in Assisi, and his rage was a
prodigy even for a Baglioni. He was a black-browed,
powerful man, built like an ape with a long body and
short legs, a fine soldier, as well the world knows,
endowed with a reckless courage and a persuasive
tongue that lured men to follow him. In quitting
Perugia, he had listened for once to the voice of discretion, urged by the cold and calculating quality of
his hatred of the Borgia, and by the hope that in
alliance with Petrucci he might stir up Tuscany and
so return in force against the Duke.

But now that he had word of how cravenly — as he
accounted it — his city of Perugia had not only bent
her neck to the yoke of the conqueror, which was perhaps inevitable, but had further bent the knee in
homage and held out her arms in welcome, he repented
him fiercely of his departure, and was blinded to
reason by his rage.

He was so mad as to attempt to induce Assisi to
resist the advancing Duke. But the city of Saint
Francis bade the belligerent Gianpaolo go with God
ere the Duke arrived; for the Duke was already on his
way, and did he find Gianpaolo there, the latter would
assuredly share the fate which had visited his fellow-
rebels.

Baglioni angrily took his departure, to pursue his
road to Siena. But some three miles to the south of
Assisi he drew rein, and lifted his eyes to the stronghold of Solignola, poised, gaunt and grey, upon a
projecting crag of the Subasian hills. It was the lair

of that indomitable old wolf, Count Guido degli Speranzoni, whose pride was as the pride of Lucifer, whose fierceness was as the fierceness of the Baglioni — to which family he claimed kinship through his mother — whose defiance of the Pope was as the defiance of an infidel.

Gianpaolo sat his horse under the drizzling rain, and considered Solignola a while, with pursed lips. To-night, he reflected, Cesare would lie at Assisi, which was as ready as a strumpet for surrender. To-morrow his envoys would wait upon the Lord of Solignola, and surely, if he knew the old warrior, Count Guido's answer would be a haughty refusal to receive the Duke.

He took his resolve. He would ride up, and seek out Speranzoni. If the Count were, indeed, prepared for resistance, Gianpaolo had that to say that should encourage him. If his resoluteness had not been weakened, as had most men's, by the mere approach of Cesare Borgia, then it might yet come to pass that here they should do the thing that at Sinigaglia had so grievously miscarried. Thus should his strangled comrades be avenged, and thus should Italy be rid of this scourge. Of that same scourge, as he now dubbed the Lord Cesare Borgia, he had himself but lately been one of the thongs. But Messer Gianpaolo was not subtle.

He turned to his armoured followers — a score or so of men-at-arms who remained faithful to him in this hour of general defection — and made known his intention to ride up to Solignola. Then, by a winding mountain path, he led the way thither.

As they ascended from the vast plain of Umbria, so

leafless, grey, and desolate under that leaden, wintry sky, they perceived through a gap in the hills the cluster of little townships and hamlets, on the slopes and in the eastern valley, which formed the territory and dominion of Solignola. These lay practically without defences, and they must fall an easy prey to the Duke. But Baglioni knew that the fierce old Count was not the man to allow any such considerations to weaken his resolve to resist the Borgia, and to that resolve Gianpaolo hoped to spur him.

Dusk was descending when the little company of Perugians reached the northern gate of Solignola, and the bells of the Duomo were ringing the Angelus — the evening prayer in honour of the Blessed Mother of Chastity revived in Italy by the unchaste Borgia Pope. Baglioni's party clattered over the bridge spanning a chasm in the rocks in the depths of which a foaming mountain torrent, swollen and umber-tinted by the recent rains, hurled itself down its head-long course to join the Tiber in the valley.

Having satisfied the guard, they rode forward into the city and up the steep long street to the Rocca, regarded with awe by the burghers, who looked upon them as the harbingers of this invasion which they knew to be sweeping towards them from the north.

Thus they came to the mighty citadel and thudded over the drawbridge into the great courtyard, where they were instantly hemmed about by a swarm of men-at-arms who demanded of them not only an account of themselves, but news as well of Cesare Borgia's army. Gianpaolo satisfied them briefly, announced his name, and demanded to see Count Guido at once.

The Lord of Solignola sat in council in the Sala degli Angioli — a chamber so known from the fresco which Luini had painted on the ceiling, representing the opening heavens and a vision of angels beyond the parted clouds. With the Count sat Messer del Campo, the President of the Council of Anziani; Messer Pino Paviano, the Master of the Artificers' Guild; two gentlemen from the valley — the lords of Aldi and Barbero; a gentleman of Assisi — Messer Gianluca della Pieve; and the Count's two principal officers, the Seneschal of Solignola and the condottiero Santafiora.

They sat about a long, quadrangular oak table in the thickening gloom, with no other light but that of the log fire that roared under the wide cowled chimney; and with them, at the foot of the table, facing the Count, odd member of his warlike council, sat a woman — the Lady Panthasilea degli Speranzoni, Count Guido's daughter. In years she was little more than a girl; in form and face she showed a glorious maturity of womanhood; in mind and character she was a very man. To describe her the scholarly Cerbone had already, a year ago, made use of the term "virago" — not in its perverted, but in its literal and original meaning, signifying a woman who in intellect and spirit is a man.

It was by virtue of these endowments, as much as because she was Count Guido's only child and heir, that she attended now this council, and listened gravely to all that was urged in this matter of the Borgia invasion. She was magnificently tall, and very regal in her bearing and in the carriage of her glorious head. Her eyes were large, dark, and lustrous; her hair of a glowing copper; and her tint of the delicate fairness that is attributed to the daughters of the North. The rich colour of her sensitive lips told of the warm blood that flowed in her; their set and shape bore witness to her courage and her will.

Into this assembly, which rose eagerly to receive him, was ushered the Lord Gianpaolo Baglioni. He clanked into the room upon his muscular bowed legs, a sinister figure as seen in the gloom with the firelight playing ruddily upon his armour and his swarthy, black-bearded face.

Count Guido advanced to embrace him and to greet him with words of very cordial welcome, which at once told the crafty Baglioni all that he most desired to know. The Count presented him to the company, and invited him to join their council, since his arrival was so timely, and since, no doubt, he would be able to offer them advice of which they stood most sorely in need, that they might determine upon their course of action.

He thanked them for the honour, and dropped with a rattle of metal into the proffered chair. Count Guido called for lights, and when these were fetched they revealed the haggard air of Messer Gianpaolo, which was accentuated by the splashed harness in which he came amongst them, just as he had ridden. His smouldering eyes travelled round the board, and when they found the Assisian gentleman, Gianluca della Pieve, he smiled sombrely.

"Hard though I have ridden," said he, "it seems that another is before me with news of what is happening in Assisi."

Della Pieve answered him. "I arrived three hours

ago, and I bore the news that Assisi had thrown up her gates to receive and harbour the invader. The Communal Palace is being prepared for him; it is expected that he will remain a while in the city, making it a centre whence he can conduct such operations as he intends against such strongholds as may resist him."

"And is Solignola to be reckoned among these?" inquired Gianpaolo bluntly, his eyes upon Count Guido.

The old Lord of Solignola met his glance calmly, his shaven, hawk face inscrutable, his almost lipless mouth tight and firm. It was a face at once handsome, strong, and crafty — the face of one who never would yield lightly.

"That," he answered slowly, "is what we are assembled to determine. Have you anything to add to the information afforded us by Della Pieve?"

"I have not. This gentleman has told you all that is known to me."

"None the less your coming is most timely. Our deliberations make no progress, and we do not seem likely to agree. You, perhaps, may guide us with your counsel."

"You see, Messer Baglioni," put in the Lord of Barbero, a red-faced, jovial gentleman of middle-age, "our interests are different, and we are naturally governed by our interests."

"Naturally, as you say," agreed Baglioni with imperceptible sarcasm.

"Now, we of the valley — and my friend Francisco d'Aldi, there, cannot deny it — we of the valley lie open to attack; we are defenceless; the few townships that have walls at all have not such walls as will resist bombardment. It is a fine thing for Count Guido and the folk of Solignola itself to talk of resistance. Solignola is all but impregnable. And well-provisioned and well-garrisoned as the city is, Count Guido may, if it please him, resist long enough to enforce advantageous terms. But what in the mean while will be our fate down yonder? Cesare Borgia will avenge upon us the stubbornness of the capital. Therefore do we urge His Excellency — and we have in this the suffrage also of the Master of the Artificers' Guild — to follow the example of Assisi and your own Perugia" (Gianpaolo winced) "and send his ambassadors to the Duke with offers of submission."

Gianpaolo shook his great head. "It is not the Duke's way to avenge upon dependencies the resistance of a capital. He is too guileful, believe me. Whom he subjects he conciliates. There will be no such fire and sword as you fear for your townships of the valley. Solignola's resistance — if she resist — will be visited upon Solignola alone. That much I can say from my knowledge gained in service with the Duke. Let me remind you of Faenza. What harm was suffered by the folk of the Val di Lamone? Why, none. The strongholds surrendered, and knew no violence, although Faenza herself resisted stubbornly."

"But to little purpose," put in Paviano — the Guildmaster — sourly.

"That," said Count Guido, "is beside the point. And Faenza had not the natural strength of Solignola."

"Yet, ultimately," protested Barbero, "surrender

you must. You cannot resist an army of ten thousand men forever."

"They cannot besiege us forever," snapped Santafiora, the condottiero, rearing his cropped bullet-head.

Baglioni sat back in his chair, and listened to the hot debate that followed now. He was as one who has tossed down a ball into a field of players, and, having done so, watches it being flung back and forth in the course of the ensuing game.

Count Guido, too, took little part in the discussion, but listened silently, his eyes passing from speaker to speaker, his countenance a mask. Facing him his daughter was sitting forward, her elbows on the table, her chin in her cupped palms, intent upon every word that was uttered, her eyes now glowing with enthusiasm, now coldly scornful, as the argument turned for or against resistance. But it was all inconclusive, and at the end of a half-hour's wrangling they were no nearer a decision than when Gianpaolo had arrived.

It was at this stage that Count Guido turned again to the Perugian, and, profiting by a momentary silence, following a vigorous plea for resistance from Santafiora, invited him to speak.

"It may be that I can help you," said Gianpaolo slowly, "for it happens that my proposal supports neither one side nor the other of the discussion to which I have listened. My suggestion concerns a middle course; and since something of the sort seems to be needed here if you are not to spend your days in talk, perhaps your courtesy will give attention to what I have to say."

The company stirred expectantly, and settled into an attentive silence. Panthasilea's eyes turned with the others upon the grim face of the speaker, and never left it whilst he was delivering his message.

"Sirs," he said, "here has been talk of resistance and of surrender. Of attack, of assuming the offensive, it seems not one of you has thought."

"To what purpose?" quoth Santafiora, scowling. "We have a bare five hundred men."

But Baglioni imperiously waved the condottiero into silence. "Hear me out before you judge me, and do not outrun me by conclusions of your own. You may know — or you may not, for Italy is full of lies upon the subject — of the business in which those gallant gentlemen, who were my friends, came by their deaths in Sinigaglia — a death which I, myself, have very narrowly escaped by the infinite mercy of God." And he crossed himself piously. "It had been planned, sirs, to take this Duke, and make an end of him. An arbalester was to have shot him as he rode into the town. But he is the fiend — the incarnate fiend. He came forewarned. *Præmonitus est præmunitus.* He turned the trap about, and took in it those who had plotted to take him. The rest you know." He leaned forward, and his blood-injected eyes ran over the assembled company. "Sirs," he concluded in a thick, concentrated voice, "that which failed at Sinigaglia might succeed in Assisi."

There was a stir, breaking the rapt silence in which he had been heard. He looked at them with challenge in his glance. "Needs more be said?" he asked.

"Aye," cried Paviano, "the how and the when, the ways and the means."

"Why, that, of course. But first —" He turned to Count Guido. "Have you a mind to follow such a course; to rid Italy of this scourge at a single stroke; to save your dominions and the dominions of others from being ravished by this insatiable devourer? Destroy Cesare Borgia, and you will have destroyed the head and brain of the Pontifical forces; thus there will be an end to this conquest of the Romagna, which presently will spread into a conquest of middle Italy; for if he lives he will not rest until he is King of Tuscany. He is not easy of access, and since Sinigaglia he uses all precautions. Yet while he is resting in Assisi should be your opportunity if you have a mind to seize it."

Count Guido sat thoughtful and frowning, whilst eagerness glowed on several faces, positive fierceness of concurrence on one or two. But one dissentient there was in old Del Campo.

"It is murder you are proposing," he said in tones of chill reproof.

"And what then? Shall a mere word set up a barrier for grown men?" demanded the fierce Baglioni.

"It would not for one woman that I know of," said the clear, boyish voice of Monna Panthasilea, and so drew upon herself, with those first words she had ventured to utter in that council, the gaze of all. There was a feverish light in her dark eyes, a feverish glow in her fair cheeks. Meeting their glances she addressed them: "What my Lord Gianpaolo has said is true. While Cesare Borgia lives there is no peace for middle Italy. And there is one thing, and one thing only, that can save Solignola — the death of Cesare Borgia."

A roar of acclamation was the answer to those words — words uttered already by Baglioni — now that they fell from her red lips. It was her beauty and her glorious womanhood that swayed them — as men ever will be swayed even against reason, against honour, and against knowledge.

But old Del Campo remained untouched by the subtle magnetism of sex. He rose as the acclamations died down. He turned a calm, impassive face upon Count Guido.

"My lord," he asked, his voice ice-cold, "does this receive your countenance?"

The white face of the old Count was set and hard, as his voice was hard when, after a moment's thought, he spoke. "Upon what grounds, Messer del Campo, would you urge that it should not? — for that is clearly what you would urge."

The President of the Anziani steadily met the Count's steely glance. He bowed a thought ironically. "I am answered," he said. He thrust back his chair, and stepped from the table. "Permit, my lord, and you, sirs, that I withdraw before you go further in a matter in which I will have no part."

He bowed again to all, drew his furred robes about him, and proudly left the chamber in the ensuing silence, leaving a chill behind him.

Scarce had the door closed after him than Gianpaolo was on his feet, his face pale with excitement.

"Sir Count," he cried, "that man must not leave the citadel. Our lives may hang upon it. Too many such schemes have miscarried through less than this. Cesare Borgia's spies are everywhere. They will be in Solignola now, and should del Campo utter a word of what has passed here, the Duke may hear of it to-morrow."

There was a moment's silence. Count Guido's eyes seemed to ask Gianpaolo a question.

"There is no dungeon in your castle too deep for Messer del Campo until this thing is done," said he; and he added almost under his breath: "Indeed, I doubt if there be any deep enough."

The Count turned to Santafiora. "See to it," he said in a low voice, and Santafiora rose and departed on his errand.

Madonna Panthasilea's face grew very white; her eyes dilated. She feared the worst for old Del Campo, who had been her own and her father's faithful friend for many a year. Yet she saw the necessity for the measure, and so crushed down the womanly weakness that arose in her, and spoke no word of intercession for him.

Presently the Count solemnly addressed the company.

"Sirs," he said, "you have plainly signified your agreement with the proposal made by Messer Gianpaolo."

"A thought occurs to me," put in Francesco d'Aldi, and at once he claimed their attention. He was a scholar, a patron of the arts, a man of natural shrewdness and much worldly experience, who had dwelt much in courts and for a season had been the Orator of Solignola at the Vatican. "A doubt occurs to me as to the wisdom of my Lord Baglioni's proposal as it stands."

Angry glances, a snort or two of impatience, and a short, contemptuous laugh from Baglioni were his answers. But he fronted the disapproval calmly, and in that moment of his pause Santafiora reëntered the chamber.

"Give me your patience, sirs," said Messer Francesco, and he almost smiled. "I do not wish to bear Del Campo company in his dungeon."

Santafiora smiled grimly as he resumed his seat. That and his silence told the company all that it could have asked the condottiero.

"Say on," the Count bade the Lord of Aldi. "We all know your worth, Francesco."

Messer Francesco bowed, and cleared his throat. "Messer Gianpaolo has told us what would result from the death of Cesare Borgia — enough to justify the slaying of him so far as the ultimate consequences are at issue. But we, here in Solignola, have also to consider the immediate consequences of this act; for those immediate consequences would touch ourselves."

"Sacrifice for the State's weal is the duty of the individual," said Gianpaolo harshly.

"Since Messer Gianpaolo proposes to seek safety for himself in Siena, it is easy for him to utter these beautiful sentiments," said d'Aldi tartly.

Some laughed, Baglioni spluttered an angry oath, and Count Guido intervened to soothe him.

"Myself," proceeded Francesco d'Aldi, "I oppose the sacrifice of the individual where it is not necessary, and in this case I hold that it is not. We are to consider that with Cesare Borgia are several condottieri who are devoted to him. Such men as Corella, Scipione, Della Volpe, and others would never allow his death to go unavenged. And the measure of revenge they would exact is such as no man may calmly contemplate. Solignola would cease to exist; not a town, not a hamlet would be left standing — no man, woman, or child would they spare in their devastating fury. Can you envisage that, sirs?" he inquired, and was answered by gloomy looks and silence. "But I have an alternative proposal," he continued, "which should more effectively meet our needs, and lead to the same result for us — for Solignola, Assisi, and Perugia.

"It is that we take the Duke of Valentinois alive, and hold him as a hostage, threatening to hang him if we are beset. That should keep his condottieri in check, and meanwhile we send our envoys to the Pope. We offer His Holiness his son's life and liberty in exchange for our own lives and our own liberties, in exchange for a Bull of perpetual franchisement from the States of the Church; and to quicken His Holiness's penmanship we add a threat that if the Bull is not in our hands within a given term we will proceed to hang the Lord Cesare Borgia."

"Most shrewd!" Baglioni cried, and others echoed the applause.

"But there is a difficulty," said Francesco. "It lies in the Duke's capture."

"Indeed, yes," agreed Paviano gloomily.

"But surely by guile," urged Count Guido, "he might be lured into some — some trap."

"We should need such guile as Cesare Borgia's own," said Santafiora.

And now for a while they talked to no purpose, and first one offered a suggestion, then another; but these suggestions were all as obvious to propose as they were impossible to execute. A half-hour was spent, and they were no nearer a solution; some, indeed, were beginning to despair, when Monna Panthasilea rose slowly to her feet.

She stood at the table's end, her hands resting lightly upon the board, her tall, lithe body in its russet gown inclining slightly forward, her bosom rising and falling, and the pallor of excitement on her face, the sparkle of excitement in her liquid eyes.

"It is most fitting," she said slowly, her voice steady and composed, "that Solignola's future mistress should be Solignola's saviour in this hour. Thus shall I prove my right to rule here when the time comes — and please God it may lie very distant yet."

The silence of utter amazement that followed her words was broken at length by her father.

"You, Panthasilea? What can you do?"

"What no man of you all could do. For here is a matter that may best be fought with woman's weapons."

Against this they protested clamorously, some in horror, some in anger, all excited, save only Baglioni, who cared not how the thing were done so that it was done.

She raised a hand for silence and obtained it.

"There is between the Borgia and me this matter of saving Solignola. That alone were matter enough to spur me. But there is more." She grew deathly white and swayed a moment with closed eyes. Then, recovering herself, she continued: "Pietro Varano and I were to have wed this spring. And Pietro Varano was strangled three months ago in the market-place of Pesaro by Borgia justice. That, too, lies between me and the Duke of Valentinois; and vengeance should give me strength in this enterprise, which must be approached by such ways as only a woman's feet may tread."

"But the danger of it!" cried Count Guido.

"Think not of that. What danger shall I run? I am not known in Assisi, where I have not been since I was a little child. I am scarce known in Solignola itself, where I have been seen but little since my return from Mantua. And I shall be careful how I show myself in Assisi. Sirs, you must not gainsay me in this. I set my hand to the task to preserve our State's independence, to save thousands of lives. As Messer Gianpaolo has said, sacrifice for the State's weal is the duty of the individual. Yet here so much can scarcely be required."

Men muttered, and looked at her father. It was for him to speak. The Count took his head in his hands and sat in thought.

"What — what is your plan?" quoth Gianluca della Pieve thickly.

Her ready answer showed how fully already she had considered the matter. "I shall go down to Assisi, taking with me a dozen men of Santafiora's condotta, disguised as peasants and lackeys. And while Solignola defies Cesare Borgia, and so detains him in Assisi, I shall find ways to lure him into a snare, bind him hand and foot and bear him off to Siena, where Messer Gianpaolo will await me. For my purpose, Messer della Pieve, your house in Assisi will be necessary to me. You will lend it to me."

"Lend it you?" quoth he in horror. "Lend it to be a mouse-trap in which you — your matchless womanhood — shall be the cheese? Is that your meaning?"

She lowered her eyes; a crimson flush overspread her face.

"Solignola," she replied, "is in danger of being conquered. In the valley thousands of women and little children are in danger of homelessness, of death and worse than death. Shall one woman hesitate" — and now she raised her eyes again and flashed them defiantly upon the company — "shall one woman hesitate to endure a little insult when at the price of it she can buy so much?"

It was her father who returned the answer that none other dared return. He uncovered a face that had become grey and haggard.

"She is right," he said, and — odd argument for an Italian of the cinquecento — "it is her sacred duty to the people she was born to rule," he informed them. "Since there offers no way by which a man's strength may prevail against Valentinois, Della Pieve, you will lend your house; you, Santafiora, the men that she requires."

Assisi, conquered without bloodshed, all trace of conquest sedulously removed as was the way of Cesare Borgia, was settling down to its workaday aspect, which the Duke's occupation had scarcely ruffled.

Though princes perish, thrones crumble in ruin, and dynasties be supplanted, citizens must eat and live and go about their business. Thus, whilst some remained in Assisi who scowled as Cesare Borgia, Duke of Valentinois, went abroad, the greater portion bared their heads and bowed their duty to the conqueror, the great captain who had made it his life's task to reconsolidate into one powerful State these petty tyrannies of the Romagna.

The half of Cesare's army was encamped in the

surrounding country. The other half, under Michele da Corella, had advanced to lay siege to Solignola, which had returned a defiant answer to Cesare's envoys when these had gone to invite Count Guido to surrender.

It was a difficult place to take, and Cesare was too wise a captain to be in haste where haste must prove expensive. Assisi afforded him pleasant quarters, and was a convenient centre for the transaction of such business as he had with Florence and Siena, and so he sat down very patiently to await the result of certain operations which he had indicated to Corella.

The chief feature of these was the preparation of a mine under the walls on the southern side of the city, almost under the very citadel itself at the point where it was flanked by the hill. Between the difficulties of access to the place, and the vigilance and continual sorties of the defenders, it became apparent at the end of a week that at the present rate of operations it would take Corella a month to effect a breach. Cesare began to consider the wisdom of opening a bombardment, deterred, however, by the difficulty there would be in effectively mounting a park of artillery upon those rocky slopes.

The matter of this obstinate but futile resistance offered by Solignola, intrigued His Highness of Valentinois, and he was assured that some explanation for it must exist that was not obvious. That explanation he sought on every hand, for the Sinigaglia affair had rendered him doubly wary and alert.

One fair morning in early February, on which the deeper golden of the sunlight told of approaching spring, Cesare rode down the steep borgo from the

market-place, the centre of a brilliant group of horsemen — captains in steel, courtiers in silk, and, beside
him, upon a snow-white mule, the handsome scarlet
figure of Cardinal Remolino, the Papal legate *a latere*.

It was a joyous cavalcade, most if its members being as young as the young Duke himself; and gay talk
and laughter leaped from them as they rode forward
to visit Corella's camp under Solignola.

In the open space before the Convent of Santa
Chiara their progress was arrested for a moment by a
mule litter that struck across their course towards
one of the streets that led to San Rufino. It was attended by two footmen, and a very elegant cavalier
on a big roan horse who rode on the litter's farther
side.

The Cardinal-legate was speaking to Cesare, and
Cesare was allowing his eyes to stray, as do the eyes
of a man not over-interested in what he is being told.
They chanced to fall upon the litter, and what he saw
there caught his roving glance, and held it.

The curtain had been drawn aside, and at the very
moment that he looked, the cavalier was — or so it
seemed to him — stooping to point him out to the
lady who sat within. It was this lady's splendid
beauty that now engrossed his gaze; and in that instant her eyes, large and solemn as a child's, were
raised to his.

Their glances met across the little intervening space,
and Cesare saw her lips part as in surprise, saw the
colour perish in her cheeks, leaving them ivory white.
In homage — not to the woman, but to the beauty
that was hers, for like all of his race he accounted
beauty the most cardinal of all the virtues — the con-

queror doffed his hat, and bowed to the very withers of his horse.

The Cardinal, checked in full flow of argument, scowled at this proof of inattention, and scowled more darkly still when, to reveal the full extent of it, Cesare asked him softly:

"Who is that lady, do you know?"

The prelate, who had a famous eye for feminine beauty, followed Cesare's indication promptly. But in that moment the curtain fell again, thus baffling his eager glance.

Cesare, a smile on his lips, uttered a slight sigh, and then fell very pensive, intrigued by the element of abnormality, slight as it was, that the incident had offered. He had been pointed out to her, and at sight of him she had turned pale. What was the reason? He could not recollect that he had ever seen her before; and had he seen her, hers was not a face he had forgot. Why, then, did the sight of him affect her in so odd a manner? Men enough had turned pale be. fore him, aye, and women too. But there had ever been a reason. What was the reason here?

The litter and its attendants vanished into the by-street. But still Cesare was not done with it. He turned in his saddle to an Assisian gentleman who rode behind.

"Did you mark the cavalier who accompanied that litter?" quoth he, and added the question: "Is he of Assisi?"

"Why, yes, Excellency," was the answer. "That is Messer Gianluca della Pieve."

"Della Pieve?" said Cesare, thoughtful. "That is the member of the Council who was absent when the

oath was taken. Ha! We should have more knowl-
ledge of this gentleman and his motives for that absence." He rose in his stirrups as his horse moved
forward, and called over the heads of some others:
"Scipione!"

One of the steel captains pushed forward instantly
to his side.

"You saw the litter and the cavalier," said Cesare.
"He is Messer Gianluca della Pieve. You will follow
them, and bring me word where the lady resides, and
at the same time you will bring me Messer della
Pieve. Let him await my return at the palace.
Should it be necessary you will use constraint. But
bring him. Away with you. Forward, sirs."

Baldassare Scipione backed away, wheeled his
charger, and departed in discreet pursuit of the litter.

Cesare pushed on, his cavaliers about him; but he
went thoughtful, still pondering that question: "Why
did she turn pale?"

The reason, had he known it, might have flattered
him. Madonna Panthasilea had come to Assisi to
destroy by guile one whom she had never heard de-
scribed save as an odious monster, the devastator of
all Italy. She had looked to see some horror of a man,
malformed, prematurely aged and ravaged by disease
and the wrath of Heaven. Instead she found a youthful cavalier, resplendent of raiment, superb of shape,
and beautiful of countenance beyond all men that she
had ever seen. The glory of his eyes when she had
found them full upon her own, seeming to grope into
her very soul, had turned her faint and dizzy. Nor
did she recover until the curtain fell again, and she
remembered that, however noble and gallant his pres-

ence, he was the enemy of her race, the man whose destruction it was her high mission to encompass as she stood pledged.

Reclining in her litter as it moved forward, she half-closed her eyes, and smiled to herself as she remembered how avid had been his gaze. It was well.

The litter curtain was slightly lifted from without. "Madonna, we are being followed," murmured Gianluca.

Her smile grew broader, more content. The affair was speeding as it should. She said so to her cavalier.

Her smile and her words caused an anger to flare out in Gianluca — an anger that for a moment had manifested itself that night when first she had committed herself to this task, and had been smouldering since.

"Madonna," he cried in a voice that was hoarse, "this is a Delilah's work to which you are committed."

She stared at him, and paled a little to hear this brutally true description of the task; then she took refuge in haughtiness.

"You are presumptuous, sir," she told him, and so lashed him with that answer that he lost his head.

"Presumptuous enough to love you, Madonna," he replied almost fiercely, yet muttering, that her attendants should not overhear him. "That is why I abhor to see you wedded to a task so infamous; making a lure of your matchless beauty, a base —"

"Stop!" she commanded him so sternly that he obeyed her despite himself.

She paused a moment as one who chooses words, nor looked at him again after that first imperious glance.

"You are singularly daring," she said, and her voice was pitiless. "We will forget what you have said, Messer Gianluca — all of it. As long as I am in Assisi I must continue under your roof, since my mission demands it. But I trust, sir, that you will relieve me of your attendance, thus sparing me the memory of your offence, and yourself the sight of one whom you condemn so harshly."

"Madonna," he cried, "forgive me. I meant not as you think."

"Messer della Pieve," she answered, with a little cruel laugh of scorn, "to be frank, I care not greatly what you meant. But I beg that you will respect my wishes."

"Depend upon it that I will, Madonna," he answered bitterly, "and suffer me to take my leave of you."

He let the curtain fall, and even as he did so the litter came to a halt before the portals of his house — one of the handsomest palaces in Assisi, standing by the Duomo of San Rufino.

With a white, sullen face he watched her alight, leaning upon the arm of a footman who had hastened to discharge the pleasant duty that usually was Gianluca's own; then he doffed his hat, bowed frigidly, and, wheeling his horse, he rode slowly away, nursing his sorely lacerated pride, which the young Assisian mistook for injured love, just as he had mistaken for love the ambition which had caused him to lift his eyes to the future high and mighty Countess of Solignola.

It was, therefore, a very short-tempered young gentleman who found himself suddenly confronted and hailed by a tall, warlike fellow on a tall horse.

Messer Gianluca scowled at Cesare's captain. "I do not know you, sir," said he.

"That misfortune I am here to amend," said the bland Scipione.

"I do not seek your acquaintance," said Gianluca, still more rudely.

"You shall have it, none the less. For I have orders to force it upon you if necessary."

Now, these were ugly words to one whose conscience was not clear of treason. Della Pieve's dark mood was elbowed aside by fear.

"Is this an arrest?" he asked.

Scipione laughed. "Why, no," said he. "I am sent to escort you; that is all."

"And whither, sir?"

"Now, here's a catechism! To the Communal Palace, to repair your omission to wait upon His Highness of Valentinois."

Gianluca looked into the other's rugged face, and observed that it was friendly; he took courage, and made no more demur. And as they rode, he sought to draw information from Scipione, but finding the captain as close as an oyster, and mistrusting this closeness, he grew afraid again.

At the Communal Palace matters were no better. He was left to cool his heels in an ante-chamber for two hours and more, to await the return of the Duke, who was abroad. It was in vain that he begged to be allowed to depart, vowing that he would return anon. He was desired, for only answer, to be patient; and so the conviction was forced upon him that in some sort he was a prisoner. He remembered Baglioni's words, that the Duke had spies everywhere, and he began to fear the worst. So engrossed was he with these fears that all thought of Panthasilea faded utterly from his mind — that lesser matter being supplanted by this greater.

At length, when his torture of suspense had reached a climax, and he had begun to shiver in that chilly ante-room, an usher came to inform him that the Duke awaited him. Whether it was of intent that the Duke had submitted him to this suspense, to the end that through fear his spirit might be softened as metal in the furnace, it is not possible to say. But it may well be that some such purpose this crafty Duke had sought to serve, desiring as he did to ascertain precisely what was the attitude towards himself of this puissant gentleman of Assisi who had failed to come with his brother Anziani to take the oath of allegiance. Certain it is that Della Pieve was a very subdued and morally weakened young man when at length he was admitted to Cesare Borgia's presence.

He was ushered into the gloomy hall of the palace, which was lighted by windows set high in the wall, and decorated by a multitude of rampant lions — the Assisian emblem — frescoed in red upon a yellow ground, unpleasantly bewildering to the eye. The place was chill, for all that a wood fire was burning in the vast fireplace. About this stood a group of Cesare's captains and courtiers, talking and laughing, when Gianluca was admitted. His advent, however, was followed by a general and somewhat disconcerting silence, and he became the object of a no less disconcerting attention on the part of those same gentlemen, whilst here he caught a smile, and there a shrug, all serving to heighten his uneasiness.

He gained the middle of the chamber, and hung there pausing awkwardly for a moment. Then from the group the Duke's tall figure detached itself. His Highness was all in black, but his doublet was embroidered in arabesques of gold thread, so finely wrought that at the little distance separating them Gianluca thought him to be wearing damascened body-armour.

Cesare advanced, his pale young face very set and grave, fingers toying with his tawny beard, eyes sad and thoughtful.

"I have waited a week to give you welcome, Messer della Pieve," said he coldly. "As I seemed in danger of having to forgo the honour, I was constrained to send for you." And he paused, as if awaiting an explanation.

But Della Pieve had nothing to say. His mind seemed benumbed under the Duke's steady glance, under the eyes of all those gentlemen at the room's end.

It was Cesare's aim to determine whether Della Pieve's recusancy was that of active or of passive enmity. If passive, the man might go his ways; but active, Cesare must know more of it. And meanwhile he had been gathering information.

He had ascertained that Gianluca della Pieve had quitted Assisi on the eve of his own arrival, and had returned upon the morrow of that event, bringing with him a very beautiful lady, a kinswoman of his, it was put about. That lady was lodged in his palace, and was shown a great deference by her attendants.

Such was the sum of Cesare's information. Slight in itself; most certainly too slight to have aroused the

least suspicion against Della Pieve, had he but come
to take the oath. Viewed, however, in the light of
that recusancy and in conjunction with the sudden
pallor of the beauty in the litter at sight of Cesare, His
Highness judged that there was matter to be probed.
And now he had Della Pieve's confused and guilty
bearing to confirm him in that judgment.

As the Assisian offered no explanation, Cesare
passed to questions.

"Although you are one of the first citizens of Assisi,
you were not among the Anziani when the oath was
taken on Sunday last," he said. "I shall rejoice to
hear your motives for that absence."

"I — I was not in Assisi at the time, Magnificent,"
said Della Pieve.

"Aye — but dare you tell us where you were?"
cried Cesare sharply — and his tone was the tone of
one who questions upon matters fully known to him.
"I do not wonder that you hesitate to answer," he
added after a moment's pause, and thus completed
Gianluca's assurance that his movements were already
known.

"My lord," he faltered, "Count Guido was my
father's friend. We owed him many favours."

Here was knowledge gained, and upon it Cesare
built rapidly.

"I am not quarrelling with your visit to Solignola,"
he said slowly, and the stricken Gianluca never suspected that he, himself, had just afforded the first
intimation of that same visit. "Nor yet am I quarrelling with your friendship for Count Guido. My
displeasure is with the motives that led you to seek
him."

That fresh vague, random shot of Cesare's went home as had done the others. Gianluca blanched. Plainly all was known.

"My lord," he cried, "I swear before Heaven that I took no willing part in any of the measures determined at Solignola."

So! Measures had been determined at Solignola! Cesare turned it over in his mind, recalled the fact that Della Pieve had gone alone and had returned accompanied by a lady — the lady of the litter, the lady who had turned pale at the sight of him that day. Undoubtedly she was from Solignola. It remained to ascertain her identity.

"How am I to believe you?" he asked.

Della Pieve clenched his hands. "I have, of course, no means of proving what I say," he admitted miserably.

"Indeed you have, sir. There is one proof you are overlooking." Cesare's voice was very cold. "It is yours to use frankness with me now, and so convince me of your honesty. Yet you are careful to tell me nothing." His eyes narrowed, and again in that tone of one who is possessed of the fullest knowledge: "Not even," he added, "in the matter of this lady whom you fetched from Solignola with you on your return."

The Assisian recoiled as if he had been struck, unable to follow the simple method of inference by which Cesare had arrived at the conclusion that the lady was from Solignola, never dreaming that the Duke was but groping for information, and assured that the identity of Panthasilea must be known to this man with as many eyes as Argus.

He took refuge at the last in falsehood, touching the

motives of his visit to Count Guido's stronghold. "Magnificent," he began by way of preface, "since you know so much you will understand the rest."

"My present aim," said Cesare, "is to test your honesty."

Gianluca plunged headlong into the falsehoods he contemplated, praying Heaven that Cesare's information might be sufficiently limited to admit of his being believed.

"Why, is it not natural, Excellency, that, being determined upon this resistance, Count Guido should have desired to place his daughter in safety — to remove her from the perils and discomforts of a place besieged? In my having given her the shelter of my house, is there anything that reflects upon my honesty towards Your Highness? I have said that my father owed great favours to Count Guido. Could I, then, do less than I have done?"

Cesare stood surveying him, his face inscrutable. So! The lady was Count Guido's daughter. That was valuable knowledge gained. But that Count Guido's daughter should have come to Assisi — into Cesare's very camp — to seek safety and shelter was a foolish, clumsy lie. Therefore, there must be some other motive for her presence, which Gianluca found himself forced to withhold.

Thus reasoned the Duke. And having formed his sound conclusions, he shrugged and laughed scornfully. "Is this your honesty?" he asked. "Is it thus that you would prove that you are not my enemy?"

"It is the truth, my lord!"

"It is a lie, I say," the Duke retorted, raising his voice for the first time. "I am too well informed, sir, to be hoodwinked so easily." Then, dropping back to his calm, level tones: "You abuse my patience, sir," he said, "and you forget that there are the rack and the hoist below-stairs with which I can force the truth from you if necessary."

Gianluca's manhood rebelled at the threat. He braced himself by an effort of will, and looked the Duke boldly between the eyes, sustained by the courage of the desperate.

"Neither hoist nor rack could extract another word from me," he said; "for I have no more to tell."

Cesare continued to ponder him in silence. He was not prone to needless or fruitless cruelty. And he fancied that, having learned so much already, the rest might be discovered without resorting to the violence of the rack. For the moment, however, it was plain that Della Pieve would say no more. He nodded slowly.

"You have no more to tell me, eh? An ambiguous phrase, sir. But I think I read its real meaning."

He turned to the group about the hearth, which included the tall captain Scipione. He beckoned the condottiero to him.

"Baldassare," said he, "take Messer della Pieve hence, and place him under arrest until I make known my pleasure. Let him be closely confined with guards you can trust to allow him to commune with none."

It was not Cesare's intention to run the risk of Panthasilea's learning that her identity was known to him; for in that case the present gain would all be wasted, and the true aim of her presence in Assisi remain undiscovered.

The matter intrigued Cesare Borgia not a little. He took counsel that night with Agabito Gherardi, his shrewd, white-faced secretary; and Agabito, though by nature a mild and kindly man, had no hesitation in recommending that the torture should be employed to squeeze the last drop of truth from Messer della Pieve.

"We may come to it in the end," said Cesare. "But the moment, I fancy, is not propitious. There was in this fellow's face this morning a look as of willingness for martyrdom which does not augur well. I infer that he loves Count Guido's daughter, and, so, is strengthened in obstinacy. What is at the bottom of it all I cannot even guess. I swear it would baffle that crafty Florentine Secretary Macchiavelli — which is as much as to say the Devil himself."

And at that same hour Monna Panthasilea degli Speranzoni was in earnest talk with one of her faithful followers from Solignola, a youth named Giovanni. Until to-night the manner of approaching her task had baffled her completely, since Della Pieve had failed her in her original scheme. She had desired him to make pretence of loyalty to the Duke, and to present her as his kinswoman, Eufemia Bracci of Spoleto. But Della Pieve, out of repugnance for the whole affair, had refused, and so had thwarted her.

But now that at last she had seen her man, and taken his measure as much by his brave appearance as by the very ready gallantry expressed in the obeisance to which the mere sight of her had moved him, she saw her way; and she was laying her plans for the morrow with Giovanni.

The morrow dawned fair and clear, a day that was

more of April than of February. A soft wind was blowing from the south, warm and subtly fragrant, and from a cloudless, cobalt sky the sun shone genially upon the plain of Umbria, and struck fire and silver from the tumbling waters of the Tescio.

It was at the ford, almost under the very walls of Assisi, that Cesare Borgia, returning with a half-dozen gentlemen from an early morning ride to the camp under Solignola, came suddenly and unexpectedly upon Madonna Panthasilea.

She was seated upon the ground in a forlorn and dejected attitude, resting her shoulders against a grey boulder that had partly concealed her from the Duke's eyes until he was abreast of her. She was dressed in that bright russet gown in which you beheld her at her father's council; cut low in the bodice it revealed the perfection of her throat, the splendid column of her neck. Her bright hair was partly unbound, and strands of it caught the breeze and fluttered distractingly about her faintly tinted cheeks. Her veil had fallen back and slipped down on to her shoulders.

In the meadow, at some little distance, a riderless mule was cropping the short grass.

At sight of her, Cesare instantly swung himself from the saddle, and she had leisure to admire the athletic ease of the movement and the matchless grace of the man as he approached her, cap in hand, his long, bronze-coloured hair gleaming in the sunlight.

At a glance he had recognized her; at a glance perceived the plight — real or pretended — in which she found herself; and, however that might be, he rejoiced in this chance to come to grips with her.

He bowed profoundly, and she found herself looking into the gentlest and most beautiful eyes that she had ever seen. The appeal to her womanhood of this very perfect manhood, this splendid youth and strength of which he was the incarnation, was instant and irresistible. A pang shot through her at the thought of her task; her first qualm beset her with that first glance of his. But it was no more than the momentary outcry of her instincts under the shock of the encounter; immediately Reason's cold hand seized the reins of her will and governed it.

"You are hurt, Madonna," he murmured, in that gentle yet richly melodious voice that was one of his greatest charms. "The mischance you have suffered is very plain to see. Permit that we assist you?"

She smiled at him, and even as she smiled her mouth assumed a painful twist and grew as quickly smooth again. "It is my ankle," she complained, and put a hand to the injured limb.

"It must be bound," said he, and swifty loosed a scarf he wore about his body.

"No, no!" she cried — a cry of real alarm, as his sharp ears detected. "My women will tend it when I reach home. It is not far."

"Believe me," he insisted, "it should be bound at once."

She crimsoned under his glance. She looked up piteously and very beautiful, and made the crimsoning do service for a blush of virgin modesty.

"I implore you not to pain me by insisting," she pleaded. And he, playing his part as she played hers, lowered his eyes in submission, and shrugged his regret at such injudicious obstinacy.

She proceeded to tell him how she came in such a plight. "My mule had crossed the ford," she said, "and was mounting the hither bank when it slipped upon those stones, came down upon its knees and threw me off."

He looked grave concern. "Ungracious beast," said he, "to cast off so fair a burden!" And he added: "You should not ride forth alone, Madonna."

"It is not my custom. But on such a morning the spring, I think, was in my soul, and I was athirst for freedom."

"A dangerous thirst," said he, "the quenching of which has been the death of many. You should have considered all the Borgia soldiery aswarm about the countryside."

"What should I fear from them?" she asked him, bewitchingly innocent, her eyes wide. "You, yourself, are one — are you not? Must I, then, fear you?"

"Ah, Madonna," he cried, "'tis you fill me with fear."

"I?" quoth she, lips parting in a half-smile.

"Fear for this same freedom which you seem to prize, and which I prize no less. What man can account himself free who has met your glance? What man can be other than a slave thereafter?"

She laughed lightly as she turned aside that thrust in the high lines. "Why, here's a courtier," said she. "And I deemed you but a soldier."

"I am a courtier here, Madonna," he said, bowing low before her. "Elsewhere I am the Duke."

He watched the pretty play of feigned surprise upon her face; the simulated sudden confusion. "The Duke — you!"

"Your slave," said he.

"My lord, I have been blind — very blind. It had been better had I been as dumb. What must you deem me?"

He looked at her, and sighed. "Life is so short! I should not find it long enough to tell you."

She flushed again under his burning gaze; for despite suspicion and all else he found her — as all men must — very good to see; and his admiration showed clearly in his glance.

"We are forgetting my poor foot, my lord," she reminded him. "And I detain you. Perhaps one of your gentlemen will come to my assistance."

"Nay, in this office I will not be supplanted. But one of them shall fetch your mule." He turned, and sharply gave an order which sent his gentlemen all spurring towards the grazing beast. "Can you rise with help?" he asked her.

"I think I could."

He stooped, and crooked his arm. But she drew back. "Highness!" she murmured in confusion, "it were too much honour! By your leave, I will await one of your gentlemen."

"Not one of them shall have my leave to help you," he said, laughing, and again, insistently, he thrust his arm upon her notice.

"From such masterful ways — how can I defend myself?" said she, and taking his arm she rose painfully on her one sound foot; then lost her balance, and fell heavily against him with a little cry.

His arm flashed round her waist to steady her. Her hair lay an instant against his cheek; the sweet fragrance of her filled his brain. She murmured piteous excuses. He smiled, silent, and held her so until the mule was brought. Then, without a word, he lifted her in his arms as though she had been a child, and set her in the saddle. And the strength of him amazed her, as it had amazed many another to more hurtful purpose.

One covert but very searching glance he bestowed upon the mule's knees. As he had expected, they were smooth and glossy, and showed no slightest hurt or stain. It left him no doubt that her ankle was in like case, and with a little smile he turned and vaulted lightly into his own saddle. Then, coming beside her, he took the bridle of her mule in his right hand, and called to one of his gentlemen to protect her on the other flank.

"Thus, Madonna, you will be safe," he assured her. "And now — forward!"

They went down the short incline to the water, and splashed across the ford, and so rode forward into Assisi. As they went, the Duke talked slightly, and she responded with a ready tongue and many a side-long glance of admiration for his person and of pleasure in the flattering homage of his words, which was not wholly feigned. As they were entering the town, he asked her whither did she desire them to conduct her.

"To the house of my kinsman, Messer Gianluca della Pieve, by San Rufino."

Her kinsman! Here, considered Cesare, was more deception. How did she propose to call herself, he wondered; and bluntly asked her.

Her reply came readily. "I am Eufemia Bracci of Spoleto, Your Highness's devoted subject."

He made no answer to Eufemia Bracci of Spoleto.

But he smiled fondly upon her, such a sweet, guileless smile as assured her that Gianpaolo Baglioni had by much overrated his acuteness.

At the door of Della Pieve's house he took his leave of her. And at the last moment, and purely out of malice, he promised to send his own physician Torella to attend her; and he dissembled his amusement and his perception of the sudden fear that leaped for a moment to her eyes. She implored him not to think of it, assured him that a day's rest would mend her foot, and she was obviously relieved that he took her word for this, and did not insist.

He rode away bemused, and once back at the Communale he sent for Agabito Gherardi and told him what had passed.

"And so, Agabito," he concluded, "the Lady Panthasilea degli Speranzoni is here in Assisi, calling herself Eufemia Bracci of Spoleto, the kinswoman of Della Pieve. She has thrust herself upon my notice, and sought to enlist my interest and ensnare my senses. Can you read me this riddle?"

Agabito's round white face was contemptuously placid. "It is extremely simple," said he. "She is the bait in a trap that has been set for you."

"That, Agabito, is what I have been telling you. What I desire to know is the nature of the trap itself. Can you hazard me a guess?"

"The matter is too serious for guessing," replied the secretary, unmoved. "If I might venture to advise you, Highness, it is that you go armed abroad and with all precaution, and that you do not adventure yourself within the doors of the Palazzo Pieve save with an ample escort."

Cesare opened his black doublet to show Agabito the gleam of steel mesh he wore beneath. "Armed I am," said he. "But for the rest of your advice —" he shrugged. "There is a way of handling these traps so that they close upon those who set them. There was such a trap prepared for a man in Sinigaglia, not so long ago. But you know that story."

"In that case, my lord, you had precise knowledge of what was intended."

Cesare looked at the other, smiling cruelly. "Knowledge which the torture wrung from Messer Ramiro de Lorqua," he said. "Bid them prepare a hoist in the hall below to-night; and let the executioner and his assistants be summoned to await my pleasure."

Agabito departed, and the Duke turned his mind to other matters. That evening he sat late at supper with his gentlemen, and when he dismissed them it was to closet himself with Agabito and his clerks and keep them at work upon despatches for Rome and Florence until far into the night.

Towards midnight he turned to Agabito to inquire had all been made ready for the examination of Della Pieve; and then, even as the secretary was answering him, the door was opened and a servant entered quickly.

"What now?" demanded Cesare, frowning.

"Soldiers from the camp under Solignola, Magnificent, with a prisoner."

He raised his brows, surprised. "Admit them," he said. And a youth in peasant garb and cross-gartered leggings, his hands pinioned behind him, was led in between two men-at-arms. With them came a young officer of Corella's, whom Cesare instantly addressed.

"What is this?"

The officer saluted. "We took this man, Magnificent, less than an hour ago, upon the slopes under Solignola. He had eluded our sentries and was through our lines, and but that in the dark he loosed a boulder, and so drew our attention, he had gained the city. We found him to be the bearer of a letter written in cipher. But Don Michele was unable to induce him to say whence this letter or for whom."

He handed Cesare a small square of paper the seal of which had already been broken. The Duke took it, ran his eye over the array of baffling ciphers, examined the seal, and finally bore the paper to his nose and sniffed it. Very faintly he caught a fragrance that reminded him of a woman in a bright russet gown; just such a fragrance had he inhaled that morning during those brief moments in which she had lain in simulated helplessness against his breast.

He advanced towards the travestied messenger, his solemn eyes upon the man's calm, intrepid face.

"At what hour," he asked quietly, "did Madonna Panthasilea degli Speranzoni despatch you with this letter?"

The man's countenance changed upon the instant. Its calm was swept away by a consternation amounting to fear. He recoiled a step, and stared wild-eyed at this Duke, who watched him with such awful impassiveness.

"Men speak the truth of you!" he cried at last, carried away by his excited feelings.

"Rarely, my friend — believe me, very rarely." And the Duke smiled wistfully. "But what have you heard?"

"That you have made a compact with the Devil."

Cesare nodded. "It is as true as most things that are said of me. Take him away," he bade the officer. "Let him be confined in strictest solitude." Then to the youth: "You have nothing to fear," he said. "You shall come by no harm, and your detention shall not exceed a week at most."

The youth was led out in tears — tears for the mistress whom he served, persuaded that from this terrific Duke nothing was concealed.

Cesare tossed the note to Agabito. "Transcribe it for me," he said shortly.

"It is in cipher," said Agabito, bewildered at the order.

"But the key has been obligingly supplied. The last word is composed of eleven numerals, and of these the second, sixth, and last are the same. Assume that word to be 'Panthasilea.' It will simplify your task."

Agabito said no more, but bent, quill in hand, over the letter, whilst Cesare — a long scarlet figure in a furred robe that descended to his ankles — thoughtfully paced the chamber.

Soon the secretary rose, and handed Cesare the transcription.

I engaged his attention at last this morning, and I have made an excellent beginning. Within a few days now I count upon an opportunity to carry out the business. I am prepared. But I shall proceed slowly, risking nothing by precipitancy.   PANTHASILEA

Cesare read, and held the paper in a candle flame, reducing it to ashes. "It tells no more than we already knew. But that much it confirms. Mend the seal of the original, and let means be found to convey it to

Count Guido. Let one of my men replace the original messenger, then let him pretend that he is wounded, and so induce some rustic with a promise of good payment from Count Guido to bear the letter to Solignola.

"And let Corella be advised that he is to see to it that he captures no more messengers at present. Thus he will find it easier to complete the mine; for as long as the folk of Solignola depend upon my defeat here in Assisi and believe it to be progressing, they are not likely to be as vigilant as if they had but their own efforts to depend upon. And now for Messer della Pieve. Let him be sent for."

The Assisian gentleman had been confined in no dungeon. He was comfortably lodged in one of the chambers of the palace; his bed and board were such as befitted a gentleman of his station; and his jailers used him with all deference. Therefore it is no matter for marvel that he slept soundly on the night in question.

From that sleep he was rudely roused to find four men-at-arms in his chamber, looking grim and fantastic in the light of the single smoky torch that was held aloft by one of them.

"You are to come with us," said the man whose heavy hand still rested upon Gianluca's shoulder.

Della Pieve sat up in alarm, blinking, but wide-awake, his heart beating tumultuously.

"What is it?" he demanded in a quavering voice. "Whither must I go?"

"With us, sir," was all the answer he received — the man who answered him obeying to the letter the orders he had been given.

The poor gentleman looked fearfully from one to another of those bearded faces, gloomy and mysterious in the shadows of their steel morions. Then, resigning himself, he flung back the covers, and stepped from the bed.

A soldier cast a mantle over his shoulders, and said: "Come."

"But my clothes? Am I not to dress?"

"There is not the need, sir. Come."

Frozen now with fear, assured that his last hour had struck, Gianluca permitted them to conduct him barefoot as he was along chill passages, down a dark staircase, and into the very hall where yesterday he had been given audience by the Duke.

Into this was he now ushered, and so into a scene that Cesare had carefully prepared with the object of torturing the man's soul — a merciful object, after all, since thus he hoped to avoid the maiming of his body.

Ranged against the wall, midway up the chamber, stood a table draped in black. At this sat the black figure of the questioner, gowned and cowled like a monk. He was flanked by a clerk on either hand, and before each of these were paper, ink-horns, and quills. On the table stood two candle-branches, each bearing a half-dozen candles. There was no other light in that great vaulted chamber, so that the greater portion of it remained mysteriously in shadow.

On the hearth at the room's far end stood an iron tripod supporting a brazier in which the charcoal was glowing brightly. Thrust into the heart of this fire Gianluca observed with a shudder some wooden-handled implements to be heating.

Across the chamber, facing the questioner's table,

grey ropes, like the filaments of some gigantic cob-web, dangled from pulleys that were scarcely visible in the upper gloom of the groined ceiling — the tor-ture of the hoist. By these ropes stood two men in leathern vests, their muscular, hairy arms bared to the shoulder. A third man, similarly dressed, stood in the foreground making knots in a length of whipcord.

In mid-chamber — the one spot of colour in all that hideous greyness — stood Cesare Borgia in his long scarlet gown, thumbs hooked into his silken girdle, a scarlet cap upon his head. His eyes were infinitely sad and wistful as they rested now upon Gianluca.

The young Assisian stood there and looked about him in dread fascination. He knew now to what purpose he had been awakened and dragged from his bed. He fought for air a moment; the beating of his heart was stifling him. He reeled, and was steadied by the leathern-clad arm of one of the soldiers.

No word had been spoken, and the silence entered into alliance with the chill breath of the place, with the gloom and with the horror of preparations indis-tinctly revealed, to make the scene appear to Gian-luca as some terrific nightmare. Then at a sign from Cesare the executioner's assistants advanced, almost silent-footed, to receive the patient from the soldiers. These surrendered him and clattered out.

Gianluca was led forward to the table, and stood there between his two fearsome guards to face the questioner.

From the depths of the cowl a cold voice spoke, and to Gianluca it seemed to ring and boom through the vaulted place.

"Messer Gianluca della Pieve," said the voice,

"you are guilty of having conspired with Count
Guido degli Speranzoni, Tyrant of Solignola, against
the High and Mighty Lord Cesare Borgia, Duke of
Valentinois and Romagna; and of having prepared
here in Assisi a pitfall for this same High and Mighty
Lord. Thereby you have deserved death. But worse
than death have you deserved when it is considered
that His Highness is Gonfalonier of Holy Church,
that the battles he fights are the battles of Holy See.
Therefore have you sinned not only against the
Duke's Magnificence, but against God and His
Earthly Vicar, our Holy Father the Pope. Yet, since
the Church has said, 'Nolo mortem peccatoris, sed ut
magis convertatur et vivat,' His Highness in our
Holy Father's name desires to spare you so that you
make frank and full confession of your sin."

The booming voice ceased; yet echoes of it still
reverberated through the tortured brain of Gianluca.
He stood there, swaying feebly, considering his course.
He hung his head.

"Look behind you," the voice bade him, "and
behold for yourself that we do not lack the means to
unseal your lips should you prove obstinate."

But Gianluca did not look. He did not need to
look. He shivered; but still said no word.

The questioner made a sign. One of the executioners whipped the cloak from Gianluca's shoulders,
and left that poor gentleman standing in his shirt.
He felt himself seized by strong — cruelly strong —
hands. They turned him about, and dragged him
across the room towards the hoist. Midway he hung
back, throwing his entire weight upon their arms to
check them.

"No, no!" he pleaded through ashen lips.

Suddenly the Duke spoke. "Wait!" he said, and, stepping forward, barred their way. He waved his hand, and the executioners fell back, leaving Gianluca alone with His Highness in mid-apartment.

"Messer della Pieve," said Cesare gently, and he placed a hand upon the Assisian's shoulder, "consider what you do; consider what is before you. I do not think the questioner has made that clear enough. You have seen the hoist at work; you have perhaps seen it wrench a man's shoulders from their sockets." And his steely fingers tightened about the shoulder that he held, until it seemed to Gianluca that a thousand threads of fire were coursing down his arm. He gasped in pain, and the Duke's grip at once relaxed. Cesare smiled — a smile of tender, infinite pity.

"Consider by that how little you are fitted to endure the cord. Be assured that you will speak in the end. And what do you think would follow? Your release? Indeed, no. If once the cords of the hoist have grappled you, you become the property of the law; and when the law has made you speak, it will silence you forever. Consider that. From the agonies of a broken body your release lies through the hangman's hands. Consider that you are young — that life has much to offer you, and consider above all that your silence will profit no one, your speech betray no one that is not betrayed already — that your obstinacy will lead you to sacrifice yourself for no useful purpose."

Gianluca's eyes looked piteously at the Duke from out of his ashen face.

"If — if I could believe that!" he murmured.

"It is easy to convince you, and in convincing you of that I shall convince you also of my own disinterestedness in seeking to save you even now.

"Learn, then, that Madonna Panthasilea degli Speranzoni has already spread her net for me; that to-day she thrust herself upon my notice; that to-night she sent a letter to her father informing him of this good beginning, and that within a week she looks to accomplish her treacherous work and take me in her toils.

"Knowing so much already, am I likely to fall a victim to this thing they plan? Can anything that you may add be of so much moment that you should suffer torture and death sooner than reveal it?"

Gianluca shivered. "What do you desire to know?" he asked. "What can I add? You seem already to know all — more even than do I. Or is it," he added in sudden apprehension, "that you seek my evidence to use it against this lady?"

"Already have I all the evidence I need, were such my aim. There is the letter which she wrote her father. That alone would doom her did I desire it. No, no. All that I seek to learn from you is the precise nature of this trap that has been prepared. You will see that in telling me you can no longer do any hurt to Count Guido or his daughter."

"Why — if that is all —"

"That is all," said Cesare. "A little thing. And there stands the horrible alternative awaiting you. Could I be more generous? Speak, and you may return to bed; I shall hold you a prisoner for caution's sake until Solignola falls. Then you may go your

ways in perfect freedom. I pledge you my word for
that. Be silent, and —" He waved a hand to the
grey cords of the hoist, and shrugged.

That was the end of Della Pieve's silence. He saw
clearly that no purpose could be served by persisting
in it; that he would but sacrifice himself in vain —
and this for a woman who had deemed his love presumptuous and had used him with so little mercy.
So he told the Duke the little thing His Highness
sought to know — that his abduction was the purpose of the conspiracy, the aim for which Madonna
Panthasilea was in Assisi.

Towards noon upon the morrow a very dainty page
in the Duke's livery came to Della Pieve's house bearing a scented letter in Cesare's own hand, wherein His
Highness, like the humblest suitor, craved permission to come in person and receive news of Monna
Eufemia Bracci.

Panthasilea's eyes sparkled as she read. Her plans
were speeding marvellously. Fortune for once was
arrayed against this Cesare Borgia whose proverbial
luck had caused him to be dubbed "*Filius Fortunæ*."

The permission His Highness sought she very
readily accorded, and so it fell out that the Borgia
came in person some few hours later. Leaving his
splendid cavalcade to await him in the little square,
he went alone into her house.

He came magnificently arrayed, as a suitor should.
His doublet was of cloth of gold; milk-white one silken
hose, sky-blue the other, and the girdle and carriages
of his sword were ablaze with jewels worthy many a
principality.

He found her in a chamber whose window-doors opened upon the topmost of the garden's several terraces, and it was a room that was a worthy setting for so rare a gem. Eastern carpets were spread upon the mosaic floor, rich tapestries arrayed the walls; books and a lute stood upon an ebony table that was inlaid with ivory figures. By the fireplace two of her women were at work upon the embroidering of an altar-cloth, whilst Madonna herself reclined upon a low couch of Eastern pattern. A subtle fragrance hung upon the air — the bitter-sweet of lilac essences, a trace of which he had yesternight detected in the intercepted letter.

Upon his entrance she made as if to rise; but in that he checked her. With sweet concern he forbade the effort, and swiftly crossed the room to stay her by force if need be; whereupon she sank back, smiling.

She was all in white, coiffed in a golden net from which a sapphire, large as a bean, hung upon her brow.

One of her women hastened to approach a low chair of antique design, whose feet, carved in the form of the lion's paw, were of solid silver. He sat, and solicitously inquired how fared Madonna's ankle, to receive her assurance that by to-morrow it should bear her weight again.

Their interview was brief, perforce, and flavoured by hints from him of the deep regard he had conceived for her; it was confined to pretty play of courtly speeches, a game of fence at which Madonna Eufemia Bracci of Spoleto showed herself no novice.

And yet, tightly strung to her task though she was, she feasted her eyes upon the rare grace and beauty of his resplendent presence, nor repelled the dangerous rapture which his haunting eyes and soft melodious voice aroused in her.

When at length he departed, he left her very thoughtful.

On the morrow he returned, and again upon the following day; and ever did the cavalcade await him in the square below. The game began to interest him beyond all his expectations. This thrusting of his head into the lion's maw afforded him sensations such as he had never yet experienced; this hunting the hunters, this befooling the befoolers, was no new thing to him, but never had he engaged upon it under circumstances more entertaining.

On the occasion of his third visit he found her alone, her women having been dismissed before his entrance. Wondering what fresh move in the game might this portend, he dropped upon one knee to thank her for the signal favour of it, and bore her fragrant hand to his devout lips. But her face was very grave, and for the first time she surprised him.

"My lord," she said, "you mistake me. I have dismissed my women because I had that to say to you which you must prefer that I say without witnesses. My lord, you must visit me no more."

For once in his life he was so astonished that he permitted his countenance to reflect his feelings. Yet she mistook for chagrin the sudden change she saw there.

"I must visit you no more, Madonna!" he cried, and his accents confirmed her impression. "How have I offended? Tell me, that on my knees, here at your feet, I may atone."

Gently she shook her head, gazing down upon him

with a tender sadness. "How should you have offended, my lord? Rise, I implore you."

"Not until I know my sin." And his eyes were the eyes of the humblest suppliant at a shrine.

"You have not sinned, my lord. It is —" She bit her lip; a gentle colour warmed her cheek. "It is that I — I must think of my good name. Oh, have patience with me, Highness! You will make me the talk of this scandal-mongering town if daily your escort is seen awaiting you below whilst you come to visit me."

At last he understood the fiendish subtlety at work within that lovely head. "And is that all?" he cried. "Is there no other reason — none?"

"What other reason should there be?" she murmured, eyes averted.

"Why, then, it is soon remedied. In future I will come alone."

She pondered a moment, and gently shook her head. "Best not, my lord. Indeed, that were worse. You would be seen to enter. And coming thus — oh! what would folks not say?"

He sprang up, and boldly put an arm about her. She suffered it, but he felt the shudder that ran through her. "Does it matter — what they say?" quoth he.

"Not — not to you, my lord. But me — consider me. What is a maid's fair name once it is blown upon by scandal?"

"There — there is a back way — by your garden. Thus none would see me. Give me the key, Eufemia."

Under lowered lids he watched her face, saw what he looked for, and released her. Inwardly he smiled.

He was the very prince of amorous boobies, of love-lorn fools — the most obliging numskull that ever dashed into a trap prepared for him. So she was thinking, not a doubt, in a mental glow at the subtleties of her poor strategy.

She stood trembling before him. "My lord, I — I — dare not."

So much fencing began to nauseate him; the daring of it amounted to folly and moved him to some contempt. He grew cold upon the instant.

"So be it, then," said he. "I will not come again."

He reduced her now to terror. He saw the quick alarm that leapt to her dark eyes. He admired her swift recovery of a situation that was slipping from her grasp.

"My lord, you are angry with me." She hid her face on his shoulder. "You shall have the key," she murmured.

He departed with it, persuaded that she was the most callous, heartless traitress that had ever drawn the breath of life. He might have thought differently had he seen her as she sat there after his departure, weeping bitterly and reviling herself most cruelly. And yet that night she wrote to her father to tell him that all was speeding excellently, and that the end was near.

And Solignola, lulled more and more by these messages and by the desultory manner in which the siege was being conducted, kept but indifferent watch. They heard at times the blows of picks under the southern wall of the citadel, and they knew that Corella's men were at work there. But they no longer sallied to disperse them, deeming it but an idle waste

of life now that another and more effective method
of checkmate was all but in their grasp.

The following afternoon was well advanced when
Cesare Borgia tapped upon the window-doors of the
room in which it was Panthasilea's custom to receive
him. He found her alone, and there was some confusion in her manner of receiving him now that he came
in secret, as a lover avowed. But he was that day the
very incarnation of discretion.

They talked of many things that afternoon, and
presently their talk drifting by the way of the verse of
Aquilano to the writings of Sperulo, who had followed
Cesare's banner as a soldier, the Duke fell into remi-
niscences. He spoke of himself for once, and of his
task in Italy and his high aims; and as he talked her
erstwhile wonder at the difference betwixt what she
found in him and what she had looked for arose again.
He was, she had been told, a man compounded of
craft and ambition; harsh, unscrupulous, terrible to
foe and friend alike; a man devoid of heart, and therefore pitiless. She found him so gentle, courtly, and
joyous, and of so rare a sweetness of thought and
speech that she was forced to ask herself, Might not
envy of his great achievements and his strength be
the true source of the hatred in which he was held by
those upon whom he warred?

A tall-necked Venetian flagon of sweet Puglia wine
stood that afternoon upon the table, having been left
there by her woman; and, moved by an impulse she
could scarce explain, she poured a cup for him when
towards dusk he rose to take his leave. He came to
stand beside her by the table whilst she brimmed the
goblet, and when she would have filled another for
herself, he covered the vessel with his hands.

It was as if some of the passion latent in him, at which, as if despite him, his ardent glance had hinted none too seldom, leapt of a sudden forth.

"Nay, nay," said he, his great eyes full upon her, their glance seeming to envelop her, and hold her as in a spell. "One cup for us twain, I do beseech you, lady, unworthy though I be. Pledge me, and leave on the wine the fragrance of your lips ere I pledge you in my turn. And if I reel not hence ecstatically, divinely drunk, why, then, I am a clod of earth."

She demurred a little, but his will made sport with hers as does the breeze in autumn with the leaf; and he watched her the while for all the hot passion that seemed to film his eyes. For he was acquainted with drugged wines, and such pretty artifices, and had no fancy for unnecessary risks in this game he was playing.

But this wine was innocent. She drank, and handed him the cup. He bent his knee to receive it, and drained it, kneeling, his eyes upon her face.

Thereafter he took his leave of her, and she stood at the window looking after his departing figure as it descended the garden and was merged at last into the thickening gloom. Then she shivered, a sob broke from her quivering lips, and she sank limp into a chair, again as yesterday to fall aweeping for no reason in the world that was apparent.

And again that night she wrote to the Count, her father, that all was going better than she could have dared to hope, and that within three days she looked to place in the hands of those who waited that which should enable them to purchase the emancipation of Solignola.

He came again upon the morrow, and upon the morrow of that again; and now Count Guido's daughter entered upon a season of sore experiences. In Cesare's absence she ripened her plans for his ultimate capture; in his presence she was all numb, fascinated by him, filled with horror and self-loathing at her task, the very creature of his will.

At last was reached that fateful evening that had been settled for the Judas deed. He came at nightfall, as she had begged him — urging her request as an added precaution against scandal — and he found her awaiting him in the gloom, no other light in the chamber save that of the logs that blazed upon the hearth. He took her hand and bore it to his lips. It was ice-cold and trembled in the clasp of his as trembled all her body now. He scanned her face and saw that it was drawn, for all that its pallor was dissembled by the ruddy firelight. He saw that she could not bear his gaze, and so concluded — as already he had suspected — that the snare was to be sprung to-night.

"Eufemia!" he cried. "My Eufemia, how cold you are!"

She shivered at the endearment, at the soft caress of his voice, the pleading ardour of his eyes. "It — it is very chill," she faltered. "The wind is in the north."

He turned from her and crossed again to the windows, her glance following him. He drew the heavy curtains close, and shut out what little daylight yet lingered in the sky.

"So," he said, "it will be more snug within."

He was dressed from head to foot in the warm red-brown of leaves in autumn; and as he stood there against the dark background of the curtains, the red light of the logs, playing over the smooth velvet of his doublet and the shimmering silk of his hose, turned him into a man of flame; and of shifting liquid fire seemed the girdle of gold scales that clasped his waist.

Tall, majestic, and magnificently lithe and graceful, he seemed to her now the very embodiment of perfect manhood. More than man he seemed in the fantastic, ardent panoply he borrowed from the firelight.

He moved, and fire glowed and shot, quivered, vanished, and gleamed again along his scaly girdle. He took her hands and drew her down beside him on the Eastern settle, out of the firelight's direct range, yet so that her face remained illumined.

She submitted despite herself. All her instincts cried out against this dangerous propinquity, thus in the flame-lit gloom.

"I — I will call for lights," she faltered, but made no attempt to rise or to disengage the hand he held.

"Let be," he answered gently. "There is light enough, and I have not long to stay."

"Ah?" she breathed the question and felt her heartbeats quickening.

"But a moment; and I am more grieved since it is my last evening here with you."

He noted the guilty start, the sudden spasm of fear that rippled across her face, the quivering, half-stifled voice in which she asked: "But why?"

"I am the slave of harsh necessity," he explained. "Work awaits me. To-morrow at dawn we deliver the final assault which is to carry Solignola."

Here was news for her. It seemed that not an hour too soon had she resolved to act.

"You — are certain that it will be final?" she questioned, intrigued by his assurance, eager to know more.

He smiled with confidence. "You shall judge," said he. "There is a weakness in the walls to the south under the hill, spied out from the commencement by Corella. Since then we have spent the time in mining at that spot; and there has been during these last days an odd lack of vigilance on the part of Count Guido's followers. Solignola seems as a town lulled by some false hope. This has served us well. Our preparations are complete. At dawn we fire the mine, and enter through the breach."

"So that I shall see you no more," said she, feeling that something she must say. And then, whether urged by make-believe or by sheer femininity, she continued: "Will you ever think again, I wonder, when you pass on to further conquests, of poor Eufemia Bracci and her loneliness in Spoleto?"

He leaned towards her, his head thrust forward; and his eyes, glowing in the half-light, looked deeply into hers, so deeply that she grew afraid, thinking he must see the truth in the very soul of her. Then he rose, and moved away a step or two until he stood in the full glow of the fire, one velvet-shod foot on the andiron. Outside the window he had heard the gravel crunch. Some one was moving here. Her men, no doubt.

He stood awhile like a man deep in thought, and she watched him with something in her face that he would have found baffling had he seen it. Her right hand was playing fretfully about her throat and heaving bosom, betraying by its piteous movements the stifling feeling that oppressed her.

Suddenly he turned to her. "Shall I come back to you, my Eufemia?" he asked in a hushed but very ardent voice. "Would you have it so?" And he flung out his arms to her.

Her glance upraised met his own, and her senses reeled under those imperious eyes instinct with a passion that seemed to enwrap her as in a mesh of fire. Suddenly she began to weep.

"My lord, my dear lord!" she sobbed.

She rose slowly, and stood there swaying, a poor, broken thing whelmed by a sudden longing for the shelter of those outstretched arms, yet horribly afraid, with a mysterious fear, and filled, too, with self-loathing for the treachery she had plotted. Once it had seemed to her that she did a noble and glorious thing. Now of a sudden, in the very hour of accomplishment, she saw it vile beyond all vileness.

"Eufemia, come!" he bade her.

"Ah, no, no," she cried, and hid her burning face in her trembling hands.

He advanced, and touched her. "Eufemia!" The appeal in his voice was a seduction irresistible.

"Say — say that you love me," she pleaded piteously, urged to demand it by her last remaining shred of self-respect — for in all their communion hitherto not one word of love had he included in the homage he had paid her.

He laughed softly. "That is a bombardment with which any clown may win a citadel," said he. "I ask a free surrender."

His arms went round her as she fell sobbing on his breast, willing and unwilling, between gladness and terror. She was crushed against him; his lips were scorching hers. Her sobs were stifled. If to her eyes he had seemed a thing of flame a moment since, to her senses now he was live fire — a fire that seared its way through every vein and nerve of her, leaving ecstatic torture in its wake.

Thus they clung; and the leaping firelight made one single and gigantic shadow of them upon wall and ceiling.

Then he gently disengaged the arms that had locked themselves about his neck, and gently put her from him.

"And now, farewell," he said. "I leave my soul with you. My body must elsewhere."

At that, remembering her men who waited in the garden, her terror rose about her like a flood. She clutched his breast. "No, no!" she cried hoarsely, eyes wide in horror.

"Why, what is this?" he protested, smiling; and so sobered her.

"My lord," she panted, controlling herself as best she could. "Ah, not yet, my lord!"

She was mad now. She knew not what she said, nor cared. Her only aim was to keep him there — to keep him there. He must not be taken. Her men must be dismissed. She must tell him. How, she knew not; but she must confess; she must warn him, that he might save himself. So ran her thoughts in a chaotic turbulence.

"I know not when I may see you next. You ride at dawn. Cesare, give me an hour — a little hour."

She sank down, still clutching the furred edge of his doublet. "Sit here beside me awhile. There is something — something I must say before you go."

Obediently he sank down beside her. His left arm went round her, and again he drew her close. "Say on, sweet lady," he murmured, "or be silent at your pleasure. Since you bid me stay, that is enough for me. I stay, though Solignola remain unconquered for to-morrow."

But in surrendering to his clasp once more, her courage left her; it oozed away, leaving her no words in which to say the thing she longed to say. A sweet languor enthralled her as she lay against his breast.

Time sped. The logs hissed and crackled, and the play of firelight gradually diminished. The flames lessened and died down, and under a white crust of ash the timbers settled to a blood-red glow that lighted but a little space and left black shadow all about the lovers.

At long length, with a sigh, the young Duke gently rose, and moved into the little lighted space.

"The hour is sped — and more," said he.

From the shadows a sigh answered his own, followed by the hiss of a quickly indrawn breath. "You must not leave me yet," she said. "A moment — give me a moment more."

He stooped, took up an iron, and quickened the smouldering fire, thrusting into the heart of it a half-burned log or two that had escaped consumption. Flames licked out once more; and now he could discern her huddled there, chin in palms, her face gleaming ghostly white in the surrounding gloom.

"You love me?" she cried. "Say that you love me, Cesare. You have not said it yet."

"Does it still need words?" he asked, and she accounted that caress of his voice sufficient answer.

She hid her face in her hands and fell asobbing. "Oh, I am vile! Vile!"

"What are you saying, sweet?"

"It is time that you knew," she said, with an effort at control. "Awhile ago you might have heard steps out yonder had you listened. There are assassins in the garden, awaiting you, brought here by my contriving."

He did not stir, but continued to look down upon her, and in the firelight she saw that he smiled; and it flashed upon her that so great was his faith in her, he could not believe this thing she told him — conceived, perhaps, that she was jesting.

"It is true," she cried, her hands working spasmodically. "I was sent hither to lure you into capture that you may be held as a hostage for the safety of Solignola."

He seemed slightly to shake his head, his smile enduring still.

"All this being so, why do you tell me?"

"Why? Why?" she cried, her eyes dilating in her white face. "Do you not see? Because I love you, Cesare, and can no longer do the thing I came to do."

Still there was no change in his demeanour, save that his smile grew sweeter and more wistful. She was prepared for horror, for anger, or for loathing from him; but for nothing so terrible as this calm, fond smile. She watched it, drawing back in fascinating horror, as she would not have drawn back from his poniard had he made shift to kill her for her treachery. Sick and faint she reclined there, uttering no word.

Then, smiling still, Cesare took a taper from the over-mantel, and thrust it into the flame.

"Do not make a light!" she pleaded piteously; and, seeing that he did not heed her, she hid her scarlet face in her hands.

He held the flame of the taper to each of a cluster of candles in the branch that stood upon the table. In the mellow light he surveyed her a moment in silence — smiling still. Then he took up his cloak, and flung it about him. Without another word he stepped towards the window.

It was clear to her that he was going; going without a word of reproach or comment; and the contempt of it smote her cruelly.

"Have you nothing to say?" she wailed.

"Nothing," he answered, pausing, one hand already upon the curtains.

Under the spur of pain, under the unbearable lash of his contempt, a sudden mad revulsion stirred within her.

"The men are still there," she reminded him, a fierce menace in her tone.

His answer seemed to shatter her wits. "So, too, are mine, Panthasilea degli Speranzoni."

Crouching, she stared at him, and a deathly pallor slowly overspread a face that shame and anger had so lately warmed. "You knew?" she breathed.

"From the hour I met you," answered he.

"Then — then — why —?" she faltered brokenly, leaving her sentence for his quick wit's completing.

At last he raised his voice, and it rang like stricken bronze.

"The lust of conquest," he answered, smiling fiercely. "Should I, who have brought a dozen states to heel, fail to reduce me Count Guido's daughter?

I set myself to win this duel against you and your woman's arts, and your confession, when it came, should be the admission that I was conqueror in your heart and soul as I am conqueror elsewhere."

Then he dropped back into his habitual, level tones. "For the rest," he said, "such was their confidence in you up there in Solignola that they relaxed their vigilance and afforded me the time I needed to prepare the mine. That purpose, too, I had to serve."

The curtain-rings clashed, as he bared the windows.

She struggled to her feet, one hand to her brow, the other to her heart.

"And I, my lord?" she asked in a strangled voice. "What fate do you reserve for me?"

He considered her in the golden light. "Lady," said he, "I leave you the memories of this hour."

He unlatched the window-doors, and thrust them wide. A moment he stood listening, then drew a silver whistle, and blew shrilly upon it.

Instantly the garden was astir with scurrying men who had lain ambushed. Across the terrace one came bounding towards him.

"Amedeo," he said, "you will make prisoners what men are lurking here."

One last glance he cast at the white, crouching figure behind him, then passed into the darkness, and without haste departed.

At dawn the mine was fired, and through the breach Solignola was carried by assault, and Cesare the conqueror sat in the citadel of the Speranzoni.

THE PASQUINADE

THE lute strings throbbed under the touch of the fair-haired stripling in green and gold. His fresh young voice was singing Messer Francesco Petrarca's madrigal:

> " Non al suo amante piu Diana piacque
> Quando, per tal ventura, tutta ignuda
> La vide in mezzo delle gelide acque " —

At this point, and inspired perhaps by the poet's words, Cardinal Farnese — that handsome voluptuary — leaned over the Princess of Squillace, sighing furiously and whispering things which none might overhear.

The scene was the spacious Pontifical Chamber of the Vatican — the Sala dei Pontefici — with its wide semi-circular colonnade overlooking the beautiful gardens of the Belvedere, and its wonderfully frescoed ceiling where panels recording the deeds of popes hung amid others depicting the gods of pagan fable. There was Jupiter wielding his thunderbolts; there Apollo driving the chariot of the Sun; there Venus and her team of doves, Diana and her nymphs, Ceres and her wheat sheaves; and there Mercury in his winged cap, and Mars in all the panoply of battle. Interwrought were the signs of the Zodiac and the emblems of the seasons.

The time was early autumn, when cooler breezes begin to waft away the pestilential humours that overhang the plain of Rome during the sweltering period of Sol in Leo.

A vast concourse thronged the noble apartment — an ever-shifting kaleidoscope of gorgeous human fragments — the purple of prelates, the grey steel of soldiers, the silks of rustling courtiers of both sexes, as many-hued as the rainbow itself, and here and there the sober black of clerks and of ambassadors.

At the chamber's farthest end, on a low dais, sat the imposing figure of Roderigo Borgia, Ruler of the World, Father of Fathers, under the title of Alexander VI. He was robed in the pontifical white, the white house-cap upon his great head. Although in his seventy-second year, he retained a vigour that was miraculous, and seemed a man still in his very prime. There was a fire in the dark, Spanish eyes — eyes that still retained much of that erstwhile dangerous magnetism whereof Gasparino da Varano wrote so eloquently some years ago — a ring in the rich voice and an upright carriage in the tall, full figure that argued much youth still lingering in this amazing septuagenarian.

Near him, on the stools upon which the Teutonic Master of Ceremonies had, with his own hands, placed cushions covered with cloth of gold, sat the lovely, golden-haired Lucrezia Borgia, and the no less lovely, no less golden, Giulia Farnese, named by her contemporaries Giulia La Bella.

Lucrezia, in a stomacher stiff with gold brocade and so encrusted with gems of every colour as to lend her a splendour almost barbaric, watched the scene before her and listened to the boy's song with a rapt expression in her blue eyes, her fan of ostrich plumes moving slowly in her jewelled fingers. She was in her twenty-second year, divorced of one husband and widowed of the other, yet preserving a singular and very winsome childishness of air.

In the corner of the room, on the far right hand of the dais, her brother Giuffredo, Prince of Squillace, a slim, graceful, pale-faced youth, stood gnawing his lip, his brows contracted in a frown as he watched his Aragonese wife, who, in the distance, was shamelessly wantoning with Farnese.

A certain bold beauty was this Donna Sancia's endowment despite the sallowness of her skin, a tint that was emphasized by the ruddiness of her henna-dyed hair. She was something fleshy, with full red lips and large liquid eyes of deepest brown, low-lidded and languorous, which of themselves betrayed her wanton nature and justified her husband's constant torture of jealousy.

But with all this our concern is slight. It is no more than the setting of another tragi-comedy of jealousy that was being played that afternoon in the Sala dei Pontefici.

Over by the colonnade, Beltrame Severino, a tall, black-browed gentleman of Naples, was leaning against one of the pillars, apparently concerned with the singing-boy and the company in the chamber, in reality straining his jealous ears to catch what was passing between a youth and a maid who stood apart from the rest, in the loggia that overlooked the gardens.

The youth was one Messer Angelo d'Asti, a fair-headed son of Lombardy, who had come to Rome to seek his fortune, and was installed as secretary to the

Cardinal Sforza-Riario. He had a lively wit, and he was a scholar and something of a poet; and the Cardinal, his master, who, to a desire to be known as a patron of the arts, added an undeniable taste for letters, treasured him the more on that account.

Let the Cardinal Sforza-Riario love him to a surfeit for his verses. With that, Beltrame, his rival, had no concern. What plagued the lithe and passionate Neapolitan was Lavinia Fregosi's interest in those same verses and in their author. For, indeed, this progress of Angelo's in Lavinia's regard was growing so marked that Beltrame accounted it high time to be up and doing if he would be saved the pain of submitting to defeat.

As he leaned now against his pillar, urged by his jealousy to play the eavesdropper, he caught some such words as: "... in my garden to-morrow ... afternoon ... an hour before the Angelus ..."

The rest he missed. But what he caught was sufficient to lead him to conclude that she was giving an assignation to this Lombard poetaster — it was thus, with a man's nice judgment of his rival, that Beltrame dubbed Messer Angelo.

He narrowed his eyes. If Messer Angelo thought that to-morrow afternoon, an hour before the Angelus, he was to enjoy the felicity of undisturbed communion with Monna Lavinia, he was sowing disappointment for himself. Beltrame would see to that. He was your dog-in-the-manger type of lover, who would allow to no other what he might not himself enjoy.

As the boy's song came to an end, and a murmur of applause rolled through the room, the twain came forward through the pillars, and so upon the Neapolitan. The latter attempted to greet Lavinia with a smile and Angelo with a scowl at one and the same time; finding the performance impossible, he was feeling foolish and therefore increasingly angry, when, suddenly, a diversion was created.

A brisk step rang through the chamber, to the martial jingle of spurs. Men were falling back, and a way was opening of itself before some newcomer, who must be of importance to command so much by his mere presence. A curious silence, too, was creeping over all.

Beltrame turned, and craned his neck. Down the middle of the long room, looking neither to right nor to left, and taking no account of the profound bows that greeted his advance, came the tall figure of the Duke of Valentinois. He was dressed in black, booted and armed, and he strode the length of the Pontifical Chamber as if it were a drill ground. His face was white, an angry fire glowed in his eyes, and his brows were drawn together. In his right hand he carried a sheet of parchment.

Arrived before the dais, he bent his knee to the Pope, who had watched the unusual character of his son's advent with a look that plainly reflected his surprise.

"We have been expecting you," said Alexander, speaking with the slight lisp peculiar to him; and he added, "but not thus."

"I have had that to do which has delayed me, Holiness," replied the Duke as he rose. "The lampoonists are at work again. It is not enough that I deprived the last of these obscene slanderers of his

tongue and his right hand that he might never utter
or pen another ribaldry. Already he has an imitator
— a poet this time." He sneered. "And not a doubt
but that unless we make an example of him he will
not lack a following."

He held out the parchment that he carried, unfolded and smoothed it with an angry hand. "This
was attached to the plinth of the statue of Pasquino.
Half Rome had been to see it and to laugh over it
before news reached me, and I sent Corella to tear it
down and fetch it me. Read it, Holiness."

Alexander took the parchment. His face had reflected none of Cesare's anger whilst the latter was announcing the cause of it. It remained smooth now
that he read, until at last it broke into creases of
amusement.

"Do you smile, Holiness?" quoth Cesare in the
angry tone that he alone dared use to the father who
at once loved and feared him.

Alexander laughed outright. "Why, what is here
to fret you so?" he asked. He handed the parchment
to Lucrezia, inviting her to read. But no sooner had
her fingers closed over it than Cesare snatched it impatiently away from her, and left her staring.

"By your leave — no," he said. "Enough have
laughed already." And he looked with meaning at
the Pope. Here at least he had expected sympathy
and an indignation responsive to his own; instead of
which he had found but amusement.

"Come," said the Holy Father soothingly, "the
thing is witty, and it has none of the more usual lewd-
ness; nor yet is it so gross an exaggeration of the truth,
when all is said." And he rubbed his great nose
reflectively.

"Your indifference is comprehensible, Holiness," said Cesare. "The thing does not touch yourself."

"Pshaw!" said the Pope with a broad gesture. "What if it did? Am I the man to waste heat upon anonymous pasquinaders? My child, the great shall never lack defamers. It is the price of greatness in a mean world. Be thankful that it has pleased God to make you worth defaming. As for the earthworms that pen ribaldries — why, if their lampoons are witty, relish them; if merely stupid, ignore them."

"You may be as patient as you please, Holiness. Patience becomes your sovereign station." He seemed never so faintly, to sneer. "As for myself — I am resolved to stamp out this passion for lampoons. Slander shall be driven down into its lair of filth and mud, and choked there by my justice. Let me but find the author of this pasquinade, and, I swear to God," he went on, raising his voice and shaking his clenched hand at the ceiling, "that I will hang him though he be a prince — temporal or spiritual."

The Pope shook his great head, and smiled tolerantly upon all this heat.

"Let us pray, then," he lisped, "that you do not find him. The writer of those verses gives much promise."

"He does, Holiness. He gives great promise of a sudden death from suffocation."

The Pope's smile wavered nothing in its benignity. "You should follow my own example, Cesare, of contempt for these scribblers."

"I do, Holiness. The bargelli have my orders to make diligent search for this rhymer. When they have found him you shall see me express my contempt for him. This ribaldry shall end."

He knelt again, kissed the ring on the hand the Pope extended, and upon that withdrew as he had come, white-faced and angry to an extent that was most rarely shown by him.

"You do not seem at ease, Angelo," murmured Beltrame in his rival's ear.

Angelo turned to face the speaker fully. He had paled a little during Cesare's angry speech, and Beltrame observing this had thereafter watched him, actuated by a suspicion that was born of hope and founded upon a knowledge of Angelo's leaning towards satirical verse and of his attitude towards the family of the Pontiff.

This inimical and satirical attitude of Angelo's towards the Borgias in general and Cesare in particular was natural in a Milanese, and it had of late been fostered in his employment by Cardinal Sforza-Riario, whose house had suffered so rudely at Cesare's hands. It was, indeed, Angelo's too-fluent pen which, in the interval of singing the thousand beauties of Lavinia Fregosi, had composed that bitter pasquinade wherein was ridiculed — somewhat late in the day, it is true — Cesare Borgia's transition from the Cardinalitial purple to the steel and leather of a condottiero.

That Beltrame should comment upon his slight agitation was disturbing now to Angelo. He very readily assumed that the Neapolitan's suspicions were not only definite, but founded upon some evidence of which he must have become possessed. That it was evidence of any value Angelo could scarcely suppose; and so he set himself to dissemble and explain his obvious perturbation.

He laughed and shrugged, as one who throws off some feeling that has weighed upon him. "Why, yes," he admitted. "I am ever ill at ease when Valentinois is present. He affects me so. I cannot explain it. A natural antipathy, perhaps. Have you never experienced it, Beltrame?"

Beltrame sneered. "Not I. Perhaps I have an easier conscience."

"Oh, the conscience of a saint, I am sure, Beltrame," said Angelo, and finding that Lavinia had meanwhile moved away on her brother's arm, he turned to follow, for Marco Fregosi was his friend.

Beltrame, too, had been his friend until just lately. Until they became rivals for the affections of Lavinia, they had been deeply attached and all but inseparable. Orestes and Pylades men had dubbed them. It was to Angelo a source of secret sorrow — the one cloud in the bright heaven of his hopes — that of their friendship no more than the ashes remained. He would have mended matters had it been possible. But Beltrame made it daily more impossible; grew daily more and more hostile, until Angelo realized that it was time to be wary of the man who once had loved him, but who did not so much as trouble now to dissemble his hatred.

By a grey old sundial, creeper-clad, on a lawn green as an emerald and smooth as velvet, in a luxurious garden on the Banchi Vecchi by old Tiber, stood on the morrow's afternoon Lavinia and her two suitors.

Beltrame's unexpected coming had been a source of

deep vexation to Angelo — though it might instead have been a source of joy had he but known how much Lavinia shared that same vexation. As it was, he could but do his best to dissemble it, and maintain a smiling front.

The child — she was little more — leaned a smooth white elbow on the grey old stone, a mischievous, bewitching smile revealed her dazzling teeth in which was caught by the stem a blood-red rose, one of the last roses of the year. Her great black eyes were now veiled demurely under half-lowered lids and curved sweep of lashes, now raised distractingly to the enamoured glances of one or the other of her swains.

And they, each dissembling his annoyance at the other's presence, each revealing the joy he found in her, little dreamed what trouble lay for them in the heart of that crimson rose she flaunted, nor how one of them must pay the forfeit of his life for its possession.

Beltrame, on the spoor of his suspicions, and hoping to dash the other's easy assurance, and steady flow of talk and laughter — all of which provoked him, since he felt himself out-matched by it — dragged in an allusion to the pasquinade that had so angered Cesare Borgia.

But Angelo laughed. "He is like that," he said to Lavinia, in apology for the Neapolitan. "The skull in the cave of the anchorite — a perpetual reminder of things best forgotten."

"I can understand that you should account them so," said Beltrame darkly.

"Why, then," returned Angelo, "knowing my wishes, it will be the easier for you to respect them."

And then Lavinia, to create a diversion from this

talk which was not plain to her, but which seemed laden with much menace, playfully smote Angelo's cheek with that rose of hers, saying that she did it to punish his excessive pertness.

"Such punishment," said he, "is an encouragement to wickedness." And as he spoke his hands closed over the rose, and his eyes smiled hardily upon the lady of his adoration, with never a thought or care for his rival's presence.

Beltrame flushed darkly under his tan, and his brows came together as he looked on.

"You'll crush the flower!" she cried, and more concern could not have laden her voice and glance had it been his heart that was in danger of being crushed.

"You can show pity for the flower, Madonna, who have none for me."

"Out of pity, then, I relinquish it," said she, and letting the stem slip through her fingers, she left the rose in his enfolding hands.

"Pity for me, or for the rose?" he asked, his blue eyes very ardent.

"For which you will — for both," she laughed, and shyly dropped her eyes.

"Aye, Madonna," snapped Beltrame. "Give him your pity. I do not grudge him that. He needs it."

She stared at the Neapolitan's brooding face, alarmed an instant; then, dissembling this, she laughed. "Why, Ser Beltrame, are you angry — and for the matter of a rose? There are still many in the garden."

"In the garden, yes. But the one I coveted, the one I begged of you but a moment since — that one is gone," he reproached her.

"And I am to blame if Ser Angelo is rude and violent?" quoth she, striving to keep the matter in the realm of jest. "You were witness that I did not give him the flower. He took it without permission; seized it with ruthless force."

Beltrame smiled, as smiles the loser in the act of paying; and the gall in his soul fermented, but was repressed for the time, to bubble forth, the more violent for its repression, an hour or so thereafter when he was alone with Angelo.

They had departed together from Lavinia's garden, and together they made their way in the twilight through the Rione di Ponte. Side by side they went; Beltrame moody and thoughtful; Angelo with smiling eyes and the lilt of a song on his lips, with new words which his mind was setting to it as they paced along.

Suddenly Beltrame spoke; his voice harsh and grating.

"Touching that rose, Angelo," he began.

"'Twas culled in Paradise," breathed Angelo softly, and he inhaled its fragrance in an ecstasy.

"I covet it," said the other viciously.

"Ah! Who would not?" smiled the poet. And he quoted, with modifications to suit his own case, a sonnet of Petrarca's:

> "Cupid's right hand did open my left side,
> And planted in my heart a crimson rose."

"'A laurel green' the poet has it," Beltrame corrected him.

"Petrarca, yes. But I —"

The Neapolitan's right hand fell heavily on Angelo's shoulder, and stayed him.

"We'll keep to the master's words, by your leave, dear Angelo," he laughed; and his laugh was evil and unpleasant. Angelo stared at him, the smile of ecstasy fading from his lips. "I'll play at Cupid," explained Beltrame, with a sneer, "and here's my laurel for the purpose." He tapped his sword-hilt, nodding darkly. "It shall be red anon, as a compromise to your own poetic fancy."

Horror filled Angelo, but no fear. "Beltrame," he said solemnly, "I have loved you."

"There is a green stretch that I know of close at hand, behind the Braschi. It is as smooth and green as — as the turf in Monna Lavinia's garden. A sweet spot to die in. Shall it be there?"

Anger rose in Angelo's soul, and in the rising waxed hot and passionate as the Neapolitan's own. That this man who had been his friend should now seek his life for very jealousy, and where it could nothing profit him, incensed him by its mean unreasonableness.

"Why, since that is your mood," he answered, "it shall be where you will. But first, Beltrame —"

"Come, then," the Neapolitan bade him, harshly interrupting the appeal he guessed was on the point of following. Then he laughed his evil laugh again. "'Angel,' are you named; an angel does Monna Lavinia account you. It is high time I made an angel of you in earnest."

"And just as surely as you are a devil, just so surely shall you sup in hell this night," returned Angelo as he strode on beside the other.

But as they went the poet's eyes grew troubled. His spurt of anger spent, the folly of the thing appalled him. He must attempt to avert it.

"Beltrame," he questioned, by way of opening a discussion, "what is your sudden quarrel with me?"

"Monna Lavinia loves you. I saw it in her eyes to-day. I love Lavinia. Needs more be said?"

"Why, no, indeed," said the poet, and his eyes grew dreamy again, his lips assumed a wistful smile. "If that contents you, there is no doubt that it contents me. My thanks, Beltrame."

"For what?" quoth Beltrame with suspicion.

"For having seen what you saw, and for having told me of it. I lacked the certainty. It will make a sweet thought to die on, if God wills that I should die. Have you no fear, Beltrame?"

"Fear?" snorted the stalwart Neapolitan.

"Men say the gods love a lover."

"Not a doubt but they'll love you well enough to take you to their bosom."

On that they crossed the street, and, skirting the Braschi Palace, they descended a narrow lane where the shadows made night, to emerge again into the twilight of an open square. And as they went Angelo's poetic soul, not to be restrained even by the matter that impended, suggested an opening line for a sonnet on a lover dying. He muttered it aloud to test its rhythm to gather inspiration to continue.

"What do you say?" asked Beltrame over his shoulder. He was a pace or two in front, as became the more eager of the twain.

"I am but muttering a verse," said Angelo quietly: "'There's a sweet visage, sweet can render death.' Can you give me an unusual rhyme for 'death'?"

"I'll give you the thing itself if you'll but have

patience," growled Beltrame. "Come. This is the place."

They had penetrated a belt of acacias set about a stretch of smooth, green turf. Peace reigned there. The place was utterly deserted, and the trees made an effective screen in case any one should come whilst they were at their bloody work.

Suddenly the Angelus bell boomed on the lethargic evening air. They paused, and bared their heads, and though murder was in the soul of one of them, he offered three Aves up to heaven. The bell ceased.

"Now," said Beltrame, casting his hat upon the grass, and untrussing the points of his doublet with swift, eager fingers.

Angelo started as from a reverie, and proceeded, more leisurely, to make ready. A moment he stood, holding the rose to his lips, breathing the fragrance of it; he was loath to put it down; yet he needed both his hands, one for his sword, the other for his dagger; for Beltrame awaited him, doubly armed. At last he solved the difficulty, and set the stem of the flower between his teeth.

If God willed that he should die that evening, at least her first love token should be with him in his last moments; its perfume — fond emblem of her soul — should sweeten for him his last breath on earth.

Beltrame saw him coming, the rose between his lips; and, lacking the wit to sound a poet's fancies, he deemed it an act of mockery, a thing done derisively and exultantly. He paled a shade. He looked furtively around. They were alone. A deadly smile flickered on his lips as he raised his weapons, and fell on guard.

He was a gentleman trained in arms, was this Beltrame; and easy, he thought, should be to him the slaughter of a scribbling poet, a man versed in no weapon but the goose quill. Yet his certainty of victory was based on an even surer measure of precaution; his valour sprang from another advantage — an advantage that made him no better than a murderer, as you shall learn.

Sword and dagger met dagger and sword; parted, met again, circled, flashed, struck fire, were locked an instant, and once more were parted. For some five minutes they fought on. The sweat gathered on Beltrame's brow, and he breathed a prayer of thanks to a heaven that surely did not heed him, for the secret advantage that was his; without that it would almost seem that this scrivener must prove his better.

They fell back to breathe a moment, each welcoming the brief respite, for each was winded by the fierce vigour of the onslaught. Then they engaged once more, and Angelo knew in his heart that he was Beltrame's master. But that he held his hand, Angelo might have slain his adversary a score of times had the latter had a score of lives to lose. But he was gentle — as gentle as he was skilled — and he could not seek the life of the man who had been his friend. Instead he sought Beltrame's sword arm. If he could drive a foot or so of steel through it, there would be an end to the encounter; and by the time the wound was healed, he would see to it that their difference was healed also; he would reason with this hot-headed Beltrame during the season of his convalescence, and seek to induce him out of his murderous jealousy.

Suddenly Beltrame's point came like a snake at

Angelo's throat. Angelo was no more than in time to turn the thrust aside, and the viciousness that could aim so at a vital spot, stirred his anger anew; it also awoke him to a sense of his own danger. Unless he disabled Beltrame soon, his life would pay the price of his generosity. Beltrame was the stronger and was showing less fatigue; unless he went in soon, he might not go in at all. Since he could not reach the arm, he would take Beltrame there, high up in the right breast, above the lung, where little damage could be done, thus:

He parried a sharp thrust delivered rather high, and on the binding of the blade went in and up with a stroke that he had learnt from the famous Costanzo of Milan, who had been his preceptor in the art of swordsmanship.

His point went home unwarded; but instead of sinking through unresisting flesh, it struck something that jarred and numbed his arm; and on the stroke his rapier snapped, and he was left with a hilt and a stump of steel.

Beltrame laughed, and Angelo understood. The Neapolitan wore a shirt of mail — one of those meshes so much in fashion then, so fine that your two hands might encompass and conceal it, and yet so finely tempered as to be proof against the stoutest stroke of sword or dagger.

The poet twisted the rose to a corner of his mouth, that he might have freedom to speak, what time with his dagger and the stump that remained him, he made the best defence he could against the other's furious charge.

"Coward!" he cried in a fury of reproach. "Oh, craven hound! Assassin! Ah!...Gesu!"

Beltrame's sword had found him. A second he
stood shuddering, his lips twisted, his eyes surprised.
Then he hurtled forward, and lay prone on the turf,
horribly still, his teeth clenched fast over the stem of
his red rose. Beltrame stood over him, sword em-
brued to the hilt, a mocking, cruel smile on his
swarthy face.

Then the murderer dropped on one knee and laid
hands on Angelo to turn him over. He had killed him
for the rose. He would take it now. But in the very
act of setting hands upon his victim, he paused.
Sounds reached him from beyond the trees, over by
the Braschi Palace.

"Down there!" he heard a voice shouting in the
distance; and footsteps came beating quickly on the
stones.

He understood. Some one attracted by the clash of
blades had spied on them and had run for the bargelli.

Swift and silent as a lizard, Beltrame darted to the
dark pile of doffed garments. He snatched up his
doublet, sword, belt, and scabbard; he never waited
to don them, but, tucking them under his arm and
clapping hat on head, he was gone from that open
space of lawn thanking Heaven for the thickening
dusk that lent him cover as he ran.

In a dark alley not twenty paces from the square
he paused, laid down his bundle, and carefully wiped
and sheathed his weapons. Then he donned his doublet, girded on his belt, straightened his hat, and
sauntered boldly back, down the alley.

At the mouth of it he was suddenly confronted by
three of the bargelli. A lanthorn was raised and

flashed on his patrician garments. An officer stepped forward briskly.

"Whence are you, sir?" he asked.

"From Piazza Navona," answered Beltrame without hesitation.

"This way?" And the officer pointed up the alley.

"Why, yes. This way."

One of the bargelli laughed. The officer stepped closer to Beltrame, and bade the lanthorn-bearer hold the light in the gentleman's face.

"This alley, sir, has but one entrance — this. Now, sir, again whence are you?"

Confused, Beltrame sought shelter in bluster. He would not be interrogated. Was not a gentleman free to walk where he listed? Let them beware how they incommoded him. He was Messer Beltrame Severino.

The officer increased in courtesy, but diminished nothing in his firmness.

"A man has been done to death down there," he informed Beltrame, "and you would be well advised to return full answers to my questions, unless you prefer to go before the Ruota."

Beltrame bade him go to the devil. Whereupon the men laid hands upon him, and the officer made bold to examine his weapons. Despite his precautions, Beltrame grew afraid, for he had wiped them in the dark.

The officer looked along the sword, then peered under the quillons of the hilt. What he saw there caused him to touch the spot with his finger, and then examine this.

"Wet blood," said he, and added curtly to his men, "Bring him with you."

They carried him off that he might tell what story he pleased to the President of the Ruota, and explain his wanderings in that blind alley by the Braschi.

Now it happened that the hole that Beltrame made in Angelo d'Asti's fair body was not large enough for the escape of so great a soul. Yet might it have proved so but for another thing that happened. As they were bearing him away from the scene of the combat, wondering who he might be, and whither they should carry him, the group was met by Marco Fregosi — Madonna Lavinia's brother, and Angelo's good friend.

At sight of Angelo's face, Marco made the bearers pause, and demanded to know what had befallen. Then, upon finding that the poet's life was not yet extinct, he ordered them to carry him to his villa on Banchi Vecchi — the house which Angelo had left but an hour or so ago.

They nursed him back to health and wholeness. The beautiful Lavinia in a passion of solicitude tended him herself. Could she have done less? For you are to know that they brought him in with the red rose still tight between his teeth, and she had recognized her love token. If anything had still been wanting to complete Angelo's conquest of her virgin heart, that thing he now afforded.

It was nine days before he opened his eyes to reason and understanding, his danger overpast; life and happiness awaiting him. They told him he was at the Villa Fregosi, and the very announcement did as much to complete his recovery as their tender efforts had done to bring it thus far.

On the morrow he saw Lavinia at last. Her brother brought her to him, and seeing him awake again her eyes filled with tears, as sweet as those had been bitter with which she had watered his pillow and her own — though he knew it not, nor dreamed it — during the first days of sojourn with them, when his vital fire seemed on the point of extinction.

It was on the occasion of this visit that Marco asked him for details of what had happened, the story of how he had come by his hurt, expressing at the same time his own suspicions that it was Beltrame who had all but slain him.

"Aye," answered Angelo wistfully. "Beltrame it was — the coward! He wore a mesh of steel in secret, and forced me into a combat that must end in murder."

"And upon what grounds did you quarrel?" was Marco's next question, heedless of his sister's heightening distress.

"We fought for a rose; this." He bore his hand halfway to his lips; then, bethinking him, he smiled, and dropped it back upon the coverlet.

"I have kept it for you," said Lavinia through her tears.

The light of a great joy leaped to the poet's eyes to answer her; a flush mounted to his pale brow.

"You fought for a rose?" quoth Marco, frowning. "I hardly understand."

"You wouldn't," said Angelo. " 'Twas a rose of Paradise."

Marco looked grave. "Lavinia," said he, rising gently. "I think perhaps we had better leave him. His mind is wandering again."

"No, no," laughed Angelo, and his tone was reassuring. "Tell me — what of Beltrame?"

"He is dead," said Marco.

"Dead?" And for all that he had suffered at Beltrame's hands, for all that Beltrame had sought his life, there was distress in Angelo's voice and in the glance he bent upon Marco. "How came he to die?"

"By the will and pleasure of the Lord Cesare Borgia. He was hanged."

"And I think he deserved it, Angelo," said Lavinia. "He deserved it for his attempt to murder you, if not for the thing for which they punished him."

"For what else, then, did he suffer?"

"Do you remember," she said, "that afternoon at the Vatican?"

"Yes," he answered, mystified.

"And how the Duke of Valentinois came in, so very angry, and told of the verses that had been found that day upon the statue of Pasquino, and how his bargelli were seeking for the author?"

"Yes, yes. But what has this to do with Beltrame?"

"He was the author," said Marco.

"Beltrame?"

"It was proved so. It fell out thus," Marco related. "It was his attempt to murder you that destroyed him. He was found near the Braschi a few moments after the bargelli had discovered you. There was blood on his sword, and so they carried him before the Tribunal of the Ruota, which began his examination with the usual formality of having him searched. In his pocket was found the original of those very verses, with all the erasures and emendations and substitutions that a writer makes in perfecting his work. He denied all knowledge of them; told, I know not what, preposterous lies. But they put him to the question. At the third hoist he confessed."

"Confessed?" quoth Angelo, his eyes dilating.

"Aye; the torture drew it from him. He may perhaps have thought they would not go the length of hanging him, or else, that since you were doubtless dead, they would hang him in any case, and so that he might at least avoid further agonies by confessing and being done with it. Cesare Borgia is tired of pasquinades, and wished to make an example. And so they hanged him next morning beside the statue of Pasquino."

Angelo sank back on his pillows, and stared at the ceiling for some moments.

"He was undoubtedly a coward," said he at length, smiling bitterly, "and he met a coward's fate. He deserved to die. And yet he was not the author of that pasquinade."

"Not the author? How do you know?"

"Because — Are we alone? Because," said Angelo softly, "it was I who wrote it."

"You, Angelo?" cried brother and sister in a breath.

Angelo's eyes were wandering round the room, reflecting the bewilderment that filled his soul. Suddenly they paused, fastening upon a garment of shot silk that was thrown across a chair.

"What is that?" he asked abruptly, pointing.

"That? Your doublet," answered Marco. "They fetched it with you from the Braschi, when you were wounded."

Angelo sank back again, and he smiled never so faintly.

"That makes it clear," he said. "Beltrame took the wrong doublet in the dark. The verses were in my pocket."

Lavinia's hand stole over Angelo's where it lay upon the coverlet. He raised his eyes to hers. "We owe him much — this Beltrame," he said slowly. "I could have known no peace while they were hunting the author of that pasquinade. He has satisfied the hunters, and so removed the danger of discovery from me. That is something. But I owe him more, do I not, Lavinia?"

"Why, what else do you owe him?" inquired Marco.

"This brother of yours is a very dull fellow, Lavinia," said Angelo, smiling as the blessed smile.

DATE DUE

	APR 12		
GAYLORD			PRINTED IN U.S.A.